Multiple Equilibria in Proteins

Molecular Biology

An International Series of Monographs and Textbooks

Edited by

BERNARD HORECKER

Department of Molecular Biology
Albert Einstein College of Medicine
Yeshiva University
Bronx, New York

NATHAN O. KAPLAN

Department of Chemistry
University of California
At San Diego
La Jolla, California

JULIUS MARMUR

Department of Biochemistry
Albert Einstein College of Medicine
Yeshiva University
Bronx, New York

HAROLD A. SCHERAGA

Department of Chemistry
Cornell University
Ithaca, New York

MULTIPLE EQUILIBRIA IN PROTEINS

Jacinto Steinhardt

DEPARTMENT OF CHEMISTRY
GEORGETOWN UNIVERSITY
WASHINGTON, D. C.

Jacqueline A. Reynolds

DEPARTMENTS OF BIOCHEMISTRY
AND ANATOMY
DUKE UNIVERSITY MEDICAL CENTER
DURHAM, NORTH CAROLINA

1969

ACADEMIC PRESS   New York and London

ACADEMIC PRESS, INC.
111 Fifth Avenue, New York, New York 10003

United Kingdom Edition published by
ACADEMIC PRESS, INC. (LONDON) LTD.
Berkeley Square House, London W1X 6BA

LIBRARY OF CONGRESS CATALOG CARD NUMBER: 79-86366

PRINTED IN THE UNITED STATES OF AMERICA

Preface

The authors of this book are keenly aware of the difficulties inherent in any effort to adequately treat a rapidly developing subject without erring on the side of lack of timeliness on the one hand, or on an uncritical emphasis on the most recent work on the other. We have often felt that we were on the verge of deducing general sets of ideas which would bring order and simplicity out of an appearance of multiple and almost arbitrary diversity. We hope that parts of this book will communicate such a feeling to the reader. Such a cliff-hanging feeling has twice led to a postponement of completion of the book, and therefore to a costly updating operation. Thus, we publish it now, still on the verge.

The authors are deeply indebted to Dr. Sherman Beychok of Columbia University who contributed importantly to the early stages of the formulation of the scope of this work, and whose assistance in the initial literature search was invaluable. Thanks are also due to Mrs. Ruth Frazier and Miss Susan Moss of Georgetown University for their patient assistance in the innumerable tasks that result in a final edited draft with verified citations. Without their help, and that of a number of others over a period of nearly five years, the manuscript would still be incomplete.

J.S.
J.A.R.

September, 1969

Contents

IV.   Binding of Neutral Molecules

V.   Hydrogen-Ion Equilibria

VI.   Metal-Ion Binding

VII.   Binding of Organic Ions by Proteins

VIII. Protein–Protein Interaction

IX. Summary and Conclusions   358

Multiple Equilibria in Proteins

|

Introduction

This book is concerned with multiple interactions between small ions and molecules and a protein molecule. It deals with the physicochemical mechanisms of this interaction and the information about protein structure and the forces stabilizing that structure which can be obtained from binding studies. It is, therefore, also concerned with changes in protein structure brought about by small-ion or neutral-molecule binding as well as the converse, i.e., changes in binding induced by the alterations in protein structure. Preparation of this book has entailed an exhaustive literature search; the references selected for citation or discussion constitute a large fraction of the literature, but are not complete.

For the most part, we will be concerned with binding isotherms which characterize the interactions referred to above, the dependence of these binding isotherms on the nature of the ligands involved and on environmental parameters, the nature of the binding sites, and the forces involved in complex formation. Frequently we will relate the extent to which ligands are bound to the propensity of the protein to undergo a binding-induced conformational change. Such a change is reflected in the isotherms themselves, since as a result of the conformational change some binding sites may be destroyed and new, often more numerous, sites may appear.

We will usually exclude what may be called the characteristic reactions of enzymes, antibodies, and membrane transport proteins (Pardee, 1968) from the scope of this book. The reasons for doing so are numerous: (a) it would not be feasible to include all of them, (b) most of their characteristic binding reactions occur in molal ratios of 1 or 2 and are not examples of *multiple* equilibria, (c) the binding involved is often highly specific and implicates a

1

specialized binding site peculiar to one protein and not a general property of proteins as a class.

Understanding the relation between complex formation and protein stability furnishes one of the strongest motives for studying multiple equilibria. If the initial binding of a ligand to a protein produces a tendency to bind more ligand (often referred to as "cooperativity"), we say that binding has destabilized the native conformation of the macromolecule. On the other hand, initial binding may result in stabilization of the native structure against conformational changes induced by other agents. The organization of the folded protein is therefore affected by ligand binding. This phenomenon has been clearly demonstrated in, for example, the hemoglobin molecule, by analyses of the oxygen binding isotherm and reaction rates (Wyman, 1948, 1965; Guidotti, 1967; Roughton *et al.*, 1955; Antonini, 1965), by Perutz *et al.* (1965, 1968 a,b) by means of x-ray analysis in which clear differences are observed between oxy- and deoxyhemoglobin, and by measurements of the stabilizing effects of some covalently bound ligands of ferrihemoglobin (Steinhardt *et al.*, 1963, Molday and Steinhardt, 1969).

The presence of a prosthetic group is not essential to binding effects on stability. Stabilization and destabilization are found in the binding of other molecules and ions to proteins in which there are no prosthetic groups. Most of the evidence for such effects has been obtained with large organic ions, such as the anions of fatty acids and common detergents. This evidence will be presented and analyzed in Chapter VII. Strong indications have also been obtained that the binding of some uncharged molecules is also accompanied by conformation changes. Such evidence is of two kinds: (1) the simplest and most direct comes from uv difference spectra, optical rotation, and hydrodynamic properties; (2) the second kind of evidence rests on analysis of the binding itself, i.e., the way in which the molal binding ratio, $\bar{v}$, varies with concentration of free ligand. While the results of all such analyses are not yet fully analyzed, the most pertinent ones, for at least one protein, serum albumin, indicate that after small numbers of sites (8–12) on the native protein are occupied by certain ions, a much larger number of sites appear, at least some of which were not initially present. Here again, the most clearcut evidence based on electrophoresis measurements refers to ions rather than neutral molecules. Beyond certain low concentrations of free ligand, electrophoretic mobilities indicate that two classes of macro-ions are present, one binding only a few molecules, the other binding a very much larger number. This kind of what has been called "cooperative (nonstatistical)" binding can be explained only on the basis of a molecular transformation creating macromolecules containing a large number of binding sites. These latter binding sites may be characterized by association constants which may be smaller than, equal to, or larger than those responsible for the initial binding at the lowest ligand concentration. This conclusion is independent of whether or not microheterogeneity of the protein (Peterson and Foster, 1965) plays a part in the transformation. The situation just described is almost exactly analogous to the now well-known "unmasking" of prototropic groups, which occurs at both acid and alkaline extremes of the stability regions of numerous proteins. This phenomenon is described in detail for a number of proteins in Chapter V. The description of unmasking of prototropic groups in ferrihemoglobin, in which the effect is clear cut and large, is particularly instructive.

Except for the oxygen–hemoglobin equilibrium, almost all quantitative work on the multiple interactions of proteins prior to about 1940 consisted in the determination of the binding of hydrogen ions by proteins. That interaction remains the classical prototype for binding studies since it possesses to an outstanding degree every feature which is ever encountered in any protein binding process. That is:

(a) Very large numbers of binding sites reacting between pH 2 and 13 (about one for each five amino acid residues present); even more at greater extremes of acidity where amide groups and peptide groups protonate.

(b) Division of the binding sites into discrete sets, each member of which is characterized by the same intrinsic binding tendency (expressed as a dissociation or association constant).

(c) Interaction between sites, i.e., an effect of charges due to binding on one site on the apparent dissociation constants of the other sites.

(d) The existence of stability regions which may be characterized either in terms of the ligand concentrations which bracket them, or the amounts bound at these limits; outside these regions conformation changes occur which manifest themselves as changes in uv absorption, in shape-related parameters such as viscosity, sedimentation and diffusion velocity, and in binding properties. The changes are often but not always reversible.

(e) In numerous cases, some of the binding sites are inaccessible until the pH stability limits are exceeded. Only in the unfolded or disordered protein are the stoichiometric amounts of binding (as determined by amino acid composition) always observed.

Although the isotherms of ligands other than hydrogen ions have been much more recently studied, and are consequently less fully known or understood, most of these five features of hydrogen-ion binding are observed in every sufficiently studied case, although in any particular case, one or another of the features may be missing or barely observable. Interactions of charged sites are, of course, not observed when neutral molecules are bound, and they may be very small when the ligands are very long chain aliphatic ions. There are nevertheless very substantial differences between the binding of hydrogen ions and the binding of all other substances (with the possible exception of polyvalent metal ions) which will become quite clear in the chapters which follow. To begin with, the functional groups to which protons bind, or from which they are dissociated, are entirely known. They are the acidic and basic groups at the ends of the side chains of seven particular amino acids and are characteristic of the constituent polypeptide chains of proteins rather than of the way in which the chains are ordered (helices, pleated sheets, or folded into compact three-dimensional structures). It is the presence of "abnormal" (inaccessible) groups, rather than of "normal" (accessible) groups, which gives us insight into the native structure. With most other ligands of high affinity this is not the case. Binding sites are created by the arrangement of linearly well-separated elements on the folded chains or by the confluence of subunits. We deduce this to be the case because the high-affinity sites often disappear when the three-dimensional order is modified or destroyed, or because such binding has not been clearly demonstrated in smaller wholly covalent model compounds. Thus, the binding isotherms of ligands other than hydrogen ions are characteristic of elements of higher structure, and are charged with information about this structure if only we can read it.

There is another important difference between the multiple binding of hydrogen ions and of other substances. When hydrogen ion dissociates from carboxyl, imidazole, phenolic, sulfhydryl, and amino groups, partially covalent bonds of measurable strength (low in the case of carboxyl, moderate with imidazole and sulfhydryl, fairly high in the others) are broken, and work is done. This work is largely of enthalpic origin (it is larger—in aqueous solutions—in the case of the ε-amino groups of lysine, even though no work of charge separation is involved, than in the case of carboxyl groups where charge separation is required). When other ions or molecules are bound, whether or not coulombic interactions are involved, enthalpy effects are nearly always very small, and are commonly positive. These substances therefore cannot be bound in the same way as hydrogen ion, by large changes in molecular orbitals. The work required to separate a dodecylsulfate ion from native serum albumin is larger than the work required to dissociate a hydrogen ion from the phenolic group in one of its constituent tyrosines, but it arises from changes in entropy rather than from changes in enthalpy (Kauzmann, 1959).[1]

There is another difference between the interaction of proteins with hydrogen ions and their interactions with other ions: hydrogen ions exist in solution partially covalently bound to water as H_3O^+, $H_5O_2^+$, etc. Thus the association of a proton to a protein site is accompanied by its dissociation from hydronium ion. All of the thermodynamic and kinetic parameters associated

[1] It will be shown in Chapter VII that exception must be made for one of the binding sites in some proteins in which the free energy of binding anions is largely enthalpic in origin (Lovrien, 1968).

with this reaction contain partial quantities related to both the association and dissociation partial reactions. The main effect to which we call attention here is that the *total* energy of activation of the reaction is bound to be small. Thus, the reaction will proceed to equilibrium exceedingly rapidly in either direction. A consequence of this feature is that protons can redistribute themselves (under the influence of an outside force such as an approaching charge) very rapidly over vacant sites, giving rise to physicochemical behavior equivalent to that of charges on a conducting hollow body.[2] Such a resemblance is the basis of the Linderström-Lang model for describing protein acid–base titration curves (Chapter II). Although other ions are hydrated in aqueous solution, there is no obvious analog to the symmetrical acid–base interchange of protons that prevails with hydrogen ion, especially when the ions contain large hydrocarbon tails, as do the detergents. Binding of such ions to proteins therefore may not be characterized by similar low activation energies, essentially diffusion-limited rates, and rapid charge fluctuations. The relatively small number of binding sites in the native protein would also give a much cruder approach to the "conducting hollow body" than would the much larger number of hydrogen-ion binding sites.

The reference above to "fluctuations" must be carefully distinguished from other fluctuations, peculiar to multiple equilibria involving numbers of similar sites, which arise for purely statistical reasons. If the state of a simple one-step equilibrium is characterized by a "degree of dissociation," α, the numerical value of α represents the fraction of the total number of molecules or ions which have dissociated, e.g., a hydrogen ion. In the case of a polyacid having identical acidic groups, which are not subject to interaction with one another (because of high ionic strength), the quantity $\bar{v}$ which is analogous to $(1 - \alpha)$ represents the ratio of bound ions to the total number of molecules. Unlike α, its value may greatly exceed unity. Unlike α also, it represents the *average* number of bound ions, rather than a detailed description of how the bound ions (or molecules) are distributed over the proteins. It is easily calculated statistically that the fraction of the total number of molecules which binds precisely $\bar{v}$ ligands is very small if $\bar{v}$ is at all large. Thus, for example, Edsall (in Cohn and Edsall, 1943) has shown that the number of instantaneously isoelectric protein ions in an isoelectric protein solution may be very small. The class is smaller, the steeper the titration curve at the pH of interest. It is apparent, therefore, that a uniform population (with respect to the extent of binding) is to be found only when the concentration of free ligand is far removed from the intrinsic dissociation constant of any sets of binding sites on either high or low side of it. Just how far it must be depends on the presence or absence of intersite interaction. In the absence of such interactions, a factor

---

[2] Conduction occurs in the innermost water layer rather than on the surface of the ion.

of 100 gives a high degree of charge uniformity. The foundation of the quantitative aspect of these relations is presented in Chapters II and V.

Multiple equilibria, when accompanied by conformation changes which make initially inaccessible sites in the native protein available to ligand, furnish an opportunity to study analogs to the "conformational adaptability" (Koshland and Neet, 1968) or "allostery" (Monod et al., 1965) which has been invoked in the study of enzymes and other proteins which undergo subunit dissociation. Monod postulated an essential role of molecular symmetry in cooperative interactions with substrate. It will be shown in Chapter VII, following ideas developed in Foster's laboratory and by Steinhardt and his collaborators, that even in the absence of subunit structure, cooperativity is manifested whenever (1) inaccessible groups are made available by ligand-induced unfolding and (2) the new binding sites are much more numerous or have a higher affinity for ligand (substrate) than the sites being filled at the ligand concentration where unfolding occurs. For example, if acid unfolds a protein at pH 4, a cooperative type isotherm will be found near pH 4 provided the initially hidden groups have pK values appreciably above 4, and therefore combine practically quantitatively at pH 4.[1] This concept is experimentally demonstrable only in the case of multiple equilibria which do not involve dissociation into subunits (as in serum albumin) and has not been invoked in the case of the enzymes and respiratory proteins to which symmetry arguments have been applied.

It will be clear from the foregoing that unmasking may occur without overt manifestations if unfolding makes accessible only combining groups which do not react until higher ligand concentrations are reached than are required to unfold. The absence of cooperative effects from a binding isotherm can never be taken as an indication that all normally reactive groups are accessible to solvent and dissolved ligand in the native protein. Only comparison of the isotherms of native and denatured proteins after allowance for possible differences in the interactions between sites, in the two states—usually requiring fast reaction techniques—can establish that there are no hidden sites in the native protein.

When unfolding complicates the interpretation of binding data it is important to distinguish whether unfolding occurs simply because the algebraic conditions given in Chapter VII are fulfilled (a consequence of many sites remaining inaccessible as long as the protein remains folded), or whether some correlate of the binding process itself, such as the accumulation of a large net electrostatic charge, overcomes the cohesive forces that hold the

[1] Parallels may be found in the two-step oxidation of certain hydroquinones, where the removal of the first hydrogen leaves a free radical which is more easily oxidized than the original substance, and is therefore observed only under special circumstances (Michaelis, 1932, 1933, 1939, 1946).

molecule together. With anion binding, the destruction may be established by counteracting the accumulating net charge of the molecule due to anions by changing the amounts of hydrogen ion bound. Very few such studies have been made (Reynolds and Steinhardt, 1969), and they are incomplete. This recourse is not available in the case of proton binding, and the destruction of structure may be operationally vague.

In the foregoing pages an attempt has been made to delineate the scope of the subject of this book, to indicate the unique features of the reactions it embraces, to mention some of its difficulties, possibilities, and the gaps in our knowledge; and above all, to indicate why the subject is important to both molecular biology and to physical chemistry. The arrangement of the book follows as simple a sequence as possible. Chapter II sets forth the basic physicochemical concepts and relationships which are essential to the development of the subject. It is not an exhaustive treatment, and the serious student is advised to supplement it by making use of articles by Klotz (1953), Edsall and Wyman (1958), Tanford (1961), Beychok and Steinhardt (1964), and Joly (1965) for more complete accounts of portions of the material, as well as of the specific references given there. Chapter III presents an enumeration and critical discussion of most of the methods which have been used to determine extents of binding and complete binding isotherms. To avoid at the outset some of the difficulties and uncertainties inherent in electrostatic interactions between sites, Chapter IV gathers together our present knowledge and hypotheses of the multiple interactions of proteins with uncharged molecules. The principal arrangement is by individual proteins with appropriate subsections for classes of ligands. Large parts of this chapter are necessarily concerned with the serum albumins and hemoglobins. Rather arbitrarily, most of the quantitative work on zwitterions is included here because the net charge is the same as that of a neutral molecule. Many sulfonamides exist in solution largely in the undissociated form; it has been a convenience to arbitrarily collect all the data on sulfonamides in a single chapter although some are ionic at neutral pH.

Chapter V is devoted to the most familiar multiple equilibria, those represented by hydrogen-ion titration curves. Since a number of excellent reviews of this subject are still reasonably up to date (Tanford, 1962; Steinhardt and Beychok, 1964) the subject is developed in a summary fashion. An effort has been made to include all of the more recent data, at least in tabular form. Detailed examples are given of unusual isotherms complicated by the intrusion of binding-induced conformation changes and unmasking of hidden groups.

Chapter VI deals with the binding of metallic ions of valence higher than one. This group of substances merits a separate chapter because the binding of metal ions is more closely interrelated to the binding isotherms of hydrogen ions than is the case with any other ions. Equilibria involving these ions are often important in the catalytic function of enzymes, sometimes because they are determinants of enzyme conformation in the active state. Metallic ions are also important, because, with few exceptions, they constitute the only large class of cations the binding of which to proteins has been subjected to adequate study.

Chapter VII considers the binding of all other ions by proteins. Its principal organization is by three classes of ligand: (a) long-chain hydrocarbons with ionic terminal groups (detergents); (b) dyes, and other predominantly aromatic ions; and (c) small ions, including monoatomic ions. This organization has been adopted in an effort to separate and distinguish the several principal types of binding forces which are involved in the binding of all except the smallest ions: hydrophobic interactions; coulombic interactions in which entropic effects on polarized water molecules are importantly involved; and hydrogen bonding or charge delocalizations. An effort is made to develop and apply the algebra of a general model of all multiple equilibria in which binding-induced conformation changes occur. Considerable attention is given to the physicochemical criteria of such unfolding.

In Chapter VIII a limited number of examples of biologically important multiple equilibria are given, as well as a very brief treatment of protein–protein interactions, including dissociation into subunits. Chapter IX is a summary which attempts to draw together the principal characteristics of multiple equilibria in proteins, the nature of binding sites, the interrelations between complex formation and induced changes in structure, and suggestions for further work.

It may help the reader in going through the book if he keeps before him what we consider to be the central questions relating to multiple equilibria in proteins. These questions are:

(A) What are the differences, if any, between the processes that are responsible for multiple equilibria (especially when whole families of substances are involved) and those responsible for the highly specific binding which is characteristic of enzyme–substrate, membrane–protein substrate, and hapten–antibody reactions?

(B) What characteristics must a protein have to be a strong binder of many equivalents of a large variety of ligands or of groups of particular types of ligands (obviously *lysozyme* lacks whatever the characteristics are that are responsible for the binding of hydrocarbons)?

(C) Within homologous groups of chemical substrates, e.g., organic anions, what are the characteristics (parameters) which may make them ligands for proteins in general or for particular proteins?

(D) Why does the binding of a small number of equivalents of certain ligands, such as the longest-chain detergents, result in large conformation changes with most proteins? The total concentration of some such substances which is required to produce extensive unfolding of bovine serum albumin (BSA) in 0.1 % solution is considerably less than 10^{-3} M; thus these substances are far more potent initiators of unfolding than the common reagents, urea and guanidine hydrochloride, used as denaturants.

(E) How are the properties enumerated above utilized physiologically, as for example, in such a versatile transport protein as serum albumin?

We will return to these questions in Chapter IX.

REFERENCES

Antonini, E. A. (1965). *Science* **158**, 1417.

Cohn, E. J., and Edsall, J. T. (1943). "Proteins, Amino Acids, and Peptides as Ions and Dipolar Ions," Chapter 20. Reinhold, New York.

Edsall, J. T., and Wyman, J. (1958). *Biophys. Chem.* **1**, Chapter 11.

Guidotti, G. (1967). *J. Biol. Chem.* **242**, 3794.

Joly, M. (1965). "Physical-Chemical Approach to Denaturation of Proteins." Academic Press, New York.

Kauzmann, W. (1959). *Advan. Protein Chem.* **14**, 1.

Klotz, I. M. (1953) *in* "The Proteins" (H. Neurath and K. Bailey, eds.), 1B, Chapter 8. Academic Press, New York.

Koshland, D. E., Jr., and Neet, K. E. (1968). *Biochem. Am. R.* **37**, 359.

Lovrien, R. Jr. (1968). *Polymer Preprints* **9**, 219,

Michaelis, L. (1932). *J. Biol. Chem.* **96**, 703.

Michaelis, L. (1933). *Cold Spring Harbor Symp. Quant. Biol.* **1**, 224.

Michaelis, L. (1939). *Cold Spring Harbor Symp. Quant. Biol.* **7**, 33.

Michaelis, L. (1946). "Biochemical Research" (D. E. Green, ed.), Wiley (Interscience), New York.

Molday, R., and Steinhardt, J. (1969). B.B.A. (in press).

Monod, J., Wyman, J., and Changeux, J. P. (1965). *J. Mol. Biol.* **12**, 88.

Pardee, A. (1968). *Science* **162**, 632.

Perutz, M. F. (1965). *J. Mol. Biol.* **13**, 646.

Perutz, M. F., Muirhead, H., Cox, J. M., Goaman, L. C. G., Mathews, F. S., McGandy, E. L., and Webb, L. E. (1968a). *Nature* **219**, 29.

Perutz, M. F., Muirhead, H., Cox, J. M., and Goaman, L. C. G. (1968b). *Nature* **219**, 131.

Peterson, H. A., and Foster, J. F. (1965). *J. Biol. Chem.* **240**, 2503, 3858.

Reynolds, J., and Steinhardt, J. (1969) *Biochem.* (in press).

Roughton, F. J. W., Otis, A. B., and Lyster, R. H. J. (1955). *Proc. Roy. Soc. London* **B144**, 29.

Steinhardt, J., and Beychok, S. (1964). *In* "The Proteins" (H. Neurath, ed.), Vol. II, Chapter 8. Academic Press, New York.

Steinhardt, J., Ona, R., Beychok, S., and Ho. C. (1963). *Biochemistry* **2**, 256

Tanford, C. (1961). "Physical Chemistry of Macromolecules," pp. 337–344. Wiley, New York.

Tanford, C. (1962). *Advan. Protein. Chem.* **17**, 69.

Wyman, J. Jr. (1948). *Advan. Protein Chem.* **4**, 407.

Wyman, J. Jr. (1965). *J. Mol. Biol.* **11**, 631.

II

Thermodynamics and Model Systems

I. Introduction

This chapter deals with the mathematical description of complex formation, the thermodynamic analysis of binding data, and various theoretical models which can be used to describe the phenomena of small molecule–macromolecule interactions. The discussion includes binding with and without interaction between multiple identical sites. In addition, the problem of binding-induced conformational changes is treated.

The experimental quantities of interest in the study of multiple equilibria are the molal binding ratio, defined as the average number of moles of ligand bound per mole of protein, and the ligand concentration in equilibrium with the ligand complex. These two experimentally determined quantities permit one to calculate the association constants of ligand for the site or sites on the protein as well as the free energy of the complex formation. When binding is measured as a function of temperature, other thermodynamic quantities such as enthalpy and entropy of binding can also be determined.

Recent general treatments of parts of these subjects, and more extended treatments of some of them are to be found in Edsall and Wyman (1958), Tanford (1961), and Steinhardt and Beychok (1964).

II. Some Concepts in Thermodynamics

Chemical equilibria are determined by the changes in free energy (ΔF) which occur when reactants combine or move from one phase to another.

From the second law of thermodynamics it is known that

$$dF = dH - T\, dS \tag{2-1}$$

where dH is the change in enthalpy in the system and dS is the change in entropy in the system. The free energy of any system is a function of temperature, T, pressure, P, and quantities of chemical components, n_i,

$$F = f(T, P, n_i) \tag{2-2}$$

and

$$dF = \left(\frac{\partial F}{\partial T}\right)_{P,\,n_i} dT + \left(\frac{\partial F}{\partial P}\right)_{T,\,n_i} dP + \sum_{i=1}^{n} \left(\frac{\partial F}{\partial n_i}\right)_{T,\,P} dn_i \tag{2-3}$$

where $(\partial F/\partial n_i)_{T,P}$ is the increase in free energy per mole of added component, n_i, when the amount of n_i added is sufficiently small that the composition of the solution remains essentially unchanged. At constant T and P, Eq. (2-3) becomes

$$dF_{T,\,P} = \sum_{i=1}^{n} \left(\frac{\partial F}{\partial n_i}\right)_{T,\,P} dn_i \tag{2-4}$$

where $(\partial F/\partial n_i)_{T,P} \equiv \mu_i$ is the partial molal free energy of the ith component, called by Gibbs the chemical potential.

At equilibrium $dF_{T,P} = 0$, and Eq. (2-4) becomes

$$\sum_{i=1}^{n} \mu_i\, dn_i = 0 \tag{2-5}$$

The composition-dependent free energy of a system at a particular constant T and P is

$$F(n_i)_{T,\,P} = \sum_{i=1}^{n} \left(\frac{\partial F}{\partial n_i}\right)_{T,\,P} n_i \equiv \sum_{i=1}^{n} \mu_i n_i \tag{2-6}$$

Differentiation of Eq. (2-6) gives

$$dF(n_i)_{T,\,P} = \sum_{i=1}^{n} \mu_i\, dn_i + \sum_{i=1}^{n} n_i\, d\mu_i \tag{2-7}$$

Combining Eqs. (2-5) and (2-7)

$$\sum_{i=1}^{n} n_i\, d\mu_i = 0 \tag{2-8}$$

which is the well-known Gibbs-Duhem equation for the equilibrium state.

Thus, when a multicomponent system at equilibrium undergoes an infinitesimal displacement, the sum of the products of concentration of each component and its change in chemical potential is zero.

An important relationship between chemical potentials is suggested by the ideal gas law, $PV = nRT$. It can be shown that for a mixture of two ideal gases

$$\mu_1 - \mu_2 = RT \ln(p_1/p_2) \tag{2-9}$$

where p_1 and p_2 are the partial pressures of each gas and are proportional to the molar concentrations. Each gas has been referred to a standard reference state of chemical potential μ_0. That is,

$$\mu_1 = RT \ln p_1 + \mu_0 \quad \text{and} \quad \mu_2 = RT \ln p_2 + \mu_0 \tag{2-10}$$

In an ideal solution the chemical potential of each component may be defined in a manner similar to Eq. (2-10)

$$\mu_i = RT \ln m_i + \mu_i^0 \tag{2-11}$$

where m_i is the molar concentration of component i, and μ_i^0 is a standard chemical potential chosen arbitrarily.

For a real solution (nonideal) we can define a quantity, a_i, which we call the activity of a specific component and which is a function of the molar concentration, m_i

$$a_i = \gamma_i m_i \tag{2-12}$$

where γ_i is called the activity coefficient. The standard chemical potential μ_i^0 is customarily chosen equal to unit activity for real solutions, and a_i is made to approach m_i at infinite dilution of real solutions. Thus Eq. (2-11) becomes for real solutions

$$\mu_i = RT \ln a_i + \mu_i^0 \tag{2-13}$$

and the difference in chemical potential for any component in two states (e.g., dissolved and crystalline) in a solution at equilibrium may be written

$$\mu_1 - \mu_2 = RT \ln(a_1/a_2) \tag{2-14}$$

Application of Eq.(2-14) to any chemical system in equilibrium as defined by the law of mass action leads to the relation

$$\Delta F^\circ = -RT \ln K \tag{2-15}$$

where ΔF° is the standard free energy change in the reaction and K, the mass action equilibrium constant.

III. Multiple Binding without Interaction between Sites

The mathematical description of simple binding may be approached from a very general standpoint. For further discussion the reader is referred to a number of comprehensive reviews (Klotz, 1953; Edsall and Wyman, 1958; Tanford, 1962; and Weber, 1965). In addition to these references the early works of Michaelis (1925) and Langmuir (1918) as well as a more recent derivation by Hill (1960) are instructive accounts of various approaches to the problem treated in this section.

Given a number of uniform particles (S) in solution each with n independent, indistinguishable, and identical sites, the following equations define the equilibrium between a ligand and the sites on the particles:

$$S + nL \rightleftarrows SL_n \tag{2-16}$$

or alternatively, following the stepwise addition of ligand

$$S + L \overset{k_1}{\rightleftarrows} SL_1$$

$$SL_1 + L \overset{k_2}{\rightleftarrows} SL_2 \tag{2-17}$$

$$SL_{n-1} + L \overset{k_n}{\rightleftarrows} SL_n$$

where at equilibrium

$$k_i = \frac{[SL_i]}{[SL_{i-1}][L]} \tag{2-18}$$

It is important to note that the above equations and the discussion to follow are strictly applicable only when the association is thermodynamically reversible. Furthermore, since we are discussing real solutions, the quantities $[SL_i]$, $[SL_{i-1}]$, and $[L]$ properly refer to activities as discussed in Section II of this chapter and not to concentrations. In general the activity coefficients are not readily ascertainable, but at constant ionic strength, they are combined with the *apparent* association constants k_0 in K[in Eq. (2-23) and (2-26)].

The number of possible combinations of n binding sites taken exactly i at a time (or alternatively, the number of equally probable forms of the complex $[SL_i]$) is

$$P_{SL_i} = \frac{n!}{i!(n-i)!} \tag{2-19}$$

Thus, for example, there are n equally probable forms of SL_1 and only one form of SL_n. Since all the sites are by definition equal, they all must have, if present alone, the same intrinsic association constant for ligand which we will call k_0. Taking into account the number of equally probable forms of each complex, we may define the k_i's in terms of an invariant equilibrium constant k_0 as follows:

$$k_1 = nk_0$$

$$k_2 = \frac{n-2}{2} k_0$$

$$k_i = \frac{n-i+1}{i} k_0 \tag{2-20}$$

$$k_n = \frac{1}{n} k_0$$

The average number of ligand molecules bound may be defined as

$$\bar{v} = \frac{\text{moles combined L}}{\text{total moles S}} = \frac{[SL_1] + 2[SL_2] + \cdots + n[SL_n]}{[S] + [SL_1] + [SL_2] + \cdots + [SL_n]} \tag{2-21}$$

And, by systematic application of Eq. (2-18),

$$\bar{v} = \frac{k_1[L] + 2k_1k_2[L]^2 + \cdots + nk_1k_2 \cdots k_n[L]^n}{1 + k_1[L] + k_1k_2[L]^2 + \cdots + k_1k_2 \cdots k_n[L]^n} \tag{2-22}$$

Substituting the relationship between k_i and k_0 defined by Eq. (2-20) in Eq. (2-22) we obtain

$$\bar{v} = \frac{\sum_{i=1}^{n} i \left\{ \prod_{i=1}^{i} \left(\frac{n-i+1}{i} \right) \right\} k_0{}^i[L]^i}{1 + \sum_{i=1}^{n} \left\{ \prod_{i=1}^{i} \left(\frac{n-i+1}{i} \right) \right\} k_0{}^i[L]^i} \equiv \frac{\sum_{i=1}^{n} i \frac{n!}{(n-i)!\,i!} k_0{}^i[L]^i}{1 + \sum_{i=1}^{n} \frac{n!}{(n-i)!\,i!} k_0{}^i[L]^i} \tag{2-23}$$

Note that the denominator of Eq. (2-23) is the general expression of the binomial theorem [Eq. (2-24)] and the numerator is the first derivative thereof [Eq. (2-25)]:

$$(1 + k_0[L])^n = 1 + \sum_{i=1}^{n} \frac{n!}{(n-i)!\,i!} (k_0[L])^i \tag{2-24}$$

$$k_0[L] \frac{d(1 + k_0[L])^n}{d(k_0[L])} = k_0[L](1 + k_0[L])^{n-1} = \sum_{i=1}^{n} i \frac{n!}{(n-i)!\,i!} (k_0[L])^i \tag{2-25}$$

Substituting Eqs. (2-24) and (2-25) in (2-23), we obtain (after substituting K for the product of the combined activity coefficients and k_0)

$$\bar{v} = \frac{nK[L](1 + K[L])^{n-1}}{(1 + K[L])^n} = \frac{nK[L]}{1 + K[L]} \quad \text{or} \quad \frac{\bar{v}}{n - \bar{v}} = K[L] \tag{2-26}$$

Equation (2-26) will be recognized as an analog of the law of mass action for a single combining site or, alternatively, the equivalent Langmuir adsorption isotherm where $\bar{v}/n = \theta$ or degree of saturation. Equation (2-26) can be rearranged to give

$$\frac{\bar{v}}{[L]} = nK - \bar{v}K \tag{2-27}$$

$$\frac{1}{\bar{v}} = \frac{1}{n} + \frac{1}{nK[L]} \tag{2-28}$$

$$\frac{n - \bar{v}}{\bar{v}} = \frac{1}{K[L]} \tag{2-29}$$

The three linear equations given above provide a convenient means for determining K when the molal binding ratio is known as a function of free ligand concentration. Note that in applications of Eq. (2-29) an assumption must be made with respect to the value of n. If n is known then Eq. (2-29) should give a linear plot of $\log [(n - \bar{v})/v]$ vs. $\log [L]$ with a slope of -1. Slopes other than -1 or failure to obtain a straight line suggest that the simple model described here is incorrect. The interpretation is often made that such deviations indicate heterogeneity of binding sites, but it will be shown that other causes such as interaction between sites, and initiation of conformation changes may produce these effects.

If there is more than one set of sites on the surface of the macromolecule such that set 1 has n_1 sites and an intrinsic association constant K_1, set 2 has n_2 sites and an intrinsic association constant K_2, etc., Eq. (2-26) may be generalized in the following manner:

$$\bar{v} = \frac{n_1 K_1[L]}{1 + K_1[L]} + \frac{n_2 K_2[L]}{1 + K_2[L]} + \cdots + \frac{n_n K_n[L]}{1 + K_n[L]} \tag{2-30}$$

This treatment assumes complete independence of sets of sites, in particular the absence of any conformational change of the surface as a result of binding, such that a previously masked set is exposed or an exposed set destroyed. If the values of K_i are separated by more than about 10^4, then at any particular value of $[L]$ only one term of Eq. (2-30) depends on $[L]$, and $\bar{v}$ in each such region is determined by one particular K_i.

If there is only one set of sites but two ligands competing for this set, each with a different association constant, Eq. (2-26) becomes

$$\bar{v}_A = \frac{K_A[L_A]}{1 + K_A[L_A]} (n - \bar{v}_B)$$

$$\bar{v}_B = \frac{K[L_B]}{1 + K_B[L_B]} (n - \bar{v}_A) \tag{2-31}$$

thus taking account of the fact that part of the n sites will be filled by each ligand. Algebraic combination of the above equations leads to

$$\bar{v}_A = \frac{nK_A[L_A]}{1 + K_A[L_A] + K_B[L_B]}$$

$$\bar{v}_B = \frac{nK_B[L_B]}{1 + K_A[L_A] + K_B[L_B]}$$

(2-32)

A special case of sites which are similar but not identical, with a statistical distribution of K's around a mean, was made use of by Karush and Sonnenberg (1949) in an attempt to fit some anion binding data obtained with bovine serum albumin. These authors proposed a Gaussian distribution function to describe the site energy distribution, and Sips (1948, 1950) later showed that a distribution function close to Gaussian leads explicitly to the following equation:

$$\frac{\bar{v}}{n} = \frac{K[L]^a}{1 + k[L]^a}, \qquad 0 \le a \le 1$$

(2-33)

where K is the intrinsic association constant, and a is an index of dispersion of K around the mean. Halsey and Taylor (1947) showed that an exponential distribution of binding energies leads to an equation of the form $\bar{v}/n = K[L]^a$ which does not reach a saturation limit at high values of $[L]$. There is no direct evidence that either of these two models represents physical reality.

IV. Binding with Interaction between Sites

Sets of otherwise identical sites will not behave in accordance with Eq. (2-26) if the state of each site (combined or uncombined) affects the binding properties of the other sites. Interaction between binding sites in the same molecule can result from one or more of the following factors:

(1) Steric interference between bound molecules may occur.
(2) When the ligand is charged, electrostatic interaction may arise from the increasing charge on the protein as more ions are bound.
(3) Conformational changes of the binding body may be induced by interaction with the ligand.

In the present discussion steric interference is not dealt with at length. It can be treated in the manner of electrostatic interaction by increasing the exponent in the free energy law [Eq. (2-36)] to a large number.

Conformational changes induced by binding have been known for many years. Early examples are the expansion of linear polyelectrolytes with increasing charge (Arnold and Overbeek, 1950; Harris and Rice, 1952) and the unfolding of proteins as a function of hydrogen ions bound (Steinhardt and Zaiser, 1955). This subject is discussed in some detail in Section VII of this chapter. This section is concerned primarily with the problem of electrostatic interaction.

It is intuitively apparent that if the ligand is a charged species, the first bound ion will have a repulsive effect on the approach of the second ligand molecule to the same neighborhood, or if the surface is a conducting one, to any point on the surface. This repulsive effect must be taken into account when determining the association constant of the charged ligand for the specific sites on the surface. In the case of small ions early efforts to take this effect into account were made by Bjerrum (1923), who estimated the electrostatic contribution to the second ionization constant of dibasic acids. Gane and Ingold (1931) and Kirkwood and Westheimer (1938) later refined these calculations.

The general case of identical and indistinguishable sites is considered here first.[1] The standard free energy of the reaction defined by Eq. (2-16) is defined by

$$\Delta F° = -RT \ln K' \qquad (2\text{-}34)$$

where we now write K' for K. The additional contribution to the free energy made by electrostatic interaction when the ligand is charged is just the difference in the charging energy between $[SL_{i-1}]$ and $[SL_i]$—in other words, the electrical work done in increasing the charge on the surface by an amount equivalent to the binding of one charged ion. This may be expressed formally by defining a function $f(\bar{v})$ such that $f(\bar{v})$ is zero at $\bar{v} = 0$, and thereby defining a K' for reactions (2-17) which varies with the number of bound ligands.

$$K' = K \exp[-f(\bar{v})] \qquad (2\text{-}35)$$

$$\Delta F' = -RT \ln K + RT f(\bar{v}) \qquad (2\text{-}36)$$

A restrictive assumption implicit in the above statements is that the *average property* of a complex in solution is identical to the same property of an *average complex*. It follows from Eqs. (2-35) and (2-36) that

$$\bar{v} = \frac{nK \exp[-f(\bar{v})][L]}{1 + K \exp[-f(\bar{v})][L]} \qquad (2\text{-}37)$$

It will be useful to make the following distinctions in considering the effects of electrostatic interaction. The charges on most proteins are

---

[1] This description of the contribution of electrostatic interaction to the free energy of binding is similar to that in Tanford (1961, pp. 535–539), to which the reader is referred for a more detailed explanation.

(1) negative from the conjugate bases of carboxylic, phenolic, and thiol groups and (2) positive from protonated secondary amines. At any given pH the algebraic sum of the positive and negative charges may be zero, positive, or negative. The simplest, and historically the first, assumption made in developing models for electrostatic interaction was that this sum, the *net* charge, creates a field that determines the work done in bringing a charged ligand to the surface of the protein. (It is clear experimentally that binding often occurs when the coulomb forces due to the *net* charge on the protein are either absent or unfavorable, but the free energy of binding is not entirely, or even, predominantly, coulombic.) The second approach is to calculate the contribution of *each* charge on the surface to the electrical work of binding. Here it is necessary to specify not only the location of the charge on the surface (which may fluctuate, so that only a time average which depends on the saturation of sites may be specified) but also its radial separation from the surface. Case (2) presents great difficulties, so we address ourselves first to case (1).

A. Debye-Hückel-Born Treatment of Electrostatic Interaction

The evaluation of $f(\bar{v})$ rests on the calculation by Debye and Hückel of the electrical work necessary to charge an ion in a continuous medium of given dielectric constant. The assumptions inherent in the calculation are given below, but the reader is refered to Tanford (1961) and to the original work of Debye and Hückel (1923) and of Born (1920) and the extension of this work to proteins by Linderström-Lang (1924) for a more complete discussion.

(1) The ion may be treated as a point charge, i.e., a rigid sphere with a net charge, Ze, distributed uniformly on a conducting surface or at the center.

(2) If the radius of the central ion is b, then the closest approach which a small spherical ion of radius r can make to the central ion is the distance between centers $a = b + r$, as with hard spheres.

(3) The sphere is impenetrable to the medium in which it is immersed.

The potential at the surface due to the charge Ze is

$$\psi_1 = \frac{Ze}{Db} \tag{2-38}$$

in which D is the dielectric constant of the surrounding medium, e is the electronic charge, and Z the total number of charges on the ion. The ion atmosphere of equal and opposite charge to the central ion gives rise to another contribution to the potential at the surface.

$$\psi_2 = -\frac{Ze}{D}\left(\frac{\kappa}{1 + \kappa a}\right) \tag{2-39}$$

where κ is the well-known Debye reciprocal length:

$$\kappa = \frac{4\pi e^2}{DkT} \left(\sum c_s Z_s^2 \right)^{1/2} \tag{2-40}$$

and c_s is the molar concentration of the small ions and Z_s, the number of charges on each of the small ions. The potential at the surface of the central ion is then

$$\psi_T = \frac{Ze}{Db} - \frac{Ze}{D} \left(\frac{\kappa}{1 + \kappa a} \right) = \frac{Z\varepsilon}{D} \left(\frac{1}{b} - \frac{\kappa}{1 + \kappa a} \right) \tag{2-41}$$

The electrostatic free energy is the work of charging this sphere to a value Ze and is given by

$$F_{elec} = \int_0^{Ze} \psi_T \, d(Ze) = \frac{Z^2 e^2}{2D} \left(\frac{1}{b} - \frac{\kappa}{1 + \kappa a} \right) \tag{2-42}$$

and

$$\Delta F_{elec}^\circ = \frac{d(F_{elec})}{dZ} = \frac{2Ze^2}{2D} \left(\frac{1}{b} - \frac{\kappa}{1 + \kappa a} \right) = RT \ln f(\bar{v}) \tag{2-43}$$

If we define w such that

$$w = \frac{e^2}{2DRT} \left(\frac{1}{b} - \frac{\kappa}{1 + \kappa a} \right) \tag{2-44}$$

then

$$\Delta F' = -RT \ln K + RT 2wZ \tag{2-45}$$

and

$$K' = K \exp(2wZ) \tag{2-46}$$

Equation (2-26) may then be written

$$\bar{v} = \frac{nK \exp(-2wZ)[L]}{1 + K \exp(-2wZ)[L]} \tag{2-47}$$

Rearranging algebraically

$$\frac{\bar{v}}{n - \bar{v}} = K \exp(-2wZ)[L] \tag{2-48}$$

and taking the log of both sides

$$\ln \left(\frac{\bar{v}}{n - \bar{v}} \right) = \ln K + \ln[L] - 2wZ \tag{2-49}$$

$$\log \left(\frac{\bar{v}}{n - \bar{v}} \right) = \log K + \log[L] - 0.868wZ$$

Equation (2-49) was deduced by Linderström-Lang (1924) and elaborated by Scatchard (1949) who showed that the "restrictive" assumption stated on p. 17 is unimportant if $n > 4$. When applied to hydrogen-ion titration curves of globular macromolecules, it takes the form

$$\log \frac{\alpha}{1 - \alpha} + \mathrm{pH} = \mathrm{p}K - 0.868 \, wZ \qquad (2\text{-}50)$$

where

$$\alpha = \bar{v}/n$$

It is readily shown that $f(\bar{v}) = 0.868wZ$ does not depend on the assumptions made as to the shape or impenetrability of the central ion, but only on those assumptions which are inherent in the Debye-Hückel approximation. The value of w, however, does depend on the physical model. In general, w is smaller the more asymmetric or more penetrable the ion. In the case of flexible, linear polymers w may itself be a function of Z rather than a constant (Tanford, 1961).

B. Tanford-Kirkwood Model for Electrostatic Interaction

A more exact theory of electrostatic interaction must take into account the location of charge density on a nonconducting surface in terms of the distance between charged sites and the position of these sites relative to the interface between the binding surface and the medium in which it is immersed. (When there are a large number of rapidly fluctuating charged sites on the binding surface, a globular protein may behave as a conducting sphere and titration data for such a protein will then be fit reasonably well by the model in the preceding section.) A more realistic model for electrostatic interactions in proteins was proposed by Tanford and Kirkwood (1957) and Tanford (1957). This model is shown diagrammatically in Fig. 2-1. The theoretical basis for

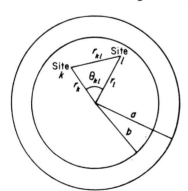

FIG. 2-1. Protein ion showing location of charged sites, k and l. [C. Tanford (1957) *J. Am. Chem. Soc.* **79**, 5340.]

the calculations to be discussed in this section was developed by Kirkwood and his collaborators (Kirkwood, 1934, Kirkwood and Westheimer, 1938). There is a concise review by Tanford (1961).

This section outlines briefly the central features of the Tanford-Kirkwood treatment with special emphasis on its application to hydrogen-ion titration curves of proteins. In principle, the treatment is equally applicable to the binding of any charged species to macromolecular surfaces.

In the model pictured in Fig. 2-1, the sites k and l must be treated as singularities and the potential field created by these charges is no longer symmetrical as in the Debye-Hückel approximation. The final expression for the electrical contribution to the free energy is

$$F_{\text{elec}} = \frac{e^2}{2b} \sum_{k=1}^{p} \sum_{\substack{l=1 \\ k \neq l}}^{p} \mathscr{L}_k \mathscr{L}_l (A_{kl} - B_{kl}) - \frac{e^2}{2a} \sum_{k=1}^{p} \sum_{l=1}^{p} \mathscr{L}_k \mathscr{L}_l C_{kl} \quad (2\text{-}51)$$

Figure 2-1 may be useful to the reader in following the terminology employed.

$$A_{kl} = \frac{b}{D_i r_{kl}}$$

$$B_{kl} = \frac{1 - 2\delta}{D_i (1 - 2\rho_{kl} \cos \theta_{kl} + \rho_{kl}^2)^{1/2}}$$

$$+ \frac{1}{D\rho_{kl}} \ln \left\{ \frac{(1 - 2\rho_{kl} \cos \theta_{kl} + \rho_{kl}^2)^{1/2} + \rho_{kl} - \cos \theta_{kl}}{1 - \cos \theta_{kl}} \right\} \quad (2\text{-}52)$$

$$\delta = \frac{D_i}{D} \quad \text{and} \quad \rho_{kl} = \frac{r_k r_l}{b^2}$$

$\mathscr{L}_k = +1$ for a positive charge and -1 for a negative charge. The quantity C_{kl} is a complicated function of the ionic strength and represents the interaction of the fixed sites with the ion atmosphere. At low ionic strength it reduces to

$$\left(\frac{1}{D}\right) \frac{\kappa a}{1 + \kappa a}$$

The factor involving the A_{kl} represents the work of charging in an unbounded medium of dielectric constant D_i; the factor involving the B_{kl} represents the modification introduced by having a bounded cavity surrounded by the medium of high dielectric constant.

Equation (2-51) reduces to the following at low ionic strength:

$$F_{\text{elec}} = \frac{e^2}{2b} \sum_{k=1}^{p} \sum_{\substack{l=1 \\ k \neq l}}^{p} \mathscr{L}_k \mathscr{L}_l (A_{kl} - B_{kl}) - \frac{Z^2 e^2}{2D} \left(\frac{\kappa}{1 + \kappa a}\right) \quad (2\text{-}53)$$

In the first term of Eq. (2-53), $k = l$ represents the work of creating an individual point charge (self-energy) and is omitted since the self-energies will cancel in the applications to be considered here.

The free energy change (ΔF_{elec}) involved in charging each site is determined by the difference between F_{elec} [Eq. (2-53)] when the site is occupied and when it is unoccupied. In the case of hydrogen-ion titration curves this amounts to $\mathscr{L} = 1$ and $\mathscr{L} = 0$.

An additional complication in computations which use this model arises from the fact that there are numerous possible configurations of charge distribution on a real protein molecule. These configurations arise from the phenomenon of charge fluctuation. For example, i protons on n carboxyl groups can be arranged in $n!/i!(n-1)!$ different charge configurations. The probability of a given configuration is $\exp(-\Delta F_{elec}^i/kT)$, where ΔF_{elec}^i is the electrical free energy of the ith configuration. In order to calculate a theoretical titration curve for a protein it is necessary to include this probability factor for each possible charged state of the macromolecule in using Eq. (2-53) (for details see Tanford, 1957).

The application of Eq. (2-53) to real binding data obviously requires a complete knowledge of the location of each site. Calculations of simple geometrical models have been made and lead to the following generalizations.

(1) The intrinsic pK of any given set is predicted to decrease as the ionic strength is increased, a phenomenon consistent with experimental observation.

(2) $\Delta F_{elec}/RTZ$ is extremely sensitive to the position of a site with respect to the surface of the protein. If w_0 is the Debye-Hückel interaction factor for an equivalent sphere and w is the Tanford-Kirkwood factor, equal to $\Delta F_{elec}/RTZ$, and d the depth below the surface of the protein–solvent interface, at

$$d = 0, \qquad w < 0.5\, w_0$$
$$d = 1\text{Å}, \qquad w \simeq w_0$$
$$d = 2\text{Å}, \qquad w > 3\, w_0$$

for a model in which eight carboxyl groups are regularly distributed at the corners of a cube or randomly distributed on a dodecahedron.

(3) When a small number of groups are being titrated w may be considerably larger than w_0.

A recent attempt to use the Tanford-Kirkwood model to calculate the theoretical titration curve for oxyhemoglobin at low ionic strength between pH 4.5 and 9.0 has been made by Ortung (1968) using the site coordinates from a model built according to Perutz (1965). Agreement with experimental data is within $h = 2$ groups for each pH using normal small molecule pK's, protein dielectric constant of 4, and a site depth of 0.6 Å. Eighteen histidines and four to six arginines are assumed to be masked.

C. HILL MODEL FOR CYLINDRICAL RODS

It is possible to calculate the charging energy as discussed in the previous two sections for an infinite cylinder. Hill (1955) computed W_{elec} for real cylinders of finite length, L, assuming that the electrostatic field at the ends of the cylinder (which is somewhat different than that in the middle) can be neglected. This assumption is probably valid for long rods. His final expression for an impenetrable cylinder of radius R and radius of exclusion, a, is

$$W_{elec} = \frac{Z^2 e^2}{DL} \left[\frac{K_0(\kappa a)}{\kappa a K_1(\kappa a)} + \ln \frac{a}{R} \right] \tag{2-54}$$

$K_0(\kappa a)$ and $K_1(\kappa a)$ are modified Bessel functions of the second kind. The application of this equation to paramyosin (Riddiford and Scheraga, 1961) is discussed in Chapter V.

V. Method of Data Treatment

In the vast literature related to the binding of small organic and inorganic molecules to biopolymers a common method of handling the binding data makes use of linear equations such as (2-27) or (2-28). Both of these equations suffer from the limitation of a relatively uncertain extrapolation, and the error inherent in taking the slope of a line drawn through experimental points, which are themselves subject to a finite uncertainty. The difficulty is compounded when binding at two or more different sets of sites overlap or when there is interaction between sites or a binding-induced conformational change, since all of these processes produce curvature as $\bar{v}$ rises.

The binding of charged ligands is often described by the use of Eq. (2-49). In these cases, the experimental w obtained by plotting $\log \bar{v}/(n - \bar{v}) - \log[L]$ against Z may be compared with that calculated from the Debye-Hückel approximation, Eq. (2-49). When the binding data do not appear to be linear, even with the application of an electrostatic interaction factor, there may be more than one set of sites, each with a different association constant, or a cooperative effect as is produced in unfolding.

In the specific case of binding of protons to rigid, compact macromolecules such as proteins, the experimental data are substituted in the Linderström-Lang equation (2-49), which has been found to be a good model for many globular proteins. It is obvious that the titration of flexible polyelectrolytes, which vary in shape and extensibility with net charge, or of polyampholytes which undergo conformational changes as the result of proton binding, will not yield constant values of w. Rather, w will depend on the charge and vary throughout the titration range. In these cases the experimental determination of w is neither easy nor particularly meaningful.

Since proteins in general contain more than one type of binding site for protons (e.g., COO^-, ε-amino, imidazole) the numbers, n_i, of each set of sites with identical K's must be determined either from a separate experiment (e.g., amino acid analysis) or from an approximate group count from a binding isotherm. The numbers determined by the two methods need not agree, if some of the prototropic groups are hidden from the surface. Figure 5-2 shows a typical hydrogen-ion titration curve for ribonuclease with the number of identical sites within each set marked on the figure. Once such a count has been established, the Linderström-Lang equation is applied as in Figs. 5-7 or 5-8 and w and K determined from the slope of the line and the intercept at $Z = 0$, respectively. Tanford (1962) has described and discussed in detail an iterative process for finding the exact number of groups in each set. The procedure for the binding of other substances is comparable except that there is usually no structural or analytical clue to the number of binding sites or the relative proportion of each type.

Two useful statistical parameters for describing the states of multiple equilibria have been introduced by G. Weber (Weber, 1965, and Weber and Anderson, 1965). His definitions are very slightly modified here. One of these, which we designate $\bar{p}_A$ is the probability that a given ligand molecule will be bound. The other, $\bar{p}_B$, is the probability that any given site in a molecule is occupied by ligand. These are related to $\bar{v}$ and equilibrium concentration C, as follows:

$$\bar{p}_A = \frac{\bar{v}[P]}{\bar{v}[P] + C} = \frac{nK[P]}{1 + nK[P] + KC} \tag{2-55}$$

and

$$\bar{p}_B = \frac{\bar{v}}{n} = \frac{KC}{1 + KC} \tag{2-56}$$

where $[P]$ is protein concentration, and C is concentration of unbound ligand. Probability $\bar{p}_B$ is directly proportional to $\bar{v}$ and is independent of the concentration of protein; $\bar{p}_A$, however, depends on protein concentration and is not *directly* proportional to $[P]$ unless $n[P]$ is much smaller than C, a condition that obtains only at very high values of C. At fixed $[P]$, the dependence of $\bar{p}_A$ and $\bar{p}_B$ on C appears to be quite different. However, the dependence of $\bar{p}_A$ on $[P]$ is *functionally* similar to the dependence of $\bar{p}_B$ on C. The inverse dependence of p_A on C simulates the dependence of $\bar{p}_B$ on C. Thus, $\bar{p}_A$ and $\bar{p}_B$ both go from 0.90 to about 0.10 as C changes by about 2 log units, and from 0.99 to 0.01 when C changes by about 4 log units. However $\bar{p}_B$ is 0.5 when $C = 1/K$, but $\bar{p}_A$ is 0.5 when $C = n[P] = 1/K$. It is clear that K is easily determined from $\bar{p}_B$ but that the value of C at which $\bar{p}_A = 0.5$ hardly depends on K at all, especially if K is large. On the other hand, at fixed $[P]$ the value of C at which

$\bar{p}_A = 0.5$ is equal to $n[P]$ and thus may be used to obtain a value of n. Anomalies in the behavior of $\bar{p}_A$, when plotted against log C, may serve as a useful clear-cut signal that more than one set of groups is being occupied, or that conformation changes which affect the number and affinity of binding sites are occurring.

Weber has used both $\bar{p}_A$ and $\bar{p}_B$ to apply a number of simple algebraic tests to experimental binding data to determine whether they can be accounted for by any number of sets of sites each having its own binding constant, or whether conformation changes (or other initiators of so-called "cooperative" phenomena) must be invoked. These parameters are well suited for this purpose, as well as for gaining insight into the accuracy in estimating K which is attainable with a given set of data. One of the results of Weber's investigations with these parameters has been a demonstration that K may be determined with a more consistent accuracy if both $[P]$ and C are varied, as in a dilution series, than when only one of them is varied, as in a titration. In such an experiment $\bar{p}_A$ is a more readily useful dependent variable than $\bar{v}$.

VI. Thermodynamics of Multiple Equilibria

The experimental determination of an equilibrium as a function of temperature for any chemical reaction allows the determination of its enthalpy and entropy. Thus,

$$\Delta F^\circ = -RT \ln K \tag{2-57}$$

$$\Delta H^\circ = -R \frac{d \ln K}{d(1/T)} \tag{2-58}$$

$$\Delta S^\circ = \frac{\Delta H^\circ - \Delta F^\circ}{T} \tag{2-59}$$

The equilibrium constant, K, should properly be calculated in terms of activities of the various species since the concentrations are equal to activities only in the limit of infinite dilution. In actual practice, an equilibrium constant, K' (characteristic of a specific ionic strength) is often expressed in terms of concentrations, in moles per liter.

The enthalpy determined by means of Eq. (2-58) from binding isotherms has been tabulated for many systems. In general, gas–solid interactions have negative enthalpies; small molecule interactions with macromolecules have negative, positive, and zero enthalpies. It is obvious that chemical equilibria with zero or positive enthalpy are entropy-driven processes. It is generally considered that the largest contribution to the entropy term in aqueous systems arises from structural changes in the solvent when solute–solvent interactions are replaced by solute–solute interactions. The entropy changes are at their largest when the solvent is water (Kauzmann, 1959).

In the case of binding by charged ligands, Eq. (2-58) should be written

$$\Delta H^\circ = -2.303 \, RT^2 \left(\frac{d \ln K}{dT} \right)_{\bar{v}, Zw} \tag{2-60}$$

and applies only at constant $\bar{v}$ and Zw. This is approximately equivalent to the requirement of the same standard state for the species which are being examined at two different temperatures. ΔH°, for example, is proportional to the changes in pH at which the same degree of protonation exists at two different temperatures, and may be read off directly from two titration curves at different temperatures.

VII. Binding-Induced Phase Transitions

The binding of small molecules and ions to macromolecules often results in conformational changes which are observed as changes in viscosity, changes in optical properties, and anomalies in the shape of the binding curves. Figures 2-2–2-4 show examples of these three phenomena. Note that the

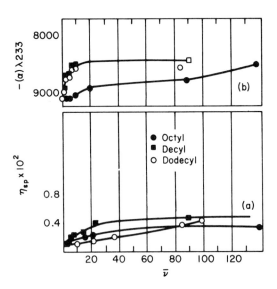

Fig. 2-2. Viscosities (a) and specific rotation (b) of BSA–alkyl sulfonate complexes as a function of molal ratio $\bar{v}$. (b) At Cotton effect trough (233 mμ). [J. Reynolds, S. Herbert, H. Polet, and J. Steinhardt (1967). *Biochemistry* **6**, 937.]

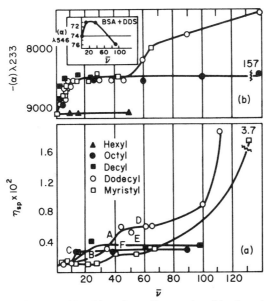

FIG. 2-3. Specific viscosities (a) and specific rotation (b) of various BSA–detergent sulfate complexes as a function of molal ratio $\bar{v}$. (b) At the Cotton effect trough (233 mμ). The insert shows results with dodecylsulfate 546 mμ. [J. Reynolds, S. Herbert, H. Polet, and J. Steinhardt (1967). *Biochemistry* **6**, 937.]

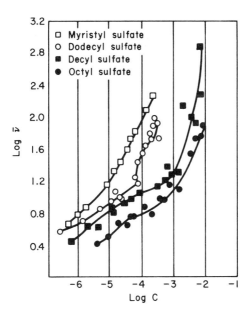

FIG. 2-4. Logarithmic plots of binding isotherms of BSA at 23° and pH 5.6 with various detergent sulfates. [J. Reynolds, S. Herbert, H. Polet, and J. Steinhardt (1967). *Biochemistry* **6**, 939.]

binding isotherm of sodium dodecylsulfate to bovine serum albumin (Fig. 2-4) shows a sharp discontinuity at log $C \cong -4.0$. By itself this does not prove conformational change in the protein since the large increase in binding over a relatively narrow range in C_{eq} could also be caused by micelle formation. (A sharp discontinuity in the binding isotherm is often referred to as evidence of a "cooperative process.") However, taken together with the viscosity and optical data, the singularity in the binding isotherm in this specific case is recognized as due to massive unfolding of the protein which leads to exposure of a large number of new sites with an association constant which may differ from that of the first set of sites on the native molecule. Binding of sufficient protons to macromolecules also usually results in conformational changes. A few which have been reported include alkaline phosphatase, hemoglobin, myoglobin, and serum albumin (Chapter V).

The mechanism by which conformational changes occur as a result of binding has been the subject of much investigation in recent years. The driving force for any degree of unfolding brought about by ligand-macromolecule interaction may be one or a combination of the following: (a) electrostatic repulsion between charges of a bound ionic ligand, including the net charge on the protein; (b) penetration of a hydrophobic tail into apolar regions of the macromolecules with the resultant replacement of conformation-stabilizing segment–segment interactions by ligand–segment interactions; (c) a ratio of the number of binding sites and their association constants in the native form to those in the unfolded form, which is favorable to unfolding.

The effect of increased net charge on a macromolecule has been investigated theoretically by Tanford (1961) and by Hill (1952). The latter has shown in an elegant application of Gibb's grand canonical ensemble to protein binding that a first-order phase transition is predicted as the number of binding sites for a charged ligand becomes very large.

An examination of Eq. (2-51) and (2-53) shows that the denominator of the first term contains the vector r_{kl} which is the distance between two binding sites on a macromolecular surface. Clearly, an increase in r_{kl} will lead to a decrease in W_{elec} and a consequent decrease in the free energy of the system. Thus, as the number of occupied binding sites is increased (when the ligand is a charged species), the macromolecule will tend to expand if by so doing it can reduce the free energy of the system.

Hydrophobic bonds (defined as a change in entropy of adjacent solvent water), hydrogen bonds, and dipole interactions have been shown to be important in stabilizing protein structure (Kauzman, 1959). If a segment–segment interaction such as a hydrophobic bond, hydrogen bond, or charge–charge interaction is replaced by a ligand–segment interaction through binding to the macromolecule, the stability of the protein *may* be reduced. Thus far there have been no proven examples of this type of macromolecular disruption although the explanation has been invoked without strong supporting evidence.

The third type of force responsible for unfolding brought about by ligand binding was first stated explicitly by Foster and Aoki (1958) in discussing the N → F transition (native to unfolded at pH ~ 4.0) of bovine serum albumin. Subsequently, Reynolds *et al.* (1967) considered a similar two-state model in which each protein molecule was considered to exist in two possible conformations—one native, the other unfolded. The total concentration of protein present at any equilibrium position during the binding of a ligand was expressed by means of the following enumeration:

$$\sum_{0}^{n} [\text{PA}_i] = [\text{P}] \sum_{s=0}^{n} [\text{A}]^s K^s \frac{n!}{s!(n-s)!} \qquad \text{(state 1—native)} \qquad (2\text{-}61)$$

$$\sum_{0}^{m} [\text{DA}_i] = [\text{D}] \sum_{n=0}^{n} [\text{A}]^r J^r \frac{m!}{n!(m-n)!} \qquad \text{(state 2—unfolded)} \qquad (2.62)$$

in which the concentration terms are [A] (ligand), [P] (native protein), and [D] (denatured protein).

The following simplifications and assumptions were employed:

(1) Activity coefficients are approximately 1, or constant, thus allowing substitutions of concentrations for activities.

(2) Each set of binding sites consists of identical, indistinguishable sites.

(3) Any set on the native proteins is destroyed when the macromolecule undergoes a phase transition and is replaced by a new set on the perturbed protein.

(4) The protein can exist in the perturbed state in the absence of bound ligand.

This is equivalent to the statement that

$$\text{P} \rightleftharpoons \text{D}$$

has a finite equilibrium constant.

The ratio of protein present in the two states [F(A)] is obtained by dividing Eq. (2-62) by (2-61)

$$F([\text{A}]) \equiv \frac{U \sum_{n=0}^{m} [\text{A}]^r J^r \dfrac{m!}{r!(m-r!)}}{\sum_{s=0}^{n} [\text{A}]^s K^s \dfrac{n!}{s!(n-s)!}} \qquad (2\text{-}63)$$

where $U = [\text{D}]/[\text{P}]$. An examination of the function $F([\text{A}])$ shows the conditions under which a minimum will obtain (stabilization of the protein structure in state 1) and also the conditions under which a transition from state 1 to state 2 is predicted.

Stabilization conditions:

$$K \gg J, \qquad n \leq m$$
$$K \geq J, \qquad n > m$$

Transition conditions:

$$m > n, \qquad K \geq J$$
$$m \leq n, \qquad K \ll J$$

Stabilization of protein conformation by ligand binding is a very general phenomenon observed in many systems (e.g., Markus *et al.*, 1964). Also, it should be pointed out that other mechanisms of unfolding may be operative in conjunction with the one just described. Electrostatic repulsion may induce a phase transition *before* the ligand-induced transition conditions above are fulfilled. [See Chapters IV, VII, and IX.]

As a result of the unfolding described the actual binding isotherm contains terms for binding by both native and unfolded protein. The complete expression for $\bar{v}$ is

$$\bar{v} = \frac{[A]}{1 + F([A])} \left[\frac{nK}{1 + K[A]} + \frac{F([A])mJ}{1 + J[A]} \right] \qquad (2\text{-}64)$$

See Figs. 7-14 and 7-15 for the agreement of experimental data with Eq. (2.64).

VIII. Linked Functions

It is appropriate at this point to discuss briefly the theory of linked functions as presented by Wyman (1964) since it can be related directly to alterations in the equilibrium constant between native and denatured states as a function of ligand binding. (See Chapter VIII for application to hemerythrin.)

Assume an equilibrium between two states of a macromolecule, each of which binds ligand

$$x_i P \rightleftarrows x_j D + (x_i - x_j) L \qquad (2\text{-}65)$$

where x_i is the number of ligand molecules bound to P and x_j, the number of ligand molecules bound to D.

$$K = \frac{\sum\limits_{s=0}^{m} (x_j[D])}{\sum\limits_{i=0}^{n} (x_i[P])} \qquad (2\text{-}66)$$

where n is the number of sites on P and m, the number of sites on D, or

$$K = \frac{[D] \sum\limits_{j=0}^{m} k_j x_j}{[P] \sum\limits_{i=0}^{n} k_i x_i} \qquad (2\text{-}67)$$

where k_j and k_i are the individual site equilibrium constants for binding to states D and P.

As in the last section, the equilibrium constant [D]/[P] (referring to uncombined macromolecules) is independent of x_i.

Equation (2-67) may be rewritten

$$\ln K = \ln[D] \sum\limits_{j=0}^{m} k_j x_j - \ln[P] \sum\limits_{i=0}^{n} k_i x_i \qquad (2\text{-}68)$$

$$\frac{d \ln K}{d \ln x} = \frac{d \ln \sum\limits_{j=0}^{m} k_j x_j}{d \ln x} - \frac{d \ln \sum\limits_{i=0}^{n} k_i x_i}{d \ln x} \qquad (2\text{-}69)$$

If $\bar{v}_i$ is the amount bound to P and $\bar{v}_j$ is the amount bound to D

$$\bar{v}_i = \frac{\sum\limits_{i} i k_i x^i}{\sum\limits_{i} k_i x_i} = \frac{d \ln \sum k_i x^i}{d \ln x} \qquad (2\text{-}70)$$

and

$$j = \frac{\sum\limits_{j} j k_j x^j}{\sum\limits_{j} k_j x_j} = \frac{d \ln \sum k_j x^j}{d \ln x} \qquad (2\text{-}71)$$

Substituting (2-70) and (2-71) into (2-72) we obtain

$$\frac{d \ln K}{d \ln x} = \bar{v}_i - \bar{v}_j = \Delta \bar{v} \qquad (2\text{-}72)$$

In the notation of Section VII, Eq. (2-72) becomes

$$\frac{d \ln F([A])}{d \ln x} = \Delta \bar{v} \qquad (2\text{-}73)$$

In other words, if the equilibrium concentrations of P and D are known (by absorbance, electrophoresis, or gel filtration, for example) at a given concentration one has a direct measure of the difference in number of ligand molecules bound to each state. When [D]/[P] is a function of pH (or other environmental parameter other than [A]) the dependence of Δv on this parameter may also be obtained.

A further discussion of linked functions in which the effects of protein hydration have been incorporated has recently appeared (Tanford, 1969). The simple treatment given above is extended to include water as a ligand, so that the case of two protein states with two ligand molecules is presented. The final result

$$\frac{d \ln K}{d \ln a_x} = \Delta \bar{v}_x = \frac{n_x}{n_w} \Delta \bar{v}_w \qquad (2\text{-}74)$$

shows clearly that as long as transitions take place at low a_x (n_x/n_w is very small) the effect of hydration or bound water is negligible. It may not necessarily be negligible for a transition, the mid point of which occurs at $2M$ NaCl, such as the dissociation of hemoglobin.

REFERENCES

Arnold, R., and Overbeck, J. Th. G. (1950). *Rec. Trav. Chim.* **69**, 192.

Bjerrum, N. (1923). *Z. Physik. Chem.* **106**, 219.

Born, M. (1920). *Z. Physik. Chem.* **1**, 45.

Debye, P., and Hückel, E. (1923). *Z. Physik. Chem.* **24**, 185, 305.

Edsall, J. T., and Wyman, J. (1958). "Biophysical Chemistry," Vol. I, Chapters 5, 8. Academic Press, New York.

Foster, J. F., and Aoki, K. (1958). *J. Am. Chem. Soc.* **80**, 5215.

Gane, R., and Ingold, C. K. (1931). *J. Chem. Soc.* 2153.

Halsey, G., and Taylor, H. (1947). *J. Chem. Phys.* **15**, 640.

Harris, F. E., and Rice, S. A. (1952). *J. Chem. Phys.* **25**, 955.

Hill, T. L. (1952). *J. Phys. Chem.* **57**, 324.

Hill, T. L. (1955). *Arch. Biochem. Biophys.* **57**, 299.

Hill, T. L. (1960). "Introduction to Statistical Thermodynamics." Addison-Wesley, Reading, Massachusetts.

Karush, F., and Sonnenberg, M. (1949). *J. Am. Chem. Soc.* **71**, 1369.

Kauzman, W. (1959). *Advan. Protein Chem.* **14**, 1.

Kirkwood, J. G. (1934). *J. Chem. Phys.* **2**, 331.

Kirkwood, J. G., and Westheimer, F. H. (1938). *J. Chem. Phys.* **6**, 506, 513.

Klotz, I. M. (1953). In "The Proteins" (H. Neurath and K. Bailey, eds.), Vol. I, p. 727. Academic Press, New York.

Langmuir, J. (1918). *J. Am. Chem. Soc.* **40**, 1361.

Linderström-Lang, K. (1924). *Compt. Rend. Trav. Lab. Carlsberg* **15**, No. 7.

Markus, G., Love, R. L., and Wissler, F. C. (1964). *J. Biol. Chem.* **239**, 3678.

Michaelis, L. (1925). *Z. Physik. Chem.* **152**, 183.

Ortung, W. H. (1968). *J. Am. Chem. Soc.* **91**, 162.

Perutz, M. F. (1965). *J. Mol. Biol.* **13**, 646.

Reynolds, J. A., Herbert, S., Polet, H., and Steinhardt, J. (1967). *Biochemistry* **6**, 937.

Riddiford, L. M., and Scheraga, H. A. (1962). *Biochemistry* **1**, 95.

Scatchard, G. (1949). *Ann. N. Y. Acad. Sci.* **51**, 660.

Sips, R. (1948). *J. Chem. Phys.* **16**, 490.

Sips, R. (1950). *J. Chem. Phys.* **18**, 1024.

Steinhardt, J., and Zaiser, E. M. (1955). *Advan. Protein Chem.* **10**, 155, (part 3). Academic Press, New York.

Steinhardt, J., and Beychok, S. (1964). "The Proteins" (H. Neurath, ed.), Vol. II p. 139. Academic Press, New York.

Tanford, C. (1957). *J. Am. Chem. Soc.* **79**, 5340, 5348.

Tanford, C. (1961). "Physical Chemistry of Macromolecules." Wiley, New York.

Tanford, C. (1962). *Advan. Protein. Chem.* **17**, 69.

Tanford, C. (1969). *J. Mol. Biol.* **39**, 539.

Tanford, C., and Kirkwood, J. G. (1957). *J. Am. Chem. Soc.* **79**, 5333.

Weber, G. (1965). *In* "Molecular Biophysics" (A. Pullman and M. Weissbluth, eds.), p. 369. Academic Press, New York.

Weber, G., and Anderson, S. R. (1965). *Biochemistry* **4**, 1942.

Wyman, J. (1964). *Advan. Protein Chem.* **19**.

III

The Measurement of Complex Formation

I. Introduction

The binding of one substance by another—the formation of identifiable complexes between them—may be measured in a number of ways, most of which fall into two broad categories:

(a) In some cases the amount of complex formed when two or more species are mixed together may be determined directly (e.g., spectroscopic determination of the concentration of the complex). This method is particularly attractive when there is one-to-one stoichiometry, and it is not necessary to distinguish between complexes containing different amounts of ligand. Enzyme–substrate reactions are a good example, since the velocity of the catalyzed reaction may be proportional to the amount of complex formed. In many cases, however, even when a simple one-step reaction is involved, the change in a particular property that distinguishes the formation of complex is difficult to distinguish from allosteric or solvent effects. Furthermore, the proportionality of this change in property to the amount of complex formed must be determined by calibration.

(b) The more general method depends on measuring the change in thermodynamic activity, or concentration, of the ligand as a result of the binding of part of it to another separate chemical species. Such a determination is often easier to make than the determination of the concentration of ligand complexes described above, but it usually involves uncertainties which must be circumvented by any of a number of expedients selected for their suitability in the particular system under study. The most direct methods are measurements of the change in vapor pressure of the ligand when it can exist in the gaseous form or of the change in potential of a reversible electrode, specific to a ligand ion. Few such electrodes are readily available, and they may be subject to poisoning by the other reactive groups of the binding body. When the ligand constitutes the only ionic species present, a membrane selectively permeable to ions *having the same charge as the ligand* can be interposed between the mixture and a solution containing a known activity of ligand alone. A membrane potential will develop which can be used to calculate the activity of the ligand in the presence of a binding body. By far the most generally applicable method, however, is to use a membrane permeable to all the ions present, except the protein, and to measure the concentration of free ligand on the side that contains no protein. If the total electrolyte concentration is high enough to reduce the Donnan potential and its accompanying osmotic differential across the membrane to a negligible value, the concentration of uncombined ligand on both sides of the membrane will be the same. Since the total ligand introduced and all the volumes are known, the amount of ligand bound follows from a simple subtractive calculation.

As a practical matter the method of equilibrium dialysis which has just been described, although more widely useful than any other, suffers from a number of serious disadvantages, which are described on pp. 46–50.

Regardless of which subtractive method is used, determination of an isotherm requires knowledge of the total amount of ligand added and the amount left uncombined. When the affinity is very low (little complex formed), only a small fraction of the ligand added is bound, and there is usually no great difficulty in determining the free ligand, since the latter differs only slightly from the total added. Unless a method is used that measures the bound ligand directly, there is likely to be a substantial range of uncertainty in the amount of complex formed, unless very high affinities are involved, since calculation of the latter depends on the *difference* between two numbers which do not differ greatly from one another, and at least one of which is subject to error.

On the other hand, when the affinity is very great (practically all the ligand bound), there is little if any uncertainty in the value of $\bar{v}$, the average molal ratio of the complex. The latter approaches closely to the ratio of total ligand to protein. Thus there is no difficulty in making up a solution characterized by a given $\bar{v}$, for determination of its physical properties. However, determination of the amount of free ligand in equilibrium with the complex, C_{eq}, is another matter, since the quantity may be so small as to occasion a very substantial percentage of error in its determination. It may even elude analysis—or detection—altogether. Determination of the association constant, or of the free energy of binding, is very strongly affected by this elusive quantity. Thus, the possibility of substantial error arises when the binding constant exceeds 10^5. Since K is proportional to $1/C$ for any given value of $\bar{v}/(n - \bar{v})$, binding constants of about 10^7 may be indistinguishable experimentally from others 10 to 100 times greater.

These figures are not absolute since they depend on methods of analysis, which differ greatly in their accuracy from one ligand to another. In the case of antibodies very much higher binding constants have proved to be measurable because of the remarkable sensitivity and specificity of complement fixation (Karush, 1969).

Determination of binding isotherms, especially in cases of multiple equilibria, requires the measurement of paired values of $\bar{v}$ and C_{eq} over a range of C_{eq} which covers from 2 to 4 logarithmic units. To some extent, therefore, even a high-affinity determination runs into the difficulties described above for a low-affinity complex, at the highest values of $\bar{v}$ and C_{eq}. The reverse is also true for low-affinity complexes at the lowest values of $\bar{v}$ and C_{eq}. Both of these difficulties may be minimized by varying the concentration of the binding body (protein) in such a way as to keep the fraction of ligand bound from approaching values too close to either 1 or 0, where errors in either $\bar{v}$ or C_{eq} will be great, i.e., using low concentrations of protein when the fraction bound tends to be high, and high concentrations when the fraction bound tends to be low. This expedient is available only if the isotherms at different concentrations of protein can be shown to be identical.

One of the most troublesome sources of error, particularly important when ligands of high affinity ($K \gg 10^5$) are involved, is the presence of traces of impurities of lower affinity which are indistinguishable by the methods of analysis from the ligand of interest. Almost all the methods of analysis which are available for high-affinity ligands are incapable of distinguishing between different ligands of the same class, e.g., anionic long-chain alkyl sulfates or sulfonates which differ in molecular weight or in stereoisomerism. Even radioisotope labeling cannot be relied on when highly purified starting products (not usually available) are employed. Free radical formation and subsequent formation of new compounds may occur and lead to the presence of contaminants which may be included in the ligand titer. Methods which depend on determination of counterions rather than of ligand ions (Karush, 1950), such as sodium flame photometry or sodium electrodes, are still less specific.

The presence of trace impurities, assayed as ligand, can have even more serious consequences than introduction of error in the determination of C_{eq}. These consequences are more serious the greater the free energy of binding of the ligand under investigation. When, for example, conditions (protein and ligand concentrations) are such that the fraction of the ligand which is combined exceeds 99%, and 0.5% of the amount introduced is an impurity of very low affinity, nearly half of the measured value of C_{eq} represents the impurity. The isotherm will then be seriously distorted to an extent that increases as $\bar{v}/n$ approaches zero (Fig. 3-1).

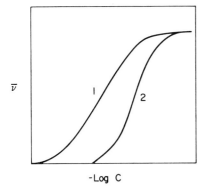

$\bar{v}$

-Log C

Fig. 3-1. Difference between true isotherm (curve 1) and apparent isotherm (curve 2) when traces of lower-affinity homologous ligands are present and assayed as ligand.

Disruption of a still more serious consequence may be illustrated by postulation of specific values of K. If $K = 10^7$, in the absence of impurity $\bar{v}/n = 0.5$ when $C_{eq} = 10^{-7}$. If the protein concentration is $10^{-5}\,M$ and $n = 10$, the total ligand employed is about $5 \times 10^{-5}\,M$ and the fraction combined is thus about 0.998. If only 0.1% of the "ligand" represents low-affinity impurity, the apparent C_{eq} rises from 10^{-7} to 1.5×10^{-7}, and the apparent K falls to 6.7×10^6. However, if 10 times more concentrated protein is employed (a more usual figure), the total ligand used will also be roughly 10 times as great, and, to a first approximation, C_{eq} will not be greatly changed. However, the unbound trace impurity will now be about $5 \times 10^{-7}\,M$, rather than $0.5 \times 10^{-7}\,M$; thus the *apparent* C_{eq} will be 6×10^{-7}, and the *apparent* K will fall to 1.7×10^6.

If the impurity were 1% rather than 0.1%, a much larger error would result with all but the lowest possible protein concentrations; or the same size error would result with actual K values as small as 10^6. Errors of this type become negligible only when K is smaller than 10^4 or 10^5. It should be noted that, for convenience, we have cited as the apparent K the values of $1/C_{eq}$ for $\bar{v}/n = 0.5$. Different discrepancies would result at other ratios of $\bar{v}$ to n, larger ones for the smaller ratios, and smaller ones as $\bar{v} \to n$. The apparent isotherms are therefore distorted, i.e., will not fit Eq. (2-26) (Fig. 3-1).

It should be noted that the effects of low-affinity trace impurities just described will simulate a large effect of protein concentration on K. Failure of the isotherms to fit Eq. (2-26) at the higher protein concentrations is one indication that the situation just described may be responsible. The effect on the isotherm of intensified purification of the ligand preparation is another. When the method of measurement is equilibrium dialysis, there is a simple expedient for detecting the presence of such an effect, and for eliminating it. This expedient is described in the discussion of equilibrium dialysis. With any method the closest approximation to the true isotherm is the one which is obtained with the most dilute protein, because the ratio of impurity to true C_{eq} is lowest under that condition. Values of this ratio under about 0.1 then generally can be neglected.

In the sections which follow, data are cited which have been obtained by all of the following specific methods (we have excluded other methods that have been used only for qualitative or demonstrative purposes):

II. *Subtractive Methods*
   A. EMF measurements of free ligand activity
      1. Reversible specific-ion electrodes
         a. Hydrogen ion
         b. Other ions
      2. Permselective membranes with nonpolarizable electrodes
   B. Equilibrium dialysis, with or without Donnan effect complications, using various methods for determining free ligand (radioisotopes, complexing and extracting, partition equilibria between immiscible solvents, spectroscopy, among others)
   C. Ultrafiltration and ultracentrifugation
   D. Gel filtration
   E. Partition equilibria between phases
      1. Solid–liquid
      2. Liquid–liquid
      3. Gas–liquid
   F. Electrical conductivity
   G. Polarography
   H. Determination of free ligand without separation of phases

III. *Direct Measurement*
   A. Direct spectroscopic observation of bound chromophores (trypan blue, Biebrich scarlet)
   B. Fluorescence methods
   C. Optical rotation
   D. Nuclear magnetic resonance
   E. X-ray diffraction
   F. Refractive index
   G. Light-scattering and osmotic pressure
   H. Biological activity

IV. *Electrostatic Methods*
    A. Electrophoresis
    B. Changes in the titration curves of proteins due to the presence of bound ions
    C. The ΔpH method of Scatchard and Black
    D. Dielectric increment and dispersion
V. *Other Methods*
    A. Complement fixation
    B. Methods which depend on competition

II. Subtractive Methods

A. EMF Measurements of Free Ligand Activity

1. *Reversible Specific Ion Electrodes*

(a) *Hydrogen Ion.* The most widely used method described in this chapter is the determination of H^+ binding using a reversible electrode system. It is described in detail because of this wide use, which rests on the familiar notion that a hydrogen-gas electrode immersed in solution develops a potential related to the H^+ activity (see Chapter II). All of the more convenient secondary electrode procedures used for this purpose depend on their precise, functional correspondence to the hydrogen-gas electrode, to which they may be related by assignment of an appropriate reference potential. The emf method of measuring the extent of binding requires the conversion of the measurement of *activity* to one of *concentration*, by dividing the hydrogen-ion activity a by the appropriate activity coefficient, γ. The amounts bound are then calculated by subtracting the free concentrations from the total H^+ introduced into the system.

Unfortunately, it is a thermodynamic idealization, which is without operational correspondence, to assign an activity (or an activity coefficient) to a single ion. Furthermore, as a practical matter, the use of cells containing liquid junctions contributes a liquid-junction potential to the emf observed; and it is necessary to assure that in a series of measurements the former is either very small, or does not change within the range of the measurements, including measurement of the system in the reference state. The requirement can be met, in any one solvent, by using reproducible liquid junctions between solutions, at least one of which contains the highest possible concentrations of KCl (the "salt bridge"). When $[H^+]$ is high, however, as it is in the reference state ($E \equiv 0$ in HCl of unit activity), there is a substantial and imprecisely known contribution of the H^+ ion to the liquid-junction potential. As a practical matter, therefore, the reference state is commonly taken to be a well-studied buffer solution (partially neutralized weak acid), the hydrogen-ion activity of which has been related to the original standard by exact thermo-dynamic investigation. Usually this procedure is more useful than one which attempts to assign standard half-cell potentials to various working electrodes such as calomel cells of known composition, or silver–silver chloride elec-trodes, since great care is required in producing such electrodes if they are to give precisely the potentials they have been assigned. These expedients, how-ever, are commonly not available when systems other than dilute aqueous salt solutions are involved, and for many systems of interest it must be stated that "the relation of the pH scale to the pH scale in dilute aqueous solutions is not well defined" or efforts may have to be made to define it from first principles.

When measurements are made in sufficiently dilute aqueous systems at constant ionic strength, the hydrogen-ion *concentrations* are proportional to the activities, regardless of the validity of the activity coefficient which is assigned. The pH scale is thus easily converted to a *relative* concentration scale. However, it is obvious that the value of $\gamma_\pm[H^+]$ assigned, regardless of how it has been arrived at, has a pronounced effect on the calculated value of H^+ bound whenever the fraction, bound acid/total acid, is appreciably lower than 1, i.e., at low pH. For this reason, it is essential that the conven-tional definition of pH (or pA when other ligands A are involved) permit a close approximation to physically meaningful values of *concentration*. Methods that will achieve this over most of the pH scale will not always achieve it at extreme values, where the liquid-junction potential ambiguity adds to an already difficult experimental situation, i.e., only small fractions of ligand present are bound. Hydrogen ion introduces larger uncertainties than other ions because of its high transport number.

Assuming that the activity of a single ion can be measured, then the electrical potential difference between two identical reversible electrodes immersed in two solutions containing that ion in two different concentrations is given by substituting $\varepsilon \mathscr{F}$ for $[(\mu_i)_1 - (\mu_i)_2]$ in Eq. (2-14). Thus,

$$\varepsilon = \frac{RT}{\mathscr{F}} \ln \frac{(a_i)_1}{(a_i)_2} = \frac{RT}{\mathscr{F}} \Delta pH \qquad (3\text{-}1)$$

The determination of pH is now almost universally made by measuring the potential of the following cell:

Ag, AgCl, HCl ($\sim 0.1 M$) $\|$ glass $\|$ solution containing H^+ ions $\|$ sat'd. KCl $\|$ Hg$_2$Cl$_2$, Hg

If pH_s is the pH of a standard solution, pH_x the pH of a solution x, and ε_s and ε_x the measured emf values of these two solutions in the cell above, then setting $pH = -\log a_{H^+}$

$$pH_x = pH_s + \frac{\varepsilon_x - \varepsilon_s}{2.303RT} \qquad (3\text{-}2)$$

or, at 25°,

$$pH_x = pH_s + \frac{\varepsilon_x - \varepsilon_s}{0.0591} \qquad (3\text{-}3)$$

The present approach is to measure the emf of Eq. (3-3), using a series of standard solutions the pH values of which have been predetermined by precise measurements employing cells without liquid junction. $[H^+]\gamma_{H^+}$ is then taken to be $a_{H^+} a_{Cl^-}/[Cl^-]\gamma_{Cl^-}$; γ_{Cl^-} or γ_{anion} is calculated from the Debye-Hückel theory (Bates, 1954).

The difficulties of interpreting the pH of highly acid solutions are apparent, and these difficulties may introduce errors at the extremes of titration curves. In order to determine how much hydrogen ion is bound at any pH, one subtracts the free hydrogen-ion concentration (calculated from pH) from that which would result from introducing the same amount of acid to the same volume of solution without protein. Evidently $-\log[H^+]\gamma_{H^+}$ is not available since γ_{H^+} cannot be measured. For this special purpose pH is defined as $-\log[H^+](\gamma_\pm)_{HCl}$ and the titration is carried out at a fixed KCl concentration in which the mean activity coefficient of HCl is known (Harned and Owen, 1950). It is obvious that this procedure is not completely logical or exact.

Above pH 4 and below pH 10, the free H^+ and OH^- concentrations, respectively, are low relative to what is bound, so long as the protein concentration is higher than about 0.5% (the equivalent hydrogen-ion combining weight of many proteins is about 1000). The small uncertainty in the activity coefficient is accordingly not serious. Outside these limits, the uncertainty becomes increasingly important as the extremes of pH are approached. At pH values near 2, it is not unusual for the bound H^+ to be less than 50% of the total. At such a pH, an exact value of an activity coefficient is critical but unavailable. At these same pH values the entire definition of the pH scale when related to the cell used and the uncomfortably high value of the liquid-junction potential combine to frustrate any attempts at accuracy, with resultant vagueness in the acid end point. Linderström-Lang and Nielsen (1959) define the $\gamma_\pm$ in $-\log[H^+]\gamma_\pm$ as a "poorly-defined, empirical, miserable coefficient."

The construction of an experimental protein titration curve or hydrogen-ion isotherm is straightforward. From what has been said already, a fundamental requirement is constancy of ionic strength (essential for theoretical interpretation) and a known, fixed concentration of protein. For many proteins a concentration between 0.5% and 1% gives the most precise results. A discontinuous titration (determination of discrete points) is the most convenient way to hold protein concentration and ionic strength constant.

The first step is to prepare isoionic materials. Dintzis (1952) devised the mixed bed of Dowex 1 and Dowex 50 resins in the hydroxyl hydrogen form for this purpose. If the resin denatures the protein, then exhaustive dialysis against distilled water is used or, for proteins of rather acid or alkaline isoionic points, electrodialysis is employed.

The first point on the curve should be the pH of the isoionic protein solution at the ionic strength which will be used throughout, no acid or alkali having been added. Mean activity coefficients of HCl or KOH are known in solutions of KCl or NaCl; the former is preferable for ionic strength control because of the well-known sodium error of many varieties of glass electrodes, and because KCl is used in the salt bridge to minimize liquid-junction potential. For the same reasons, KOH is the alkali of choice.

After each aliquot of acid is added, the measured pH is converted to pC ($-\log C_H$) by adding $-\log(\gamma_\pm)_{HCl}$. The free hydrogen ion concentration so determined is subtracted from the total acid added. The difference is total *bound* hydrogen ion which, when divided by the protein concentration, yields equivalents of hydrogen bound per mole of protein if the molecular weight of the protein is known, or H^+ equivalents per gram of protein otherwise. When alkali is added, pOH is calculated from pK_w and pH and then pC_{OH} from the mean activity coefficient of the alkali (Harned and Owen, 1950), and the remainder of the procedure is the same. Bound OH^- is usually converted to the more meaningful "hydrogen ion dissociated," to which it is formally equivalent.

When results are expressed as H^+ bound/mole protein, it is essential that any pH dependence of molecular weight be recognized and taken into account.

In the interpretation of protein titration curves, it is important to be able to distinguish the various ionizable groups from one another. This subject is discussed more fully in Chapter V. It is helpful in this operation to know the numbers of groups in each set. Two of the early techniques for determining amino groups were the formol titrations of Sorensen (1907) and the acetone titration of Linderström-Lang (1927, 1928). The alcohol titration of Willstatter and Waldschmidt-Leitz (1921) have been useful in the determination of carboxyl groups.

In 1925 Strenstrom and Reinhard (1925) found that the ionization of the phenolic hydroxyl of tyrosine gives rise to a large change in its ultraviolet absorption spectrum. It is well established that the absorption of proteins between 250 and 310 mμ is primarily due to the aromatic residues tryptophan, tyrosine, and phenylalanine (Beaven and Holiday, 1952). Of these, only tyrosine is capable of dissociating a proton when it is part of a peptide chain. The phenolic hydroxyl of tyrosine in proteins is expected to titrate at pH values near 10. Thus, the spectrum is examined at pH near neutrality and at small increments of pH up to pH 13 (lower if a constant spectrum is observed independent of further pH change). Generally, the position of the maximum shifts from about 275 mμ to about 295 mμ during this titration with a substantial increase in molar extinction at the higher wavelength. If the total difference at 295 mμ between the neutral pH values and that in alkali is $\Delta\varepsilon_{295}$ max and the difference at any intermediate pH is $\Delta\varepsilon$, then $\Delta\varepsilon/(\Delta\varepsilon_{295}$ max $- \Delta\varepsilon)$ is equal to the ratio of ionized to un-ionized tyrosine. This together with the observed pH gives the apparent pK of the tyrosine ionization. Wetlaufer (1962) gives a detailed account of the basis of this method.

The first application of this technique to proteins was in the investigation by Crammer and Neuberger (1943) of the tyrosyl ionization in ovalbumin and insulin. They found that several of the phenolic hydroxyls in ovalbumin do not ionize at all until the pH is raised to about 13, while in insulin all tyrosines are fully ionized before that pH is reached.

(b) *Other Ions.* Reversible electrodes seldom have been used to measure binding of ions other than hydrogen ions. This is due primarily to the scarcity in the past of specific-ion electrodes, especially those that can be used in the presence of proteins. Studies have, however, been carried out with reversible silver–silver halide or silver–silver thiocyanate electrodes by Scatchard *et al.* (1950). The electrodes were protected from reacting with the protein by coating them with collodion (Scatchard *et al.*, 1950). Scatchard *et al.* (1957, 1959) and Carr (1953) have also used electrodes with nonreversible salt bridges to determine the activity of numerous small ions by setting up concentration potentials across anion-exchange membranes. This latter method will be discussed separately. Both methods depend on the equation

$$\varepsilon = \frac{RT}{\mathscr{F}} \ln \frac{[L]'\gamma'}{[L]\gamma} \tag{3-4}$$

in which [L] represents concentration of ligand ion and primed quantities refer to the protein-free solutions. It is usually assumed that $\gamma' = \gamma$.

The use of collodion membranes on the electrodes (Scatchard *et al.*, 1950) introduces the additional assumption that free ion activities are the same in the bulk phase, and beneath the membrane. Since the protein does not penetrate the membrane, this is equivalent to assuming that there is no Donnan inequality (which would make activity of the free ligand at the electrode higher than in the bulk phase). The validity of this approximation depends, as in all Donnan effects, on the relative concentrations of protein, ligand, and other diffusible salts.

When specific-ion reversible electrodes are used to measure the binding of other than hydrogen ions the same problems arise as with hydrogen ion: ambiguities due to liquid-junction potentials and activity coefficients. The first of these is probably negligible at all times, and the second difficulty is reduced when constant ionic strengths are maintained since a constant ratio then prevails between activities, which the potentials measure, and concentrations. As with hydrogen ion a precise determination of this ratio is important mainly when the fraction of ligand combined is small.[1] However, the maintenance of a constant ionic strength is not as simple as when interest is focused on the uptake of hydrogen ion. One or both of the ions of any salt added for this purpose is likely to be an effective ligand also, and competition may result. It may, therefore, be necessary to calculate activity coefficients rather than attempt to keep them constant for each concentration of ligand. With highly asymmetric ions, such as detergents, or with highly charged ions, such as a second protein, these calculations may fall wide of the mark.

The calculation of amounts bound follows the same procedure as in the determination of acid-titration curves. The total ligand remaining free in the experimental volume and expressed in moles is subtracted from the total introduced, and the difference is divided by the number of moles of protein present to give $\bar{v}$, the molal ratio. All of the quantities enumerated in this paragraph are *concentrations*, which must, in some cases, be obtained from activities, by the use of appropriate activity coefficients. The isotherm, itself, however, is governed by the *activity* of the unbound ligand, and in using any of the graphical methods for obtaining the association constant, a_{ligand} rather than C_{ligand} should always be plotted—unless it has proved possible, without complication, to perform all of the experiments at the same ionic strength.

2. Permselective Membranes with Nonpolarizable Electrodes

The use of membranes permeable solely to anions or to cations, together with nonpolarizable electrodes to make contact with the two separated bulk phases (only one of which contains protein) was described by Carr (1953), who used protamine–collodion, or polysulfonate–collodion membranes, depending upon the charge desired. Scatchard et al. (1957, 1959) have made extensive binding studies with anion-exchange membranes that were available commercially. Carr investigated the binding of a number of halides to several different proteins on the basis of an assumption that the activity coefficient of the permeable ion was the same on the two sides of the membrane (i.e., the protein does not affect the activity coefficient of the free ligand and the concentrations are not very different on the two sides). Scatchard et al. (1957) made a related assumption that the ratios of the activity coefficient of the ligand (anion) to the mean activity coefficient in the protein-containing and the protein-free solutions, are the same, and discussed the validity of the assumption. They added other halides as well as thiocyanate and trichloroacetate to the halides and cations studied by Carr.

---

[1] If the ratio used is incorrect, the binding constant determined from the experiments will be in error by the same proportion as the ratio.

The depression of the activity of the ligand ion in the presence of protein is taken to indicate binding of the ion since the activity coefficients have been assumed to be the same. Scatchard *et al.* (1957) made calibration curves of emf versus salt concentration by separating solutions of sodium salts of various anions by the anion-exchange membrane with each side connected by a salt bridge to a calomel electrode. When protein at stoichiometric concentration, m_2, is present in a salt solution of concentration, m_3, on one side of the membrane and the other side contains salt at m_3, then the number of moles of anion bound per mole of protein, $\bar{v}$, may be given as

$$\bar{v} = \frac{(m_3 - [X^-])}{m_2} \tag{3-5}$$

in which $[X^-]$ is the concentration of the *unbound* anion species X, calculated from the calibration curve with the assumption about mean activity coefficients stated above.

Very useful, although few, results have been obtained by this method; the increased availability of reliable permselective membranes should lead to further work at an early date. Data obtained in our laboratory indicate that the method may be limited to ions which are not as asymmetrical as long-chain detergents or polymeric ions. (Cassel *et al.*, 1969).

B. EQUILIBRIUM DIALYSIS

Probably more measurements of binding of neutral molecules and ions other than H^+ to protein have been carried out by this method than by all others combined. Results obtained by equilibrium dialysis up to about 1951 have been reviewed by Klotz (1953), who gave great impetus to the use of this method by the example of his own work.

A large proportion of all the investigations based on this method have been concerned with bovine and human serum albumin (Klotz, Karush, Pallansch, Foster, Marcus, Luck, Ray, Reynolds, among others), but the method has also been used with β-lactoglobulin (Hill and Briggs) and with a number of enzymes (ribonuclease, Loeb and Saroff; lysozyme, Rupley, etc.) and their substrates or inhibitors, as well as with simple ions. (All references are given in Chapter VII.)

The essence of the equilibrium dialysis method is to contain the protein within one compartment separated from another by a membrane permeable to all the components of the system except the protein. At equilibrium the chemical potential of all of the components (properly defined), except the protein, is the same in both compartments. The chemical potential of the free ligand in the protein-free compartment may then be determined at equilibrium, without interference by the protein. It is then converted into concentration by making use of all of the assumptions, subject to the same uncertainties, that have already been discussed in the case of reversible electrodes. Alternatively, the concentration may be measured directly by suitable analytical means. However, if this is done, additional reasoning is required to assure that concentration has the same relation to chemical potential on the two sides of the membrane. Chemical potentials (or activities) are measured by reversible electrodes or, when gases are involved, by partial pressures. Concentrations are measured by optical properties, by complexing with dyes, by extracting with suitable, almost immiscible solvents, by radioisotope labeling, by catalytic assay (see, for example, Tritsch, 1967), specific absorption (Merzbach et al., 1963), or by calculations based on measurements of electrical conductivity or amperometry (McMenamy et al., 1968), as well as by numerous other methods.

The presence of the membrane introduces the usual problem of Donnan inequalities or, if the latter are suppressed by salts, of competition with the ligand by the salts added. The concentration of the latter will usually be over a thousand-fold greater than that of the free ligand. Klotz (1953) summarizes all of the earlier data on competition. In general, competition may be expected to have significant effects when the product of free ligand concentration multiplied by its binding constant is not over 10–100 times larger than the product of buffer concentration multiplied by buffer binding constant. Klotz has shown that many buffers, including acetate, compete strongly with the binding of methyl orange to BSA—there is little competition when phosphate is used. Cassel et al. (1969) found that cacodylate competes strongly with detergent anions also. While all of the data just cited were obtained in studies of anion binding, it seems likely that buffer ion competition will also interfere with binding studies on neutral molecules. It is often not feasible to reduce buffer concentrations below about 0.03 M since the buffers are required for regulation of pH. Donnan effects may not be negligible in the binding of neutral molecules unless the protein is truly isoionic and no other ions are present. Recourse must therefore be had to the use of minimal concentrations of weak binders such as phosphate (when the protein is BSA) and to avoiding addition of neutral salts. Algebraic methods of taking the effects of competition into account are given in Chapter II. The membrane may introduce other sources of error. The rate at which equilibrium is approached is very variable, and depends on stirring, pretreatment of the membrane, the volumes on both sides, protein concentration, temperature, and nature of the supporting electrolyte. The length of time required for the attainment of equilibrium precludes studying the kinetics of the binding process. In general small volumes should be used with the largest possible surface of separation (membrane). To expedite attainment of equilibrium (always desirable if protein denaturation or putrefaction is to be avoided), the system should be stirred or otherwise agitated to renew the layer in contact with the membrane. Low temperatures are desirable. The equilibria are often almost wholly independent of temperature, and the rates of transfer are only slightly reduced as the temperature falls, but the stability of protein, and of ligand (if, e.g., esters are employed) is greatly improved at cold-room temperatures. With ligands of high affinity (large binding constant) the attainment of equilibrium is greatly expedited by starting with all of the ligand on the protein side of the membrane. Far less transport across the membrane is required than when all the ligand is initially on the other side. However, it must be established that the initially high ligand–protein ratio has not produced irreversible unfolding.

Grossly misleading conclusions may result if difficulties in attaining equilibrium are not taken into account. With serum albumin such delays are observed when neutral salts rather than buffers are used as supporting electrolytes; and when high protein concentrations ($>0.1\%$) are used, and large amounts of ligand must be transported across the dialysis membrane. Both delays occur only when the ligand and protein are initially separated by the dialysis membrane. Since thermodynamic isotherms must be attainable by approaching equilibrium from both sides, uncertainty, or incorrect conclusions, as to the association constant may result when the approach from one side takes very much longer than from the other.

When dilute protein (0.1 % BSA) and a noncompeting buffer (0.033 ionic strength phosphate) are used, all of the ionic ligands used in the authors' laboratory (Cassel *et al.*, 1969), including normal hydrocarbon sulfates and sulfonates containing up to 14 carbon atoms, attain equilibrium with the protein within 24 hours at room temperature and well within 48 hours at $2°$, unless very high molal ratios, $\bar{v}$, are involved. Unambiguous isotherms result. When NaCl is substituted for phosphate buffer, only about half the amount of combination occurs within a day, except at very low $\bar{v}$, and the transport of ligand across the membrane becomes so slow that hardly any change occurs within several additional days. If, however, all of the ligand is initially on the protein side of the membrane, the same isotherm as was obtained with phosphate is attained very rapidly. Here, of course, much smaller amounts of transport are required than in the opposite case.

When chloride is substituted for phosphate, a number of different possible effects may intervene. Binding of chloride by the protein is appreciable at $0.033\ M$ ($\bar{v}_{Cl}$ is about 7), and binding by ligand involves replacement of the chloride. This should occur much more readily if all the ligand is initially on the protein side. The displacement of chloride may occur very slowly but there is no independent experimental evidence that this is the case, nor is it obvious why the delay should be greater (as it is) at high $\bar{v}$.

Various attempts to understand these kinetic differences have not led to conclusive results. For the present, we consider three cases, when all the ligand is initially on the nonprotein side (Cassel *et al.*, 1969):

(a) no support electrolyte present;
(b) completely ionized salts present;
(c) buffers present (acidic and basic forms in equilibrium).

With no salt present the transport phenomenon may be considered to be (to a first approximation):

$$\text{Rate across membrane} = k_1[C]^2 \qquad (3\text{-}6)$$

where C represents the free ligand on the nonprotein side. The exponent reflects the need to provide for electrical neutrality at all stages of the transport, i.e., two oppositely charged ions must cross together. With ligands of high affinity the free ligand on the protein side $[C']$ can be considered to be too small to contribute an additional negative term to Eq. (3-6), at least during the early stages of the transport process.

When completely ionized salts are present the process is more complicated. It is not necessary for the ions to pass through the membrane in oppositely charged pairs. Instead, as a ligand ion passes in one direction, a supporting electrolyte ion of the same electrical sign, may compensate for it by moving across in the contrary direction. The rate will be faster than in the first case, since at the outset

$$\text{Rate}_B = k_1[C][A] \quad \text{or} \quad k_1[C][A^-] \qquad (3\text{-}7)$$

where A is the support ion of unlike charge, and $[A^-]$ the support ion of like charge. However, the fact that there is no concentration gradient in A or A^- across the membrane effectively eliminates these from Eqs. (3-7). The ratio of the two rates, if k_1 is unaffected, is obviously C/A or C/A^- (which are equivalent) and Rate_B will be much larger than the rate in Eq. (3-6). The terminal stages may, however, be greatly retarded by the gradual disappearance of the gradient in $[C]$ when explicit account must be taken of the kinetics of an equilibrium process.

When the supporting electrolyte is a buffer Eq. (3-7) still applies, but [A] or $[A^-]$ are not completely eliminated. Thus, for example, the binding of a ligand anion raises the pH on the protein side of the membrane, but buffer action in restoring the pH results in the diminution of the acidic form of the buffer, and an increase in the basic form *on the protein side*. Thus the flow of both A and A^- in the required direction to facilitate ligand transport is increased, and both the initial and final rates of transport are greater than in the other two cases.

The effects just described are more marked with large detergent ions that, at $\bar{v} > 10$, cause massive unfolding. The effects, however, may be observed with the longer-chain nonunfolders, such as decylsulfate.

The second transport anomaly has to do with the effects of protein concentration. Early work in this laboratory (Ray *et al.*, 1966) appeared to show that at $\bar{v} < 8$, 1% protein solution (BSA) in 0.033 ionic strength phosphate buffer gave much smaller values for the association constant than did more dilute solutions. The effect was not confined to ionic ligands, but was common to all ligands having 12 or more carbon atoms. Various efforts made to explain this phenomenon met with no success. The only property which appeared to differ between very low and more concentrated solutions of BSA was viscosity; but this effect, which is not understood (Reynolds *et al.*, 1967), does not appear to be related to the slow attainment of equilibrium in concentrated solutions.

It was clear that the presence of a very low concentration of a low-binding impurity could simulate an isotherm dependent on protein concentration if the assay method used failed to distinguish between ligand and impurity. In order to eliminate this possibility, Cassel *et al.* (1969) conducted experiments in which bovine serum albumin plus sodium dodecylsulfate in buffer were dialyzed repeatedly against successive portions of buffer. These experiments not only showed clearly that practically no low-binding impurity was present, but also that the results obtained after diluting originally 1% predialyzed protein solution to 0.1% were very close to the results obtained at higher concentrations.

It is clear, therefore, that the protein "concentration effect" to be explained is a kinetic one, not a thermodynamic one. It is not due solely to the larger amounts of ligand transport required at the higher protein concentration (in the absence of protein, equilibrium across the membrane is attained very rapidly, even at high ligand concentrations). It is not the same kind of delay encountered with more dilute protein when NaCl is substituted for phosphate, since a true equilibrium is eventually attained (3 days), whereas the delay with NaCl may be, to all practical purposes, of infinite duration. The possibility must be entertained that the higher concentration of protein, with or without the ligand, coats the membrane and greatly reduces its permeability. If this is so, the permeability is high enough to allow the attainment of equilibrium very rapidly when the ligand is initially on the protein side.

The thermodynamic method of choice—equilibrium dialysis—is thus not devoid of traps for the unwary. Obviously, attainment of the same isotherm when transport across the membrane is carried out in both directions removes all doubts and leads to a clear-cut result. However, attainment of equilibrium by such an ideal criterion is not always readily demonstrable.

Absorption of ligand on the membrane or other surfaces is a source of error to which equilibrium dialysis may be especially prone, although any of the subtractive methods may be affected to some degree. Absorption of ligand on the membrane is well established for some ligands, although demonstrably negligible with others (Klotz, 1953). The magnitude of the effect is not easy to establish by blank measurements made in the absence of protein. The preceding paragraph indicates that the presence or concentration of protein may affect the results. Isotopic labeling of the ligand permits measurement of the bound ligand as well as of the free ligand, and thus permits comparison of their sum with the amount introduced into the system. Recourse to this combination of "direct" and "subtractive" methods should usually be capable of detecting loss of ligand amounting to only 2–5 %. If, for example, 2 % is lost, the practical effect on the isotherm may be very small if K is large, since $\bar{v}$ will be estimated high by only the same factor, and C_{eq} will not be affected. At low affinities, however, when, for example, only 20 % is bound, $\bar{v}$ will be in error by 10 % and a reciprocal (Klotz) plot will suffer considerable distortion at low $\bar{v}$—a departure from the theoretical form of the isotherm may be evident. A more serious effect arises when the adsorption of ligand on the membrane mainly occurs when it is combined with protein. Much larger amounts may be adsorbed, and the accompanying attachment of protein to the membrane may have the effect of reducing its permeability to ligand. It is possible that such an effect is responsible for the great delays in the attainment of equilibrium already described which occur when high concentrations of BSA (1 %) are used with all of the ligand initially on the nonprotein side. This delay, unlike the one produced by NaCl, appears to be much more marked at ligand concentrations which do not produce unfolding.

One more important practical source of error remains to be mentioned. The membranes used must be demonstrably free of interfering impurities. Visking tubing seems to be relatively free of the worst sorts (see below), but it is desirable to boil it with distilled water for at least 15 minutes, followed by prolonged rinsing before use. Some investigators have resorted to boiling with dilute sodium carbonate followed by rinsing. In the absence of such treatments, material originally present in the membrane dissolves during the prolonged equilibration period and may interfere with the assay of free ligand, or of protein (the impurity has, for example, a pronounced uv absorption). It appears possible that the impurity includes sulfite. Membranes have been encountered in which the impurity converted BSA to a form having a binding isotherm very like that of unfolded protein (Reynolds et al., 1967).

An automated flow system of obtaining equilibrium dialysis data has been described which greatly reduces the time required to obtain complete isotherms (Stein, 1965).

C. Ultrafiltration and Ultracentrifugation

In this method (Flexner, 1937; Grollman, 1926), which is, in principle, identical with equilibrium dialysis, the long period of attaining equilibrium across the membrane is eliminated by starting with a single solution containing both protein and ligand, which is assumed to reach equilibrium very quickly, and separating out of it a known volume of protein-free phase which can be analyzed for free ligand. Filtration employs the same sort of membrane used in dialysis, suitably supported to withstand high pressures. In some cases of ultrafiltration a strong gravitational field is supplied by a centrifuge (Nishida, 1961). Earlier applications are listed by Klotz (1953, see refs. 9–11 cited therein). Its use with serum albumin began with the work of Boyer *et al.* (1947) on fatty acids.

If a sufficiently strong centrifugal field (100,000g or more) is applied, the membrane may be dispensed with, by making a graph of the *total* concentration of ligand as a function of the concentration of protein, as the distance from the center of rotation is varied. This graph is extrapolated to zero protein concentration to give the concentration of free ligand. This method was used by Chanutin *et al.* (1942) in an investigation of the binding of calcium by serum proteins and by casein. It has also been used by Velick *et al.* (1953) to examine the binding of diphosphopyridine nucleotide by glyceraldehyde-3-phosphate dehydrogenase; by Hayes and Velick (1954) with yeast alcohol dehydrogenase; and by Wallenfels and Sund (1957) in an investigation of the binding of pyridine nucleotides, and by Buettner (1964). Kerp and Steinhilber (1962) have used sudden freezing and subsequent sectioning of centrifuged narrow tubes to prevent convection and to minimize diffusion prior to determining the gradients of both protein and ligand; they have shown that their results with serum albumin and methyl orange agree closely with those of Klotz *et al.* (1946) determined by the method of equilibrium dialysis.

When a membrane is used, results obtained by ultrafiltration are subject to some of the sources of error and the uncertainties which have been discussed in the case of equilibrium dialysis. They may also be subject, whether or not a membrane is used, to a possible influence of protein concentration, or when a membrane is present, to effects due to piling up the protein at the membrane. It might seem that the presence of a protein concentration gradient might lead to an extrapolated value of free ligand which is substantially higher than the concentration in equilibrium with the more concentrated protein; in fact it would almost certainly do so if it were not for the fact the free low-molecular-weight ligand cannot establish a significant gradient in fields of this strength. The portion of total ligand which is bound varies throughout the tube, but the concentration of free ligand does not. The calculation of interactions of three (or more)-component systems in a centrifugal field is known to be troublesome (Cassasa and Eisenberg, 1961). What might seem to be an error inherent in the simple extrapolation has been satisfactorily resolved by the work described in the next paragraph, as well as by the good agreement with data obtained by equilibrium dialysis.

The ultracentrifuge has long been used to study interactions between proteins or between the subunits of proteins, as well as to investigate reactions with ligands that bring about dimerization (Hughes, 1947; Fredericq and Neurath, 1950; and Bresler, 1949, among others). These studies have reached a point of great refinement in Schachman's laboratory (Schachman and Edelstein, 1966) where they have been extended recently to encompass the interactions of proteins with small molecules (Steinberg and Schachman, 1966). In this work, both sedimentation equilibrium and sedimentation velocity were employed, and explicit account was taken of the change in chemical equilibrium at moving boundaries. The earlier crude methods for observing gradients are replaced by use of a photoelectric scanner and monochromator, which record the gradients at the most suitable wavelengths. A clear-cut extrapolation to zero protein concentration of a linear graph of total ligand against total protein (bound or unbound) gives the concentration of unbound ligand, while the slope is directly proportional to $\bar{v}$. Seven different dye-protein interactions were investigated with results that agreed closely with the equilibrium dialysis data obtained in Klotz's laboratory for the same systems. The results obtained by the sedimentation velocity method, adjusted for the change in equilibrium at the moving boundaries (Gilbert and Jenkins, 1960), were in satisfactory agreement with the results obtained by sedimentation equilibrium. The success of both methods depends on a theoretical demonstration that although the distributions of the various complexes may vary slightly from level to level, the equilibria are maintained at every level in the cell, and total ligand minus free ligand is always equal to the concentration of protein multiplied by $\bar{v}$. A similar demonstration was presented by Nichol and Ogston (1965).

The general applicability of the ultracentrifugal method, and its recent acquisition of a sound theoretical foundation (at least for moderate values of $\bar{v}$) appear to ensure that it will be widely used in the future with light-absorbing ligands, since the necessary optical accessories have become available.

D. GEL FILTRATION

This method[2] is, in principle, very similar to equilibrium dialysis, but is particularly useful for light-absorbing ligands which bind in low molar ratios. It is probably capable of giving more accurate values of C_{eq} with ligands of high affinity and low molecular weight than is any other method, since C_{eq} is

[2] First introduced by Hummel and Dryer (1962) in an investigation of the binding of cytidine 2'-phosphate by ribonuclease, and soon afterwards, by Pfluderer (1964) to study the binding of DPNH by lactic dehydrogenase, by Fasella, *et al.* (1965) to the binding of cytidine 3'-phosphate to the same enzyme, by Fairclough and Fruton (1966) to determine the binding of tryptophan and a number of tryptophan peptides by BSA, and more recently by Gotschlich and Edelman (1967) and by Glazer (1967).

not determined by analysis, but set at predetermined values. In its simplest form a Sephadex column is equilibrated with a solution of the ligand (solution A), and the same solution plus dissolved protein (solution B) is then applied to the column in a small volume relative to the volume of the column. When elution is carried out with a solution (A), the protein emerges at the excluded volume of the column. The small volume containing protein bound to ligand also gradually comes to contain ligand at the equilibrium concentration C_{eq} of solution A, since it has abstracted ligand from the gel until it is no longer able to do so (equilibrium) and emerges at the bottom with the free ligand essentially restored to C_{eq}. The ligand removed from the gel is revealed as a reduction in ligand concentration (a trough on the record) as solution A is eluted behind the effluent protein. All of the ligand eluted from the gel is bound by the protein, since it is determined by the amount bound in the original small volume of protein solution, plus the additional amount bound as the concentration is restored to C_{eq}.

A detailed description of the apparatus, procedure, calculations, and corrections to be applied is given by Fairclough and Fruton (1966). That the method is capable of high precision is demonstrated by the fact that these investigators were able to show by the use of Scatchard plots (Figs. 3-2–3-4) that BSA has a single strong site for tryptophan and certain tryptophan-containing synthetic polypeptides, with association constants that ranged from 191,000 for L-tryptophan to 200 for glycyl-L-tryptophan diketopiperazine. They also determined that the enthalpy of the reaction was -14.5 kcal for L-tryptophan, a surprisingly large value, about double the value of the free energy. Where comparisons were possible, the results were in good agreement with those of McMenamy and Oncley (1958) and McMenamy and Seder (1963). Recently, Fruton and Humphreys (1968) have applied this method to studying the interaction at pH 4 of a number of native and modified pepsins with small synthetic peptide substrates. The native enzyme was shown to bind at least 5 equivalents of peptide.

A more qualitative use of Sephadex introduced by Scholtan in his work on antibiotics (1964) is more akin to ultrafiltration than to gel filtration. Dry Sephadex is suspended in serum or other protein solution containing a ligand, and the concentration of the free ligand determined by elution after filtration. A somewhat similar batch method of gel filtration for the measurement of binding has been introduced by Pearlman and Crepy (1967).

E. Partition Equilibrium between Phases

1. *Solid–Liquid*

If the solubility of any ligand in a given solvent is measured in the presence of an increasing amount of dissolved protein, it is unnecessary to distinguish analytically between bound and unbound ligand. The ratio of the increment

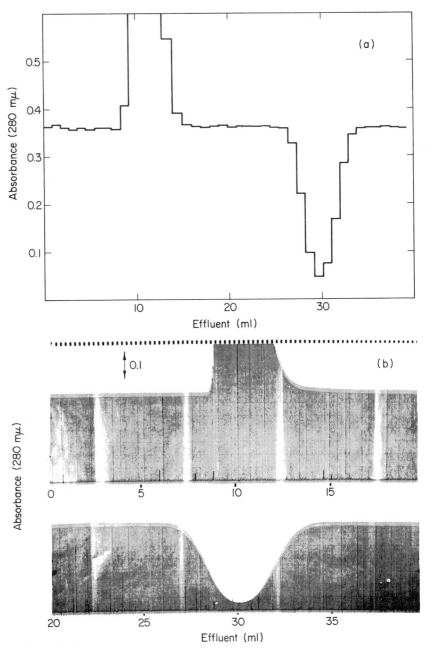

FIG. 3-2. Representative elution diagrams for the measurement of the binding of L-tryptophan by BSA. Concentration of L-tryptophan, 6.4×10^{-5} M; amount of protein, 21 mg; pH 9.0; temperature, 30.0°; spectrophotometer cell path length, 1 cm. (a) Elution diagram obtained by analysis of individual fraction of effluent solution. (b) Elution diagram recorded by means of Gilford instrument. In the original record, 5 ml of effluent corresponded to 19.3 cm on the abscissa, and an absorbance of 0.1 corresponded to 5 cm on the ordinate. [G. F. Fairclough and J. S. Fruton (1966). *Biochemistry* **5**, 673.]

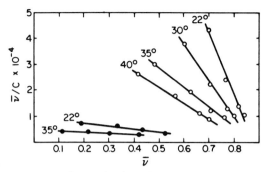

FIG. 3-3. Scatchard plots for the binding of L-tryptophan and D-tryptophan by BSA. The amount of protein varied from 10 to 23 mg; pH 9.0; ○ L-tryptophan; ●, D-tryptophan. [G. F. Fairclough and J. S. Fruton (1966). *Biochemistry* **5**, 677.]

in pure solvent divided by the increment in dissolved protein, both measured in moles, gives $\bar{v}$ at the concentration of ligand in protein-free solvent, *unless the presence of protein changes the thermodynamic activity of the components of the solid to any serious extent.* The principal limitations of this method, which is particularly well suited for work with radioisotopes, is that only a single pair of values ($\bar{v}$ at C_{eq}) can be obtained in this way at a single temperature. Nevertheless, if it has been established by other work that a normal isotherm with a single value of n and K (intrinsic) applies, this single set of values suffices to establish n or K (but not both), and is therefore useful for exploring the effect of particular environmental parameters. The method has been employed to determine the binding to proteins of naphthoquinones (Heymann and Fieser, 1948), certain steroids (Bischoff and Pilhorn, 1948), and calcium (Weir and Hastings, 1936, and others). More recently it has been employed to determine the binding of *n*-octane to BSA (Ray *et al.*, 1966).

A slight modification of this method was also used by Ray *et al.* (1966),

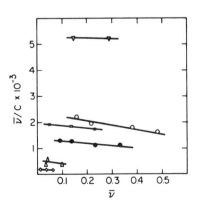

FIG. 3-4. Scatchard plots for the binding of tryptophan peptides by BSA. The amount of protein varied from 30 to 40 mg; pH 9.0; ○, glycyl-L-tryptophan, 15°; ●, glycyl-L-tryptophan, 30°; ◇, glycyl-L-tryptophan diketopiperazine, 25°; △, glycyl-L-tryptophanamide, 25°; ▽, L-tryptophylglycyl-L-tryptophanamide, 25°; □, glycyl-L-tryptophylglycyltryptophanamide, 25°. [G. F. Fairclough and J. S. Fruton (1966). *Biochemistry* **5**, 680.]

who separated the solid phase plus solvent from the protein-containing phase in measurements of the binding isotherm of n-dodecanol to BSA, in order to attain higher values of C_{eq} (saturation values) in what would otherwise have been simply an equilibrium dialysis measurement.

2. *Liquid–Liquid*

The basic procedure in this method is to determine the ratio of the equilibrium concentration of ligand dissolved in an aqueous phase to that of ligand dissolved in a suitable immiscible organic solvent, in the absence of protein, and then in the presence of a known amount of protein. Values of these two partition coefficients permit calculation of the amount of ligand which does not contribute to the chemical potential of ligand in the aqueous phase, and which is therefore " bound " by the protein. The quotation marks are inserted to indicate the nature of the thermodynamic simplifications which are introduced in this reasoning. The method has been used with BSA and a number of organic ions (Karush, 1951), antibiotics (Scholtan, 1963, Scholtan and Schmid, 1963) (see Chapter IV, p. 106), and in extensive investigations of steroids (Schellman *et al.*, 1954), including a very thorough study of the binding of testosterone by Alfsen (1963). Karush (1950) states that no corrections for Donnan effects are required. Goodman (1958) has applied the method to a detailed study of the binding of long-chain fatty acid anions by BSA.

The well-known susceptibility of proteins to unfolding, or dissociation, at interfaces indicates the need for caution in the use of this method. Alfsen has shown that, in the case of BSA, exposure to the organic solvent (heptane) leads to changes in the uv adsorption of the protein and that the results obtained by partition equilibrium do not agree in detail with those obtained by equilibrium dialysis. It is probable that small amounts of the organic solvent actually combine with serum albumin.

3. *Gas–Liquid*

Wishnia has used the solubility method described above (Section II, E, 1) to study the reaction between a number of proteins and two slightly soluble hydrocarbon gases, butane and pentane (Wishnia, 1962). Since the saturation solubility of gases is proportional to the pressure, which can be varied, the use of gases instead of solids permits determination at a single temperature of numerous pairs of values of $\bar{v}$ and C_{eq} instead of the single pair available with solids. If it can be assumed that the effects of changes in pressure on the protein and on n and K are negligible, the possibility of determining complete isotherms appears to be offered. Unfortunately, the very careful and resourceful experiments by Wishnia appear to indicate that this simple assumption of pressure independence may not apply in the case of BSA, and that more sites may become available as the pressure is increased. A more complete discussion of Wishnia's imaginative experiments is given in Chapter IV (p. 88 *et seq*,). All ofthe precautions as to purity of ligand, especially those applying to isotopic labeling, which have been alluded to in discussions of other methods, have equal applicability here.

An ingenious method for studying the binding of higher hydrocarbons and some of their derivatives has recently been introduced by Mohammed-zadeh-K, *et al.* (1967, 1969a, b). Protein solutions are equilibrated with the chosen ligand which has been dissolved in an immiscible solvent, tridecane, the solubility of which is so low that it may be neglected. Aliquots of the aqueous phase which contain protein are admitted into the high-temperature port of a gas chromatograph, and the total ligand present (both bound and free) is assayed as the area of its peak on the chromatogram. The same procedure is followed with protein-free solutions which have been similarly equilibrated with ligand dissolved in tridecane. The difference between the two assays represents bound ligand. Varying the amount originally present in the tridecane permits determination of entire isotherms.

F. ELECTRICAL CONDUCTIVITY

This is a special case of the general method of measuring the removal of free ligand from a solution containing proteins, other ionic components, and ligand. On addition of protein to a solution of, for example, sodium dodecyl-sulfate, the conductivity falls as the ions of the salt are immobilized by the protein. Since every component contributes to the conductivity, including the protein and the various protein–ligand complexes, determining the ratio of bound to free ligand from changes in conductivity is almost a *tour de force*, requiring considerable experimental calibration and refined calculation. The method is listed here solely because of the results obtained by its use with BSA and sodium dodecylsulfate by Strauss and Strauss (1958), described on p. 265. Two of the results of this investigation are especially noteworthy: (a) Values of $\bar{v}$ up to 160 could be observed at concentrations below the critical micelle concentration (in water). (b) It was possible to show that the counter-ions (sodium, in this case) were very largely dissociated, i.e., had nearly normal transfer numbers. The latter observation, if it should prove to be a general one, would bear on the interpretation of discrepancies between the results of certain other methods. Strauss and Strauss claimed fair agreement between their calculated isotherm work, and that of Pallansch and Briggs (1954) for the same salt. However, recent work has shown that the latter data yield a far lower binding constant than that obtained in later investigations. The validity of the conductometric method seems to have been well established in a study of the binding of Congo red and stearic acid to human serum albumin (HSA) (Larsen, 1964). An end point of 7 to 8 moles/mole proteins was obtained, almost the same value as was obtained by the effect of the protein on the absorption of the dye (Section III, A).

G. Polarograpy

Whenever a ligand is reducible at a characteristic potential on a mercury dropping electrode, the limiting diffusion current obtained at slightly higher potentials will depend on the concentration. Since the diffusion coefficient of a ligand bound to protein is very low relative to its diffusion coefficient when free, the diffusion current measured will give the equilibrium concentration, C_{eq}. The initial ligand concentration is known, and the difference gives the amount bound and thus permits $\bar{v}$ to be calculated. The method has been used to study the binding of metal ions (Tanford, 1951, among others), methyl orange (Stricks and Koithoff, 1949), the binding of azo-coupled antigens to antibodies (Breyer and Radcliff, 1949), the binding of thallous ions to pepsin (Lapanje, 1966), and the binding of thiocyanate ion to serum albumin (McMenamy et al., 1968).

H. Determination of free ligand without separation of Phases

Membranes, centrifugal fields, and gel filters may be dispensed with when free ligand reacts with an analytical reagent and bound ligand neither reacts nor dissociates rapidly enough during the assay to affect it. Very few systems meet these conditions. The effects of free ligand (B_{12}) on the growth of *Lactobacillius leichmannii* may be one such case (Kim et al., 1965).

III. Direct Measurements

It is clear that the measurement of virtually any property of the macromolecule or the ligand which changes when binding occurs may be used as a measure of binding. Many of the measured properties X are given by the general relationship (Rossotti and Rossotti, 1961)

$$X = \theta\left(X_A[A] + \sum_{i=1}^{n} X_i[PA_i]\right) \qquad (3\text{-}8)$$

where X_A and X_i are the appropriate intensive factors of the species A (ligand) and PA_i, respectively, and θ is a constant which depends on the measuring instrument. When the intensive factors are constant throughout the range of measure, the quantity

$$\beta \equiv \frac{X - \theta_{XA}[A]}{\theta[P]} \qquad (3\text{-}9)$$

where $\theta_{X_A}[A]$ refers to the expression in parentheses in Eq. (3-8), is a function of $[A]$ only.

From equations given in Chapter II, it will be clear that for the reaction

$$P + \bar{v}A \rightleftharpoons PA_{\bar{v}}$$

$$K = \frac{1}{[A]}\frac{\bar{v}}{n - \bar{v}} \tag{3-10}$$

Note that $PA_{\bar{v}}$ is a shorthand expression for a sum of compounds PA_i in which $\sum (i/n) = \bar{v}$. Thus

$$\bar{v} = \frac{X - \theta_{X_A}}{\theta[P]} = \frac{\displaystyle\sum_{i=0}^{n} n_i K^i[A]^i \frac{n!}{i!(n-i)!}}{\displaystyle\sum_{i=0}^{n} K^i[A^i] \frac{n!}{i!(n-i)!}} \tag{3-11}$$

Accordingly, data which relate $\bar{v}$, $[P]$, and $[A]$, allow determination of K, when n is known.

There is an ever growing number of methods of measuring interaction of small ions with macromolecules. Some are of general applicability, others suited only to a given protein or ligand. We shall not list all the methods currently or recently in use but refer the reader to the complete survey of techniques and the manipulations of expressions such as Eq. (3-11) which is presented by Rossotti and Rossotti (1961). Some of the methods which appear to have the greatest usefulness in the case of proteins are given in the sections which follow.

Direct methods are often of very superior accuracy in determining amounts bound (molal ratios) when affinities are so low as to leave much of the added ligand free in solution. They offer no advantages in accuracy, for purposes of determining association constants or free energies of binding, with ligands of very high affinity, since with these the accuracy is limited by determining the concentration of free ligand when the latter is very small, rather than by estimation of $\bar{v}$ (the latter is, to a very good degree of approximation, merely the ratio of total ligand to protein concentration). In applications of the fluorescence methods made to date, K has not been much greater than 10^5 except in the case of antibodies. The very accurate $\bar{v}$ values given by this method, combined with reasonably accurate values of C_{eq} give accurate values of K in this range.

Certain effects which depend on complex formation and which may easily be measured are inherently unsuitable because they are nonlinear and saturate at relatively low levels of binding ratio. Two of these are (a) changes in the uv absorption of the protein, which Ray *et al.* (1966), Reynolds *et al.* (1968), and Polet and Steinhardt (1968) have shown to be produced by complexing at the sites of highest affinity only; and (b) viscosity changes, because they are wholly absent when only small amounts are bound (Reynolds *et al.*, 1967). Calorimetric methods are often out of the question, except with hydrogen ion, since with other ligands the free energy of binding is entirely, or almost entirely, due to changes in the entropy (Kauzman, 1959) of the entire system. However, recent calorimetric work of Lovrien (1968) and binding studies by Fairclough and Fruton (1966) among others, indicate that just one of the most tightly bound ligands on a number of proteins, including bovine serum albumin, is characterized by a large negative ΔH.

A. CHANGES IN LIGHT ABSORPTION OF LIGAND

Although binding of ions or small molecules may change the characteristic light absorption of proteins themselves, experience to date indicates that such changes are highly individual, and likely to be nonlinear (Polet and Steinhardt, 1968) except when binding occurs at definite, identical sites, as in the case of binding of hydrogen ions by phenoxy groups, already mentioned on p. 42. Changes in the light absorption of ligands are in some of the cases investigated much simpler: the unbound chromophore has one set of extinction coefficients ε_λ and bound ligand a different set ε'_λ. It is only necessary to determine the two sets, and then select the λ at which $\varepsilon_\lambda - \varepsilon'_\lambda$ has a large, easily measured value, after demonstrating that both ε_λ and ε'_λ obey Beer's Law. The value of ε_λ is determined in the absence of protein, and ε'_λ in a large enough excess of protein to assure that essentially all the ligand is bound. All of the work which uses this method has been done with visible or uv light; the infrared, which should often be most informative, remains unexplored.

Klotz (1946) used the reduction in ε of azosulfathioazole at approximately 500 mμ and the concurrent slight red shift (Fig. 3-5) when it combines with BSA to measure the binding isotherm of this antibiotic. Although the method is well suited for use at λ above about 300 mμ, it has been used only with visibly colored molecules. A detailed investigation with the same protein and the dye trypan blue, carried out by Lang and Lasser (1967), reveals a more complicated situation than the simple case described by Klotz. At neutral pH, instead of a single ε'_λ for bound dye, there are two distinct values, associated with different classes of binding sites. Two of the three binding sites belong to one class, identified by its binding constant and characteristic adsorption spectrum (Fig. 3-6). When the third site is filled the preexisting high-energy sites disappear and all three bound dye molecules belong to a set of three identical sites having a smaller K and possessing a different absorption spectrum. At pH 3.3, where BSA is unfolded, a number of soluble complexes are formed; one of these, which has $n = 9$, is in equilibrium with

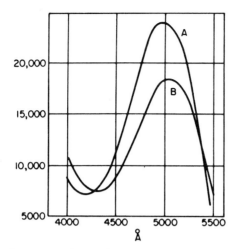

FIG. 3-5. Absorption spectra of azosulfathiazole. (A) in buffer at pH 6.9; (B), in buffer containing 0.2% bovine albumin at pH 6.9. [J. M. Klotz (1953). *Proteins* I. **B**, 737.]

an insoluble form which is characterized by $n = 31$. There are indications that the protein itself undergoes a change when more concentrated than about 0.6%. Unfortunately, the interpretation based on an analysis of the data in Fig. 3-6 was not confirmed by an independent method such as equilibrium dialysis, as in the case below.

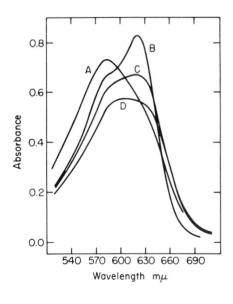

FIG. 3-6. Spectra of trypan blue at pH 3.3. Curve A, no BSA; curve B, $D_0/P_0 = 0.5$; curve C, $D_0/P_0 = 5$; curve D, $D_0/P_0 = 8$. Trypan blue concentration, 130×10^{-5} *M*. [J. Lang and E. C. Lasser (1967). *Biochemistry* **6**, 2403.]

Results with another dye, Biebrich scarlet, (6-[2-hydroxyl-1-naphthyl]azo)-3, 4-azodibenzene sulfonic acid, which combines with α-chymotrypsin at or near the binding site of the enzyme, and undergoes a red shift in its visible spectrum (Fig. 3-7) when bound (Glazer, 1967), are discussed in Chapter VII (p. 304).

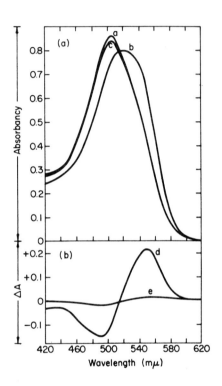

FIG. 3-7. Effect of chymotrypsin and chymotrypsinogen on the visible absorption spectrum of Biebrich scarlet. All spectra were obtained in 0.1 M phosphate buffer, pH 7.6, 22°, at a Biebrich scarlet concentration of 2.88×10^{-5} M. A 1-cm light path was used in all cases. (A) Curve a, Biebrich scarlet; Curve b, Biebrich scarlet in the presence of α-chymotrypsin ($1.8 \times 10^{-4}M$); Curve c, Biebrich scarlet in the presence of chymotrypsinogen (1.8×10^{-4} M). (B) Difference spectra obtained by scanning: Curve d, Biebrich scarlet + α-chymotrypsin (1.8×10^{-4} M) versus Biebrich scarlet; Curve e, Biebrich scarlet + chymotrypsinogen (1.8×10^{-4} M) versus Biebrich scarlet. [A. N. Glazer (1967). *J. Biol. Chem.* **242**, 4530.]

Differences produced in the spectrum of trypsin itself by substrates and inhibitors have been used by East and Trowbridge (1966) to measure the respective binding constants. This method is suitable when $n = 1$, but it cannot be assumed to give results linearly related to binding when multiple equilibria are involved. For this reason the extensive intrinsic difference spectra of BSA produced by a number of ligands have not been suggested as a means of determining binding constants unless empirical calibrations can be performed (Polet and Steinhardt, 1967).

The effects produced on the absorption spectrum of a dye when it binds to human serum albumin are different from those produced by binding to the serum albumin of 13 other species, even when the species differences in binding are taken into account (Baxter, 1963).

B. FLUORESCENCE METHODS

Following the explanation by Laurence (1952) of the fact that when a small fluorescent molecule combines with protein changes occur in the intensity or polarization of the radiation emitted, use has been made of these changes, especially by Weber and his collaborators, to study binding equilibria (Daniel and Weber, 1966). Figure 3-8 shows the fluorescence spectra of

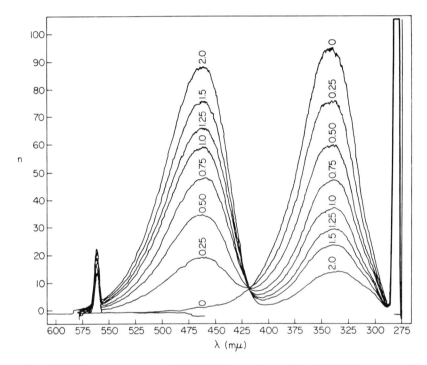

FIG. 3-8. Fluorescence spectra of ANS–BSA at various values of $\bar{v}$. BSA concentration 10 mg/ml, in 0.1 M buffer, pH 7.0. Bandwidths of excitation and emission 3.0 mμ. An isoemissive point is observed at 416 mμ. [E. Daniel and G. Weber (1966). *Biochemistry* **5**, 1894.]

1-anilino-8-naphthalene sulfonate (ANS) at various extents of combination with BSA. Each numbered curve corresponds to a different dilution of the same BSA–ligand solution having a ligand–protein ratio and an initial concentration sufficient to produce virtually stoichiometric binding. " Upon dilution, $\bar{v}$, the number of moles of ligand bound/mole of protein, takes on successively all the values from $\bar{v} = n$ to $\bar{v} \ll 1 \ldots$. In this way, the method gives a cross-section of the surface representing the probability of binding

$p \ (=\bar{v}/n)$" as a function of total ligand and total protein (Weber, 1965) and, "provided concentration-dependent protein interactions may be neglected, yields an unambiguous characterization of this surface." Dilutions as low as $10^{-8} \ M$ were successfully employed. A simple relation gives $\bar{v}$:

$$\bar{v} = (F_c/F_b)(X_0/P_0) \tag{3-12}$$

in which F_c is the fluorescence of a given solution, F_b the fluorescence of an equal concentration of ligand in sufficient BSA to bind all of it, and X_0 and P_0 are the total ligand and total protein. Equation (3-12) depends on two verified conditions: (a) a quantum yield for the free ligand which is negligibly small compared to that of bound ligand; and (b) a quantum yield of the latter which does not depend strongly on $\bar{v}$.

Figure 3-9 shows results at two pH values. From the known values of X_0

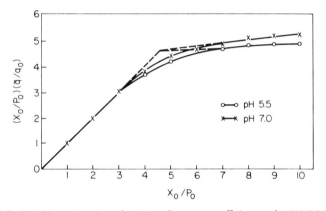

FIG. 3-9. Stoichiometric plot of relative fluorescent efficiency of ANS-BSA mixtures X_0 = molarity of total ANS; P_0, molarity of total protein; buffer = 0.1 M phosphate. [E. Daniel and G. Weber (1966). *Biochem.* **5**, 1893.]

and P_0, the concentration of free ligand (X) is obtained by using the relation

$$X = X_0 - \bar{v}P_0 \tag{3-13}$$

Titration curves are obtained by plotting $\bar{v}$ against $-\log X$ as in Fig. 3-10. The significance of the difference in the pH span (the number of log units covered in the range $\bar{v} = 0.5$ to 4.5) of the curves obtained at different pH values is pertinent to the section on mathematical models in the preceding chapter (none of the curves, except possibly the one at pH 7, is exactly in accord with the law of mass action, even with five arbitrarily selected binding constants), and to Chapter VII on the binding of ions. An appendix to the paper of Daniel and Weber (1966) explores the precision and reliability of the binding data.

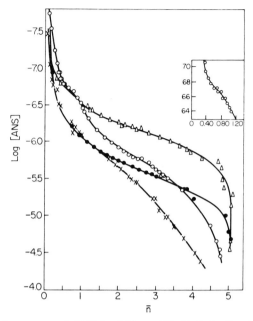

Fig. 3-10. Binding curves of ANS by BSA at 25°: O–O, buffer, 0.1 M phosphate, ph 7.0; ×–×, buffer, 0.1 M phosphate, pH 10.0; △–△, buffer, 0.1 M phosphate, pII 5.0; ●–●, buffer, 0.1 M acetate, pH 5.0. Inset: portion of curve of 0.1 M phosphate, pH 7.0. Abscissa $\bar{n}$ is equivalent to $\bar{v}$. [E. Daniel and G. Weber (1966). *Biochem.* **5**, 1893.]

In another paper, Anderson and Weber (1966) report measurements of the binding of NADH (nicotinamide adenine dinucleotide) by the five forms of beef lactate dehydrogenase by the same dilution-fluorescence technique. As in the case of BSA–ANS, the titration curves show a change in the binding process at $\bar{v} = 1$, and, somewhat less markedly, in other parts of the isotherm (Fig. 3-11). The significance of these results is discussed in Weber and Anderson (1966), and on pp. 307–310 of this book.

Weber and Daniel (1966) have shown that measurements of polarization of ligand fluorescence, and of quenching of *protein fluorescence* on binding may be used to yield information about energy transfer among ligand molecules. Both sets of data yield the weighted average distances and, in the polarization case, the mutual orientation of the oscillators participating in the transfer of energy from tryptophan residues in BSA to the bound ANS molecules. Cooperative features in the binding process have been detected by both types of observation.

Fluorescence methods have been used in recent binding studies by the following, among others: West *et al.* (1966) have studied the binding constant of acridine orange and cell proteins *in situ*; Masters *et al.* (1967) were able to

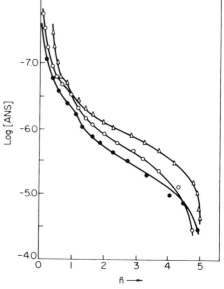

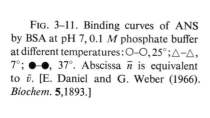

Fig. 3–11. Binding curves of ANS by BSA at pH 7, 0.1 M phosphate buffer at different temperatures: O–O, 25°; △–△, 7°; ●–●, 37°. Abscissa $\bar{n}$ is equivalent to $\bar{v}$. [E. Daniel and G. Weber (1966). *Biochem.* **5**,1893.]

distinguish between binding and the electron-transfer step in the action on NADPH by respiratory enzymes; Brand *et al.* (1967) studied the binding of alcohol by alcohol dehydrogenase; Yielding and Thompson (1967), the binding of ANS to glutamine dehydrogenase; and Attallah and Lata (1968), the binding of steroids by BSA. The association constants in the last paper are not the same as those defined in this book.

Other examples of the use of changes in fluorescence of both ligands and proteins to determine binding are given in a recent review by Edelman and McClure (1968). Fluorescence techniques have been used to measure the kinetics of binding by applying them to the temperature jump method, Froese *et al.* (1962). Bimolecular constants for the formation of two dye complexes were 2.1×10^6 mole^{-1} sec^{-1} and 3.6×10^5 mole^{-1} sec^{-1}. An antigen–antibody reaction (phenylarsonate) gave 2×10^7 mole^{-1} sec^{-1}. Combining these values with the association constants gave the first-order constants for the dissociation reaction. This is relatively slow (half-periods between 14 and 280 msec).

Polarization of fluorescence techniques have also been shown to be applicable to the binding of dyes to polypeptides, and therefore presumably to denatured proteins. Loosely bound complexes [DNS-labeled poly-Glu$_{63}$-Lys$_{37}$] are characterized by two relaxation times, but strongly bound complexes (fluorescein) show only one. The difference in interaction is also indicated by differences in the rotational relaxation time in solutions of high viscosity (50% glycerol) (Gill and Omenn, 1966).

Fluorescence studies of the binding of the 5-dimethylaminonaphthalene-1-sulfonamide group of a hapten to rabbit antibody have demonstrated that the specific combining region of the antibody is essentially hydrocarbon in nature (Parker *et al.*, 1967).

C. Optical Rotation

The use of ORD to study binding has been limited, but enough has been done to indicate its usefulness. Small amounts of the strongly bound detergent, sodium dodecylsulfate, change the depth of the Cotton effect trough when they bind to BSA (Reynolds *et al.*, 1967) but a much larger effect on the ORD of this protein occurs when larger amounts combine with the *unfolded* protein. It is possible to distinguish the binding effect from the unfolding effect kinetically (Lenz and Steinhardt, unpublished). The effects of dodecylsulfate *binding* are the same as those of certain other long-chain sulfates and sulfonates which do not unfold.

In the case of lactic acid dehydrogenase, binding of the substrate can be determined by its modification of the Cotton effect at 233 mμ; the results match those deduced from changes in uv absorption.

D. Nuclear Magnetic Resonance

When a ligand is bound to protein, the relaxation characteristics of one or more of its H atoms or one or more of those of the protein may be altered.

This alteration may show up as a " chemical shift," a frequency change, or as the broadening of a line, in the proton magnetic resonance spectrum. Selective broadening of some of the proton resonances of the small molecule is always observed when it is bound to a protein, and has been interpreted as a sign of intimate contact between such protons, or the groups to which they belong, and the macromolecule. The chemical shifts are small and difficult to measure; they arise from rapid reversible changes of the state of the ligand, from bound to unbound, and reflect not only the shifts in the nuclei which are caused by binding, but also the time average of the fraction of ligand bound.

Observation of the line-broadening has been used by Fischer and Jardetsky (1965) to study the binding of penicillin G and by Jardetsky and Wade-Jardetsky (1965) to study the binding of sulfonamides to BSA and the binding of ethanol and of DPN to alcohol dehydrogenase.

Both sulfonamides and penicillin occupy single sites on BSA. The presence of only *half* an equivalent of phenylproponal totally inhibits the sulfonamide binding. Rosenberg *et al.* (1968) have studied dodecylsulfate–protein interactions by observations of line-broadening.

The binding of certain paramagnetic metal ions (Mn^{2+} for example) is easily followed since their effect on the hydrogens of water is greatly enhanced when they are bound by protein (Cohn and Hughes, 1962). A relaxation time of approx. 3 sec is reduced to about 0.01 msec. The interaction of BSA with two Mn^{2+} ions can be shown to occur in two steps. The association constants were shown to increase more than tenfold as the pH was raised from 5 to 7. In pyruvate kinase there are demonstrably two Mn^{2+} sites. When the substrate, phosphoryl pyruvate, is also bound to the enzyme the water effect enhancement is greatly reduced. It has been demonstrated with pyridine kinase, which does not bind Mn^{2+}, that the effect of different nucleotides on the water enhancement exactly parallels their effect on the enzyme activity. The advent of equipment with stronger magnetic fields will undoubtedly lead to the possibility of greatly extending the use of this method. Since a complex ligand may give a number of relaxation times, it is theoretically possible to determine, from observing which lines are broadened by binding, which parts of the ligand are most directly involved. The effect of the environment on the extent of line-broadening may also be invoked to distinguish between, for example, hydrogen-bond formation or hydrophobic interactions. Multiple equilibria involving cooperative interactions may also be studied; for example, the binding of protons by each of the four histidines of ribonuclease may be distinguished by the effects of substrates or inhibitors on their respective lines, which are separable in part by differences in pH dependence (Meadows et al., 1967). Histidines 48 and 105 appear to have little dependence on substrate or pH, and are assumed to be deeply buried. Histidines 12 and 119 are in the active site and their NMR spectra are both pH- and substrate-dependent.

Recent NMR studies of protein complexes include lysozyme–inhibitor (Raftery et al., 1968), and hapten–antibody complexes (Burgen et al., 1967).

E. X-Ray Diffraction

Quiocho et al. (1966) have demonstrated that carboxypeptidase A crystals, insolubilized by cross-linking with glutaraldehyde, may be examined by the techniques of x-ray crystallography while bathed in various solvents, including solutions of substrate and inhibitor (e.g., β-phenylpropionate, which has an association constant of about 10,000). An inhibitor, o-phenanthroline which, in solution, removes zinc, apparently does not do so in these crystals, since washing the latter with water restores the activity. Acid can be shown to remove zinc, since the restoration of activity requires washing with zinc-containing solutions. These equilibria and others have been studied by not only measuring enzymatic activity, but more important, by analyzing the x-ray pattern which reflects accompanying conformation changes. It has been suggested that a complete analysis is not necessary since it may suffice to measure the optical density of a single suitably selected reflection in the Richards apparatus.

Stryer (1965) has obtained qualitative but highly useful information about the binding of azide and sulfate ions to myoglobin by x-ray diffraction analysis. Similar information has been obtained more recently about xenon binding (Schoenborn, 1965). The binding of lysozyme substrates and inhibitors has also been made visible by the results of x-ray investigations (Butler and Rupley, 1967).

F. REFRACTIVE INDEX

Giles and McKay (1962) have made use of discontinuities in the curve obtained when refractive index is plotted against the ratios of the concentrations of certain carbohydrates to BSA as an indication of the formation of a number of definite stoichiometric complexes. The evidence offered for this interpretation seems inadequate; the work is discussed on p. 111 in Chapter IV on the binding of neutral molecules. Observations of changes in refractive index have also been used by Paget and Vittu (1946) with sulfanilamide, and by Pankhurst and Smith (1947) with gelatin and detergents.

G. LIGHT-SCATTERING AND OSMOTIC PRESSURE

The principal value of light-scattering and osmotic pressure in binding studies is not in detecting changes in molecular weight due to such binding [unless the binding induces aggregation (Doty and Edsall, 1951)], but in the effect of binding on the second virial coefficient, which contains a term for the interaction of the protein with ions (Scatchard, 1946; Scatchard *et al.*, 1959; Edsall *et al.*, 1950). Since the second virial coefficient contains other factors which make a much larger contribution (unless the total electrolyte concentration is very low) the method has a very restricted applicability, except in the study of antigen–antibody reactions, when large shape changes or aggregation may make a large contribution. Gitlin and Edelhoch (1951) and Goldberg and Campbell (1951) were among the first to apply light-scattering in this way. When no other electrolytes are present than the ligand salt at high dilution, a Donnan equilibrium osmotic pressure permits an estimate of amounts bound (Scatchard *et al.*, 1946).

H. BIOLOGICAL ACTIVITY

Whenever the protein studied is an enzyme which catalyzes a reaction the kinetics of which fit the Michaelis-Menten model (which depends on the assumption of the existence of a dissociable enzyme–substrate complex), the isotherm for the formation or dissociation of this complex may be arrived at by kinetic studies (Michaelis and Menten, 1913). The formation of complexes with competitive inhibitors also may often be studied in the same way. Studies of "protection"—the persistence of biological activity in the presence of substances or conditions that would otherwise destroy it—when certain ligands are present have also been interpreted in terms of binding. There are innumerable papers based on either of these approaches, a few of which are specifically dealt with in the chapters that follow. Neurath and Schwert (1950) have discussed critically the use of Michaelis-Menten kinetic analysis to determine the characteristics of enzyme–substrate complexes. In recent years relaxation methods for studying biochemical systems have been greatly extended and refined (Hammes, 1968), but are only occasionally made use of in studies which have as their principal purpose the study of protein complexes.

As might be expected, since the Michaelis-Menten model is limited to enzyme–subsrate complexes, most of these studies are irrelevant to multiple equilibria.

$$E + S \overset{K_s}{\rightleftharpoons} ES \overset{K_R}{\rightarrow} EP \overset{K_D}{\rightarrow} E + P \tag{3-14}$$

where K_s, K_R, and K_D are rate constants. If K_s is not rate-controlling, application of Michaelis kinetics gives only an apparent association constant which is *not* equal to the true K of Chapter II.

IV. Electrostatic Methods

We include under this heading at least one method which might fit equally well in Section I, Subtractive Methods, because of its close relation to the others in this section, all of which depend quite strongly on the electrostatic theory of dilute solutions.

A. Electrophoresis

The interactions of proteins and ions have been studied by observing changes in the conductivity of ligand salts (metal ions, dyes) as a function of the concentration of protein [(see Klotz (1953), p. 735 for references between 1910 and 1926; Neurath and Bailey, 1953]. Since the work of Tiselius (1930) made it possible to measure accurately the mobilities of protein ions, attention has turned to the determination of changes in mobility (charge) and therefore the increases or decreases in bound ions (including hydrogen ions) which are brought about by changes in concentration or other environmental parameters. Alberty and Marvin (1950, 1951) and Alberty (1953) have presented a critical analysis of how the extent of complex formation ($\bar{v}$) may, under favorable circumstances, be determined from the constituent mobilities $\bar{u}_{\text{Proteins}+\text{L}}$ and $\bar{u}_\text{L}$ if the mobilities of free P and free L are also known under otherwise identical conditions. The $\bar{u}_\text{P}$ and $\bar{u}_\text{L}$ values are obtained by measuring the speed of both slow ascending boundaries and faster descending boundaries. The results of Alberty and Marvin (1951) on the binding of chloride to serum albumin determined in this way were in good agreement with those obtained by equilibrium dialysis. Similar agreement was obtained by Smith and Briggs (1950) with methyl orange.

The success of the method depends on two characteristics of electrophoresis: (a) the velocity of an ion in a given potential gradient depends on its charge, and therefore, in part, on the number of small ions with which it is combined; and (b) although as the boundary moves the more highly charged ions move faster, there is a continuously, instantaneously reestablished equilibrium so that the boundary moves with a constant average velocity $\bar{u}_\text{P}$ which is related in a linear fashion to the average molal ratio in the protein complex. The velocity is, of course, affected by the entire environment (other electrolytes present, counterions, etc.) so that the relation of $\bar{u}_\text{P}$ to $\bar{v}$ applies strictly only to conditions in which the environment undergoes no change other than small increments in ligand concentration. Even when this restriction is satisfied, it is necessary to make the assumption (which is known to be invalid for a number of linear polyelectrolytes) that the potential increment due to each anion bound is not altered as charges accumulate, i.e., the ratio of counterions accompanying the ion to ions bound does not depend on total or net charge. It is also necessary to assume that the frictional coefficient which depends on conformation, does not depend on $\bar{v}$.

A frequent use in the past has been to identify the formation of a protein–ligand complex by the appearance of a new boundary in the electrophoretic diagram [nucleic acids, Longsworth and MacInnes (1942); detergent ions, Lundgren *et al.* (1943) and Putnam and Neurath (1945)]. The appearance of a new boundary may, in fact, indicate the existence of complicating factors. Thus, in the case of certain detergent ions, the appearance of one or more new boundaries has been used as direct evidence of the formation of a distinctly new conformation of the protein. Measurements of the amount of migrating protein in each boundary has been used to ascertain the partition of the protein between its distinct forms [native and one or more unfolded forms (Yang and Foster, 1953; Hill and Briggs, 1956; Decker and Foster, 1966)] and partition of the ligand between these phases.

This use is seriously open to question if an equilibrium is assumed to exist between two conformations unless the *rate* of reestablishment of equilibrium as migration separates the two species is extremely slow. The existence of stable multiple boundaries lead Foster and his collaborators to the concept of microheterogeneity of the protein with an almost continuous spectrum of molecular subspecies which differ in their susceptibility to denaturation. Thus, the *appearance* of equilibrium was the consequence of continuous fractionation of the protein by the denaturant (Peterson and Foster, 1965a; Petersen *et al.*, 1965; Peterson and Foster, 1965b; Sogami and Foster, 1968).

The reader is referred to Klotz (1953, p. 715) for references to other early work by the electrophoretic technique. The theory of the application of *zone* electrophoresis to determine the formation of definite complexes has been given by Cann and Goad (1966), and by Waldmann-Meyer (1964), who applied the method to the binding of zinc and thiocyanate ions to HSA. The formation of ligand–protein complexes can be determined qualitatively by reversal of polarity after an initial period of electrophoresis (Jolley and Allen, 1965).

B. Changes in the Titration Curves of Proteins due to the Presence of Bound Ions

A series of investigations of the insoluble protein, sheep's wool keratin, by Steinhardt and his collaborators showed that the binding of hydrogen ions (measured by the simple subtractive method, titration of unbound hydrogen ions at each pH, not inferred simply from pH) depended strongly on the presence of anions (in the case of acid) or cations (in the case of base). There was a close approach to stoichiometry in the relationship. If, for example, the chloride concentration is held constant at 0.2 M, there is a displacement in the titration curve obtained at 0.02 M by 1 pH unit toward the higher pH (Fig. 3-12). If both H^+ and Cl^- are allowed to vary simultaneously, as in adding HCl only, the titration curve has twice the slope as if a mass-law equilibrium applied to the "combination" with *both* ions (Steinhardt and Harris, 1940).[3] As a simple test of the possible physical significance of this description of the titration process, titration curves were obtained with a very wide range of strong acids, the anions of which differed greatly in chemical constitution and size (Fig. 3-13). It was found that most acids, even in the absence of additional anions, gave parallel titrations which differed only— but very widely—in the positions of the titration curves on the pH axis (Steinhardt, 1941; Steinhardt *et al.*, 1941, 1942). The effect is therefore clearly due, predominantly, to differences in affinity of the various anions for the protein, and not merely, as might have been possible for the chloride data taken alone, to a complex effect akin to a Donnan equilibrium arising from the necessity of achieving electrical neutrality in the close vicinity of the individual insoluble protein fibers. It proved possible to rank the affinities of over 30 anions in roughly the order of their size. Unbranched aliphatic

---

[3] The curves obtained at constant anion concentration had almost exactly the same slope as similar curves obtained with comparable dissolved proteins.

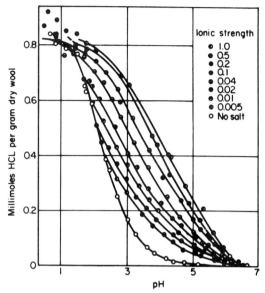

FIG. 3-12. Effect of ionic strength on carboxyl titration of wool at 0°. (From Steinhardt *et al.*, 1940a.) [J. Steinhardt and M. Harris (1940). *Natl. Bur. Std.* **24**, 335.]

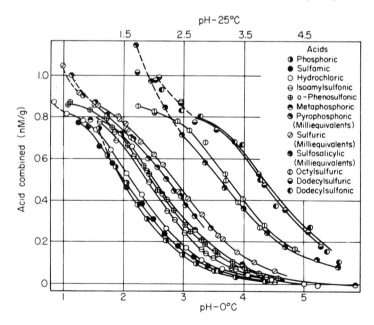

FIG. 3-13. Combination of wool protein with 12 different strong acids at 0° and 25°C. The pH scale at the top of the figure applies to the data obtained at 25°C. (From Steinhardt *et al.*, 1942.) [J. Steinhardt, C. H. Fugitt, and M. Harris (1942) *Natl. Bur. Std.* **28**, 201.]

ions formed stronger bonds than aromatic or inorganic ions of the same molecular weight. Similar effects were found with the binding of bases (Steinhardt and Zaiser, 1950). The coarse analysis provided cannot be accepted as giving reliable absolute values of the respective binding constants, nor as furnishing a quantitative theoretical explanation of how the binding of anions affects the position of the titration curves in so nearly exactly a stoichiometric manner (see next section). Nevertheless, it permitted prediction of the results obtained with *mixtures* of anions which differed in affinity (Steinhardt *et al.*, 1942). Only a few experiments were published which dealt with a *soluble* protein, ovalbumin. The results were less diagramatically clear, but sufficed to show that a different titration curve resulted from each of the acids used. The differences were less marked because at the higher amounts bound they precipitated the protein. The fact that the isoionic point of ovalbumin is on the carboxyl portion of the titration curve rather than almost exactly at the pH at which all the carboxyl groups are dissociated, as in wool keratin, prevents the titration curves from being parallel, and excludes the simple method applied in the case of wool for determining the affinity. The titration curves of insoluble proteins, and the work of other investigators, is treated more fully in Chapter V.

Attention is invited to the fact that the equilibrium curve (isotherm) *measured* is that of hydrogen ion rather than that of anion. Nevertheless, the method yields, at least in the case of insoluble proteins, the relative magnitudes of the binding constants of the anion, and therefore of the free energy of the protein–anion complexes; this is true even if the crude method used by the investigators is rejected in favor of a more refined one, possibly one based on a combination of the Linderström-Lang isotherm with considerations based on phase separation (see Chapter II or III). The clear-cut nature of the results is due in large measure to the fact that combination with hydrogen ions and with anions must be macroscopically equal, when the system is divided into two phases. With soluble protein this simple rule must be relinquished, and recourse must be had to all the complexities of electrostatic solution theory, as in the method below.

C. THE ΔpH METHOD OF SCATCHARD AND BLACK—DISPLACEMENT OF pH OF
    ISOIONIC SOLUTIONS BY ADDED SALTS

If the two ions of an added neutral salt are bound to an unequal extent by deionized protein, the Linderström-Lang titration theory provides a simple and elegant means for calculating the amount bound *within the range of validity of the simple theory*. At reasonably high concentrations of protein of isoelectric point between pH 4 and 9, the isoionic protein in water is essentially, though not exactly, isoelectric ($Z = 0$). When salt is added, there will be a change in Z if there is unequal binding of anions and cations. It is clear from Eq. (2-50) that, since $\alpha/(1 - \alpha)$ cannot change materially because no acid or alkali has been added, pH will have to vary.[4] By the same equation, if $\bar{v}_i$ is the number of salt ions of charge Z bound per molecule of protein, then

$$\Delta pH = -0.868w \sum \bar{v}_i Z_i \qquad (3\text{-}15)$$

a relationship first utilized by Scatchard and Black (1949).

This attractively easy and rapid method has been widely used, especially in investigations which have not attempted to establish complete isotherms. Its validity, of course, rests very heavily on the Linderström-Lang equation and on the validity of the assumptions made in deriving it; and on the validity of use of the Debye-Hückel theory, or other means, to calculate w (see Chapter II). Figure 3-14 gives the factor F by which ΔpH must be multiplied to obtain

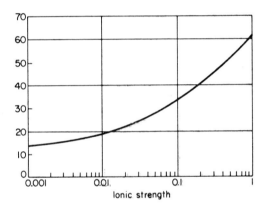

Fig. 3-14. Factor for calculation of extent of binding from displacement of isoionic pH (see text). [I. M. Klotz (1953). *Proteins* **B**, 742.]

$\bar{v}$ when $Z_i = -1$ and the Debye-Hückel theory applies.

The assumption can often be made that cations do not bind appreciably, in which case

$$\Delta pH = 0.868w\bar{v} \qquad (3\text{-}16)$$

when a neutral salt is added to isoionic (deionized) protein, provided no buffers other than the protein are present, and provided that enough unbound salt is present to provide a Debye-Hückel ion-atmosphere having $1/\kappa$ values which do not exceed a few angstroms, less than the average separation

---

[4] Variation in $\alpha/(1 - \alpha)$ due to the pH change itself (addition or subtraction of protons to or from the solvent) is negligible at protein concentrations of about 1% in the pH range 5–9. In more dilute protein solutions, corrections for changes in this term must be made (Cassel and Steinhardt, 1969).

between protein ions (Tanford, 1961). With ions of very high affinity at high dilution, therefore, additional "support" electrolyte must be added. Furthermore, if the "binding constant" is to be constant, a constant ionic strength must be maintained over the whole isotherm. Thus, the strong possibility of competition between the added electrolyte and the ligand being studied must be considered, especially at low $\bar{v}$ (see Chapter II) and the shift in pH will be smaller than predicted by Eq. (3-15). In addition, at high $\bar{v}$, ΔpH becomes very large, and the constancy of $\alpha/(1 - \alpha)$ must be examined; this is especially important when the protein is dilute, or when the isoionic pH is in a poorly buffered region of the titration curve, or when the pH is initially so acid that only a small fraction of the carboxyl groups are ionized (such as in isoionic pepsin).

Cassel and Steinhardt (1969) have shown that the ΔpH method tends to severely underestimate the extent of binding when the binding constant is very high. All of the sources of error enumerated could contribute to this result, but residual discrepancies remain, which indicate that other sources of error are present when ions of high affinity are being examined.

One or another of the sources of departure from Eq. (3-16), or the cumulative effect of all of them, may show themselves in a number of ways: distorted isotherms or underestimated values of association constants (in comparison with the constants determined in equilibrium dialysis experiments in the presence of buffers). The greater part of these errors is due not so much to underestimating $\bar{v}$, as to the large effects of an error in $\bar{v}$ on the calculation of C_{eq} when K is very large. These errors, whether due to incorrect w values, or to changes in $\alpha/(1 - \alpha)$, or to defects in the simple theory, may even result in calculated values of C_{eq} which are negative.

A recent effort to avoid these sources of error with very tightly bound ions has sought to determine the limiting value of the slope near the origin of a plot of total ligand concentration (bound plus free) divided by the protein concentration against change in pH. The reciprocal of this limiting slope gives an empirically determined value of 0.87 w, which can then be applied to the rest of the isotherm (Cassel and Steinhardt, 1969). The experiment may be automated by using automatic titration equipment which adds the ligand of interest instead of base, and uses a combined glass electrode–reference electrode for control, and recording the amounts added and pH. The values of w obtained in this way with BSA and the salts of long-chain aliphatic half-esters are only about half as large as those calculated from the Debye-Hückel theory for a spherical central ion having the volume of BSA and a conducting surface, and a ligand ion of 2Å radius. The values of w required to fit the hydrogen ion titration curve of BSA are also smaller than the Debye-Hückel values, but are closer to the theoretical values (see Table 5-4, Chapter V). The experiment is instructive, because the use of anions of very high affinity, which give the most accurate approximation to the empirical w, gives lines that do not depart measurably from the limiting slope, up to values of ΔpH which indicate the binding of all the sites in the native protein which are demonstrated by other methods (Fig. 3-15). Since C_{eq}, upon which K, the binding constant,

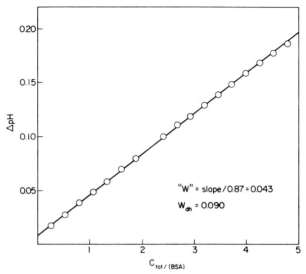

FIG. 3-15. Titration of 0.5% BSA with myristyl sulfate in 0.001 M NaCl. [J. Steinhardt and J. Cassel (1969). *Biochem.* **8**, 2603.]

critically depends, is thus only a vanishingly small fraction of C_{total} and can only be obtained in the ΔpH method by measuring the difference between C_{total} and the line of the limiting slope, it is obvious that the ΔpH method is not applicable to the measurement of large values of K. It is not merely that the measurement of C_{total} minus C_{eq} is very difficult; there is also a requirement that protein concentration be known to an unattainable accuracy, i.e., on the basis of an exceedingly accurate molecular weight.

Nevertheless it has been shown by Cassel and Steinhardt that values of K which are in acceptable agreement with those obtained by equilibrium dialysis, can be obtained by the ΔpH method (except with the long-chain aliphatic ions which can be bound by numerous high-energy sites) even when the value of w used is calculated by means of the Debye-Hückel theory. It seems probable therefore that in the successful cases the empirical and theoretical values of w converge. Their wide discrepancy in the case of the binding of long-chain aliphatic anions is attributed by Cassel and Steinhardt to the unsuitability of the Linderström-Lang model in the case of the latter.

Equation (3-15) should be just as applicable at any pH as it is at the isoionic point if $\alpha/(1-\alpha)$ is unchanged by the addition of ligand. With BSA there appears to be a tendency for $\bar{v}$ to be independent of pH and therefore of charge, in the case of dodecylsulfate over the range $\bar{v} = 1–8$. Hydrogen ion titration curves obtained with different constant ligand concentrations will therefore tend to be parallel over a protracted range, as were those of wool keratin (p. 73). However, their separation will tend to follow Eq. (3-14) and is much smaller than in Fig. 3-13.

D. DIELECTRIC INCREMENT AND DISPERSION

Dielectric dispersion measurements with human serum mercaptalbumin (Dintzis, 1952) have shown that addition of tightly bound fatty acid anions to the highly deionized protein sharply reduced its high dielectric increment (0.93 per gm protein per liter) to about half this value. A nonionic aliphatic ligand, decanol, had a smaller effect. When "free" of bound fatty acid, mercaptalbumin (monomer) had a dipole moment of 700 Debye units, but this was greatly reduced by bound ions.

Measurements of dielectric constants of protein solutions at very high frequencies (wavelengths of 1–10 cm), to which the protein ions themselves cannot respond, give information about bound water (Buchan et al., 1952). Estimates of hydration were obtained for BSA, hemoglobin, lysozyme, and β-lactoglobulin. As much as one-third of the water appears to be bound too tightly to orient in the highest frequency fields. Ions which bind to proteins change both their dielectric increment and the relaxation times of the protein; unbound ions do not (Takashima, 1963).

V. Other Methods

A. COMPLEMENT FIXATION

The great sensitivity of complement fixation (see, for example, Kabat, 1968) as a highly specific analytical method for determining concentration of antigens extends the range of such methods as equilibrium dialysis by several powers of ten in the direction of lower equilibrium concentrations; it thus permits determination of association constants as large as 10^{12}—the practical limit by any other methods described in this chapter is 10^7. The method has not been used except with materials of immunological interest.

A related and extremely sensitive method for determining n and K in antibody–antigen reactions has been developed by Karush (1969). The antigen (hapten) is attached to phage and the extent of phage neutralization determined as differing amounts of antibody are added to the system.

B. METHODS WHICH DEPEND ON COMPETITION

Whenever it is feasible to make use of a series of ligands of varying known K which occupy the same binding sites, it may be possible to determine the affinity of a new ligand by observing either (a) which of the series of known ligands it can displace, or, more satisfactorily, (b) the extent to which it shifts the equilibrium of a known ligand the affinity of which is of the same order of magnitude, making use of the equations of competitive equilibrium given in Chapter II. This recourse extends the usefulness of the *direct methods* to ligands which themselves give no readily measured direct effects, and is also useful in extending the use of radioisotopes (such as Na^+ and I^+)[5] to measure the binding of "cold" ligands (Saifer *et al.*, 1964) such as acetate.

Such procedures require clear demonstration that the same sites are occupied by both known and unknown ligands. There are many indications that there is considerable heterogeneity of binding sites in many proteins. Thus, for example, in the case of BSA there are different numbers of binding sites for sulfate half-esters which differ in chain length; there exists also spectroscopic evidence that homologous fatty acid anions may not bind to the sites which are available to the half-esters. The substrate binding sites and regulator binding sites of enzymes form large classes of binding sites which are not available to other ligands, although many enzymes are known to combine with numerous other ligands which do not compete with substrate.

REFERENCES

Alberty, R. A. (1953). *In* "The Proteins" (H. Neurath and K. Bailey, eds.), 1st ed. Vol. 1, Part A, p. 461. Academic Press, New York.

Alberty, R. A., and Marvin, H. H. (1950). *J. Phys. Colloid Chem.* **54**, 33.

Alberty, R. A., and Marvin, H. H. (1951). *J. Am. Chem. Soc.* **73**, 3320.

Alfsen, A. (1963). *Compt. Rend. Trav. Lab. Carlsberg* **33** (11), 415.

Anderson, S. R., and Weber, G. (1966). *Biochemistry* **6**, 1948.

Attalah, N. A., and Lata, G. F. (1968). *Biochim. Biophys. Acta 9*, **168**, 321.

Bates, R. G. (1954). "Electrometric pH Determination." Wiley, New York.

Baxter, J. H. (1963). *Proc. Soc. Exptl. Biol. Med.* **113**, 197.

Beaven, G. H., and Holiday, E. R. (1952). *Advan. Protein Chem.* **7**, 320.

Bischoff, F., and Pilhorn, H. R. (1948). *J. Biol. Chem.* **174**, 663.

Boyer, P. D., Ballou, G. A., and Luck, J. M. (1947). *J. Biol. Chem.* **967**, 407.

Brand, L., Galke, J. R., and Turner, D. E., (1967). *7th Intern. Congr. Biochem.* (Tokyo) IV, 781.

Bresler, S. E. (1949). *Biokhimiya* **14**, 180.

Brettner, H. (1964). *Antibiot. Chemotherapia* **12**, 95.

[5] The competitor ion was I^+; Na^+ was used to determine the Donnan corrections.

Breyer, B., and Radcliffe, F. J. (1949). *Nature* **167**, 79.

Buchan, T. J., Haggis, G. H., Halsted, J. B., and Robinson, B. G. (1952). *Proc. Roy. Soc. (London)* **A213**, 379.

Burgen, A. S. V., Jardetsky, O., Metcalfe, J. C., and Wade-Jardetsky, N. (1967). *PNAS* **58**, 447.

Butler, L. G., and Rupley, J. A. (1967). *J. Biol. Chem.* **242**, 1077.

Cann, J. R., and Goad, W. B. (1966). *Fed. Proc. Abst.* #882.

Carr, C. W. (1953). *Arch. Biochem. Biophys.* **46**, 417, 424.

Cassasa, E. F., and Eisenber, H. (1961). *J. Phys. Chem.* **65**, 427.

Cassel, J., and Steinhardt, J. (1969). *Biochemistry* **8**, 2603.

Cassel, J., Gallagher, J., Reynolds, J., and Steinhardt, J. (1969). *Biochemistry* **8**, 1706.

Chanutin, A. C., Ludewig, S., and Masket, J. (1942). *J. Biol. Chem.* **143**, 737.

Cohn, M., and Hughes, T. R., Jr. (1962). *J. Biol. Chem.* **237**, 176.

Crammer, J. L., and Neuberger, A. (1943). *Biochem. J.* **37**, 302.

Daniel, E., and Weber, G. (1966). *Biochemistry* **5**, 1893.

Decker, R. V., and Foster, J. F. (1966). *Biochemistry* **5**, 1242.

Dintzis, H. M. (1952). Ph.D. thesis, Harvard Univ.

Doty, P., and Edsall, J. T. (1951). *Advan. Protein Chem.* **6**, 39.

East, E. J., and Trowbridge, C. G. (1966). ACS Meeting, New York, Sept.

Edelman, G. U., and McClure, W. O. (1968). Accounts of Chem. Res., March, Vol. 1, 65.

Edsall, J. T., Edelhoch, H., Lontie, R., and Morrison, P. R. (1950). *J. Am. Chem. Soc.* **72**, 4641.

Fairclough, G. F., and Fruton, J. S. (1966). *Biochemistry* **5**, 673.

Fasella, P., Hammes, G. C., and Schimmel, P. R. (1965). *Biochim. Biophys. Acta* **103**, 708.

Fisher, J. J., and Jardetsky, O. (1965). *J. Am. Chem. Soc.* **87**, 3237.

Flexner, L. B. (1937). *J. Biol. Chem.* **121**, 615.

Fredericq, E. F., and Neurath, H. (1950). *J. Am. Chem. Soc.* **72**, 2684.

Froese, A., Sehon, A. H., and Eigen, M. (1962). *Can. J. Chem.* **40**, 1786.

Fruton, J. S., and Humphreys, R. E. (1968). *Proc. Natl. Acad. Sci.* **59**, 579.

Gilbert, G. A., and Jenkins, R. C. L. (1960). *Proc. Roy. Soc. (London)* **A253**, 420.

Giles, C. H., and McKay, R. B. (1962). *J. Biol. Chem.* **237**, 3388.

Gill, T. J., III, and Omenn, G. S. (1966). *Fed. Proc. Abst.* #3401.

Gitlin, D., and Edelhoch, H. (1951). *J. Immunol.* **66**, 67.

Glazer, J. A. N. (1967). *J. Biol. Chem.* **242**, 4528.

Goldberg, D., and Campbell, H. E. (1:51). *J. Immunol.* **66**, 79.

Gotschlich, E. C., and Edelman, G. M. (1967). *Proc. Natl. Acad. Sci.* **57**, 706.

Goodman, D. S. (1958). *J. Am. Chem. Soc.* **80**, 3892.

Grollman, A. G. (1926). *J. Gen. Physiol.* **9**, 813.

Hammes, G. G. (1968). *Advan. Protein Chem.* **23**, 1.

Harned, H. S., and Owen, B. B. (1950), "The Physical Chemistry of Electrolytic Solutions," 2nd ed. Reinhold, New York.

Hayes, J. E., and Velick, S. F. (1954). *J. Biol. Chem.* **207**, 225.

Heymann, H., and Fieser, F. (1948). *J. Pharmacol. Exptl. Therap.* **94**, 197.

Hill, R. M., and Briggs, D. R. (1956). *J. Am. Chem. Soc.* **78**, 1590.

Hughes, W. L. (1947). *J. Am. Chem. Soc.* **69**, 1836.

Hummel, J. P., and Dryer, W. J. (1962). *Biochim. Biophys. Acta* **63**, 530.

Jardetsky, P., and Wade-Jardetsky, N. G. (1965). *Mol. Pharmacol.* **1**, 214.

Jolley, W. B., and Allen, H. W. (1965). *Nature* **208**, 390.

Kabat, E. A. (1968). "Structural Concepts in Immunology of Immunochemistry." Holt New York.

Karush, F. (1950). *J. Am. Chem. Soc.* **72**, 2705.
Karush, F. (1951). *J. Am. Chem. Soc.* **73**, 1246.
Karush, F. (1969). Private communication.
Kauzmann, W. (1959). *Advan. Protein Chem.* **14**, 1.
Kerp, L., and Steinhilber, S. (1962). *Klin. Wochschr.* **40**, 540.
Kim, Y. P., Gizis, E., Brunner, J. R., and Schweigert, B. S. (1965). *J. Nutr.* **86**, 394.
Klotz, I. M. (1946). *J. Am. Chem. Soc.* **68**, 2299.
Klotz, I. M. (1953). "The Proteins," 1st Ed., 1B, 727.
Klotz, I. M., Water, F. M., and Pivan, R. B. (1946). *J. Am. Chem. Soc.* **68**, 1486.
Lang, J. H., and Lasser, E. C. (1967). *Biochemistry* **6**, 2403.
Lapanje, S. (1966). *Biopolymers* **4**, 85.
Larsen, B. (1964). Intl. Biochemical Congress, 6th, New York.
Laurence, D. J. (1952). *Biochem. J.* **51**, 168.
Linderström-Lang, K. (1927). *Compt. Rend. Trav. Lab. Carlsberg*, **15**, 7.
Linderström-Lang, K. (1928). *Compt. Rend. Trav. Lab. Carlsberg*, **17**, 4.
Linderström-Lang, K., and Nielsen, S. O. (1959). "Electrophoresis: Theory and Applications" (M. Bier, ed.), Chapter 2. Academic Press, New York.
Longsworth, L. G., and McLunes, D. A. (1942). *J. Gen. Physiol.* **25**, 514.
Lovrien, R. (1968), *Polymer Preprints* **9**, 219.
Lundgren, H. P., Elam, D. W., and O'Connell, R. A. (1943). *J. Biol. Chem.* **149**, 183.
Masters, B. S. S., Kamin, H., Siegel, L. M., Vorhaben, J. E., and Gibson, Q. H. (1967). Intl. Congress of Biochemistry (Tokyo), 7th, IV, 836.
McMenamy, R. H., and Oncley, J. I. (1958). *J. Biol. Chem.* **233**, 1436.
McMenamy, R. H., and Seder, R. (1963). *J. Biol. Chem.* **238**, 3241.
McMenamy, R. H., Madeja, M. I., and Watson, F. (1968). *J. Biol. Chem.* **243**, 2328.
Meadows, D. H., Markley, J. L., Cohen, J. S., and Jardetsky, O. (1967). *PNHS* **58**, 1307.
Merzbach, D., Sulitzeanu, D., and Grossowicz, N. (1963). *Bull. Res. Council Israel Sect. E* **10**, 213.
Michaelis, L., and Menten, M. L. (1913). *Biochem. Z.* **49**, 333.
Mohammadzadeh-K., A., Feeney, R. E., Samuels, R. B., and Smith, L.M. (1967). *Biochim. Biophys. Acta* **147**, 583.
Mohammadzadeh-K., A., Feeney, R. E., and Smith, L. M. (1969a). *Unpublished.*
Mohammadzadeh-K., A., Smith, L. M. (1969b). *Unpublished.*
Neurath, H., and Schwert, G. W. (1950). *Chem. Rev.* **46**, 69.
Neurath, H., and Bailey, K. (1953) "The Proteins," 1st Ed. Vol. IB, p. 735. Academic Press, New York.
Nichol, L. W., and Ogston, A. G. (1965). *J. Phys. Chem.* **69**, 4365.
Nishida, T. (1961). *Medicine Biol.* (*Japan*) **59**, 33.
Paget, M., and Vittu, C. (1946). *Compt. Rend. Soc. Biol.* **140**, 227.
Pallansch, M. J., and D. K. Briggs (1954). *Jacs* **76**, 1396.
Pankhurst, K. G. A., and Smith, R. C. M. (1947). *Trans. Faraday Soc.* **1** & **3**, 511.
Parker, C. W., Yoo, T. J., Johnson, M. C., and Godt, S. M. (1967). *Biochemistry* **6**, 3408.
Pearlman, W. H., and Crepy, O. (1967). *J. Biol. Chem.* **242**, 182.
Peterson, A. A., and Foster, J. F. (1965a). *J. Biol. Chem.* **240**, 2503.
Peterson, A. A., and Foster, J. F. (1965b). *J. Biol. Chem.* **240**, 3858.
Peterson, A. A., Foster, J. F., Sogami, M. A., and Leonard, W. J., Jr. (1965). *J. Biol. Chem.* **240**, 2495.
Pfluderer, G. (1964). "Mechanismen Enzymaticher Reaktionen," p. 300. Springer, Berlin.
Polet, H., and Steinhardt, J. (1968). *Biochemistry* **7**, 1348.
Putnam, F. W., and Neurath, H. (1945). *J. Biol. Chem.* **159**, 195.

Quiocho, F. A., and Richards, F. M. (1966). *Biochemistry* **5**, 4062.

Raftery, M. A., Dahlquist, F. W., Chan, S. I., and Parsons, S. M. (1968). *J. Biol. Chem.* **243**, 4175.

Ray, A., Reynolds, J. A., Polet, H., and Steinhardt, J. (1966). *Biochemistry* **5**, 2606.

Reynolds, J. A., Herbert, S., Polet, H., and Steinhardt, J. (1967). *Biochemistry* **6**, 937.

Reynold, J., Herbert, S., and Steinhardt, J. (1968). *Biochemistry* **67**, 1357.

Rosenberg, R. M., Crespi, H. L., and Katz, J. J. ACS Meeting, April, 1968, Abstract #203.

Rossotti, F. J. C., and Rossotti, H. (1961). "The Determination of Stability Constants." McGraw-Hill, New York.

Saifer, A., Westley, F., and Steigman, J. (1964). *Biochemistry* **3**, 1624.

Scatchard, G. (1946). *J. Am. Chem. Soc.* **68**, 2315.

Scatchard, G., and Black, E. S. (1949). *J. Phys. Colloid Chem.* **53**, 88.

Scatchard, G., Batchelder, A. C., and Brown, A. (1946). *J. Am. Chem. Soc.* **68**, 2320.

Scatchard, G., Scheinberg, I. H., and Armstrong, S. H. (1950). *J. Am. Chem. Soc.* **72**, 535, 540.

Scatchard, G., Coleman, J. S., and Shen, A. L. (1957). *J. Am. Chem. Soc.* **79**, 12.

Scatchard, G., Wu, Y. U., and Shen, A. L. (1959). *J. Am. Chem. Soc.* **81**, 6104.

Schachman, H. K., and Edelstein, S. J. (1966). *Biochemistry* **5**, 2681.

Schellman, J. S., Lumry, R., and Samuels, L. T. (1954). *Jacs* **76**, 2808.

Scholtan, W. (1963). *Intern. Cong. Chemotherapy, Proc.* 3rd Stuttgart, 261.

Scholtan, W. (1964). *Arzneimittel-Forsch.* **14**, 146.

Scholtan, W., and Schmid, J. (1963). *Arzneimittel-Forsch.* **13**, 288.

Smith, R. F., and Briggs, D. R. (1950). *J. Phys. Colloid Chem.* **54**, 33.

Sogami, M., and Foster, J. F. (1958). *Biochemistry* **7**, 2172.

Sorensen, S. P. (1907). *Biochem. Z.* **7**, 45.

Stein, H. H. (1965). *Technicon Symp. 2nd, N. Y., London*, **45**.

Steinberg, I. Z., and Schachman, H. K. (1966). *Biochemistry* **5**, 3728.

Steinhardt, J. (1941). *Ann. N. Y. Acad. Sci.* **41**, 287.

Steinhardt, J., and Harris, M. (1940). *J. Res. Natl. Bur. Std.* **24**, 355.

Steinhardt, J., and Zaiser, S. H. (1950). *J. Biol. Chem.* **183**, 789.

Steinhardt, J., Fugitt, C. H., and Harris, M. (1941). *J. Res. Natl. Bur. Std.* **26**, 293.

Steinhardt, J., Fugitt, C. H., and Harris, M. (1942). *J. Res. Natl. Bur. Std.* **28**, 201.

Strauss, G., and Strauss, O. P. (1958). *J. Phys. Chem.* **62**, 1321.

Strenstrom, W., and Reinhard, M. (1925). *J. Biol. Chem.* **66**, 819.

Stricks, W., and Koithoff, I. M. (1949). *JACS* **71**, 1519.

Stryer, L. (1965). *J. Mol. Biol.* **13**, 482.

Takashima, S. (1963). *J. Polymer Sci.* **1**, 2791.

Tanford, C. (1951). *J. Am. Chem. Soc.* **71**, 2066.

Tanford, C. (1961). "Physical Chemistry of Macromolecules." Wiley, New York.

Tiselius, A. (1930). *Nova Acta Regiae Soc. Sci. Upsalliensis* [4] **7**, No. 4.

Tritsch, G. L. (1967). *Intl. Biochem. Congress, 7th Tokyo IV*, 592.

Velick, S. F., Hayes, J. E., and Harting, J. (1953). *J. Biol. Chem.* **203**, 227.

Waldmann-Myer, H. (1964). Intl. Congress 6th Biochem., N.Y. **11**, 99.

Wallenfels, K. W., and Sund, H. (1957). *Biochemistry* **329**, 59.

Weber, G. (1965). *In* "Molecular Biophysics" (A. Pullman and M. Weissbluth, eds.), Academic Press, New York.

Weber, G., and Anderson, S. R. (1966). *Biochemistry* **6**, 1942.

Weber, G., and Daniel, E. (1966). *Biochemistry* **6**, 1900.

Weir, E. C., and Hastings, A. B. (1936). *J. Biol. Chem.* **114**, 397.

West, S. S., Nemchin, R. G., and Langley, B. C. (1966). ACS Meeting, Sept., N.Y.

Wetlaufer, D. B. (1962). *Advan. Protein Chem.* **17**, 303.
Willstätter, R., and Waldschmidt, E. (1921). *Ber. Deut. Chem. Ges.* **54**, 2988.
Wishnia, A. (1962). *Proc. Natl. Acad. Sci.* **48**, 2200.
Wishnia, A., and Pinder, T. W., Jr. (1966). *Biochemistry* **5**, 1534.
Yang, J. J., and Foster, J. F. (1953). *J. Am. Chem. Soc.* **75**, 5560.
Yielding, K. L., and Thompson, W. (1967). Intl. Cong. Biochem., 7th (Tokyo), IV, 832.

IV

Binding of Neutral Molecules

I. Introduction

The classical examples of the binding of neutral molecules by dissolved proteins are interaction with solvent and the reversible binding of oxygen, carbon monoxide, and other neutral ligands by the respiratory proteins. Neither of these cases lends itself well to a general analytical treatment of the subject. There is relatively little solid quantitative information available about the hydration of dissolved proteins; in fact, the concept itself, as will be shown later, is both conceptually and operationally vague. On the other hand, the reactions of respiratory proteins with neutral ligands are intimately related to interactions with the heme moiety, or with iron itself, and thus are a highly specialized group of interactions peculiar to the prosthetic group rather than to proteins in general.

For these reasons, our discussion will start with less widely known reactions, some of which have been studied only within the recent past. In describing these it will be assumed that the reader has read the discussion in Chapter I (pp. 6–7) of the effects of binding-induced conformation changes on binding isotherms. It is also assumed that the reader has examined the algebraic formulation of binding isotherms which includes the effects of unfolding and is given in Chapter II (pp. 26–30).

If the cooperative nature of the binding is disregarded (and therefore the sharp distinction between the two classes of macro-ions present, native and unfolded), only *average* values of bound ions will enter into the analysis, and the protein may appear to be characterized by one (initial) set of sites with large values of K (association constant) and a region beyond this in which the simple law of mass action does not seem to be obeyed. This second region may involve an unfolded state in which more binding sites are available to the ligand than in the native state. It is noteworthy that binding by the initial set of sites stabilizes the native form, and even exaggerates the "native" properties, such as compactness, of the protein (Wetlaufer and Lovrien, 1964; Reynolds *et al.*, 1967.)

Disruption of protein conformation may result from the binding of neutral molecules as well as of ions. The evidence is indirect and rests, in part, on a similarity of the binding isotherms for neutral molecules (e.g., alcohols) and their homologous ions (e.g., the sulfate half-esters). Some of the latter are known to cause the unfolding just described (see Chapter VII). It also rests in part on some of the evidence in the pages that follow of conformation changes induced by binding of neutral molecules which may be detected by changes in optical properties such as optical rotatory dispersion (Polet and Steinhardt, 1968). The fact that some proteins are denatured by some neutral molecules (ferrihemoglobin is denatured by octanol at slightly acid pH values at which it is stable in the absence of octanol) tends to support this inference (Steinhardt and Moezie, 1964). The neutral ligands most thoroughly investigated, however, have been characterized by relatively low affinities, with the consequence that only small values of $\bar{v}$ (molal binding ratio), and stabilizing rather than destabilizing effects have been observed (Wishnia, 1964). It has been reported, however, that dodecanol, which is strongly bound, does not protect BSA even at low $\bar{v}$ values (Markus *et al.*, 1964).

II. Results Obtained with Particular Proteins

A. SERUM ALBUMINS

1. *General Considerations*

There are both advantages and disadvantages in beginning a discussion of complex formation by proteins with a review of the results obtained with serum albumins. The advantages are numerous and obvious: binding by these proteins has been most extensively and, in some cases, most critically, studied. The disadvantages are threefold:

(a) Serum albumin is a very special protein, apparently designed for the purpose of combining with practically all substances (except most simple cations) in substantial quantities. It is not certain, therefore, that what may be learned about multiple equilibria with serum albumin will be applicable to other proteins.

(b) The avidity with which it combines with certain substances with which it occurs in natural association (e.g., long-chain fatty acids) has caused most investigations of BSA to be carried out with protein still containing one or two equivalents of combined fatty acid. Thus one or two of its highest-energy sites are already occupied. Alternatively, the protein has been drastically treated with acid, or acid plus organic solvents, to remove most (but not all) of the residual lipid material. Only the remarkable elasticity of this protein, which is almost instantly restored to something close to its original conformation when initial conditions are restored, has made it possible to work with such "acid-defatted" serum albumin at all.[1] However, the recent discovery by Chen (1967) that bovine serum albumin may be completely defatted in a short time by dilute acid in the presence of purified charcoal, has made available a fatty-acid-free protein for which new information is only beginning to be available (Sogami and Foster, 1968). Although this material differs perceptibly in a number of physical properties, including pH-stability profile, from the incompletely acid-defatted serum albumin with which so many binding data have been obtained, its binding isotherms with detergents do not differ perceptibly from those obtained with protein which has had no other treatment than passage through a mixed-bed resin deionizing column (Gallagher and Steinhardt, 1969). Reynolds et al. (1968) have discussed the effects of residual high-affinity fatty acid anion on binding isotherms obtained with other fatty acid anions.

(c) Finally, it has been convincingly shown that both bovine and human serum albumins are microheterogeneous, i.e., composed of a mixture of components which are not spontaneously and rapidly interconvertible and which are separable on the basis of their varying degrees of susceptibility to partial unfolding by acid (Peterson et al., 1965; Sogami and Foster, 1968; Peterson and Foster, 1965a,b). The heterogeneity has been suggested to be solely a manifestation of "extrinsic" contaminants (McMenamy and Lee, 1967) but Wong and Foster (1968) have convincingly demonstrated that this is not the case. The effect of this heterogeneity on the observed binding properties has not been determined. Its implications in preventing any simple thermodynamic analysis of the $N \rightleftarrows F$ "equilibrium" are obvious.

If the reservations based on the disadvantages just described are kept in mind, the great body of work with the serum albumin of ox and human makes an excellent subject with which to start a review and analysis of binding by proteins. The very fact that it appears to be a protein designed for material transport may make it most suitable for providing insight into the pattern of forces which are involved in binding. Just as muscle is a better tissue with which to study the conversion of biochemical to mechanical energy than is

---

[1] This ready regenerability, unparalled in any other investigated protein, may be the result of the 17–18 disulfide bridges of this protein.

a less specialized tissue, serum albumin may similarly be a better protein with which to study multiple equilibria than is one that does not form complexes so readily.

2. *Effects of Residual Fatty Acid*

Serum albumin, even after crystallization, is associated with quantities of lipid; separation of this material by repeated crystallization is not complete. The crystalline material available commercially today, prepared by methods developed in E. J. Cohn's laboratory (Hughes *et al.*, 1947), contains traces of decanol and small amounts of fatty acid (usually 1 to 2 moles/mole) (Goodman, 1958). Some of this residue can be removed by passage through a mixed-bed ion-exchange resin, but reports differ as to the amounts which remain. Goodman described a method for reducing the fatty acid content of fraction V (defatted) human serum albumin to less than 0.1 mmole/mole (Goodman, 1957), by a procedure involving treatment with glacial acetic acid in isooctane. The protein thus prepared was stated to be indistinguishable from the original material, as judged by ultracentrifugal, electrophoretic, immunological, optical rotatory, and methyl orange binding properties. It has been reported by Scatchard *et al.* (1959), that HSA prepared on deionizing columns exhibits the same binding behavior, with respect to such ions as thiocyanate and trichloroacetate, as when defatted by Goodman's procedure. Alfsen (1963) has reported that the Goodman preparation is identical with Armour crystalline serum albumin with respect to the binding of testosterone, although free fatty acid was displaced from the crystalline protein in equilibrium dialysis experiments with this ligand. It must be remembered that there is a possibility that Goodman's protein contains traces of isooctane. However, very recent work (Sogami and Foster, 1968) indicates that there are small but definite differences in the stability properties and ultraviolet absorption between protein defatted by the mild acid–charcoal method of Chen (1967) and protein that has had the more drastic acid treatment used previously.

With larger ions, and with the fatty-acid-like neutral molecules discussed in this chapter, there is a possibility that residual fatty acid anion may occupy part of the one or two sites of highest affinity which appear to characterize the binding of many substances to serum albumin. If so, some discrepancies in the low $\bar{v}$ region may be found between different protein preparations, and estimates of n and K may vary in this region. More serious, perhaps, is the fact that the residual fatty acid anion may be competitively replaced by neutral substances of very high affinity such as dodecanol or the even more tightly bound ionic detergents; while substances of lower affinity, such as chloride, may appear to have somewhat lower binding constants than they would otherwise show (see the treatment of competition in Chapter II; also Scatchard, 1950a,b).

All the evidence at hand appears to indicate that residual fatty acid does not materially complicate the isotherms obtained with deionized serum albumin—not only Scatchard's findings with smaller ions and our own findings with detergent ions (Gallagher and Steinhardt, unpublished) and Alfsen's with testosterone, but also the fact that octanol and dodecanol differ to a larger extent at larger $\bar{v}$ values than at small $\bar{v}$ values, point in this direction. With lipoproteins (i.e., lipovitellin) fat solvents remove only part of the lipid moiety unless the structure of the protein is degraded by unfolding or proteolysis (Evans *et al.*, 1968).

3. *Binding of Specific Classes of Substances*

(a) *Alkanes, Toluene.* Detailed measurements have been made by Wishnia (1962, 1964a,b) of the binding of *propane*, *butane*, and *pentane* by bovine serum albumin, β-lactoglobulin, hemoglobin, and lysozyme. The method principally employed has been determination of the solubility of these gases in solutions containing a fixed amount of protein (5%) at a number of gas concentrations (partial pressures) and temperatures. The results for serum albumin described below apply to pH values near the isoionic point; the binding is a function of pH since the transformation in conformation which occurs at pH values just below the isoionic point results in greatly reduced binding (Wishnia, 1964).[2]

It is clear from Figs. 4-1 and 4-2 that bovine serum albumin binds more

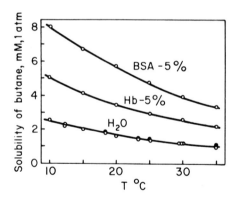

FIG. 4-1. Solubility of butane, millimoles per 1000 gm solution, 1 atmosphere. SLS refers to micellar sodium dodecylsulfate. [A. Wishnia (1962). *Proc. Natl. Acad. Sci. U.S.* **48**, 2200].

[2] It is not obvious from Wishnia's data that the pH effect can be wholly accounted for by the $N \rightarrow F$ transformation, most of which occurs over a very narrow pH interval (4.0–4.3) in dilute solutions of sodium or potassium chlorides—further measurements are required at pH values above the isoionic point.

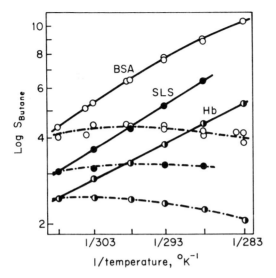

FIG. 4-2. Heats of solution, butane: O, BSA; ◑, Hb; ●, SLS; —, solubility increment, millimoles per 10^3 gm solute at 1 atmosphere; – – –, ratio of solubility in the solute S_p to solubility in water S_w. Note that values for BSA and Hb are to be multiplied by 10, for SLS by 100. [A. Wishnia (1962). *Proc. Natl. Acad. Sci. U.S.* **48**, 2200.]

butane per molecule than do hemoglobin or micelles of sodium dodecyl-sulfate. The ratio of the binding by protein to the solubility in water is essentially unchanged by temperature (Fig. 4-2). Thus the nearly constant ratios represented by the dashed lines show that the enthalpy of binding is essentially zero and the free energy of binding is principally entropic. Similar results were obtained with propane.

Wishnia gives the values shown in Table 4-1 for the changes in unitary free energies, unitary entropies,[3] and enthalpies of the combination of hydro-carbons with micelles of sodium dodecylsulfate.

TABLE 4-1

"BINDING" BY SODIUM DODECYLSULFATE AT 25°

	ΔF_u (k cal/mole)	S_u (eu)	ΔH (k cal/mole)	Molal ratio at 1 atmosphere
Propane	−4.3	+16	−0.5	—
Butane	−5.1	+17	∼0	approx. 5

[3] The unitary parameters are defined by Kauzmann (1959).

From the free energies it would appear that K_A for propane should be about 1350 and for butane about 5000. Wishnia calls attention to the similarity between the values in Table 4-1 and the corresponding values for the transfer of these gases from water to a pure liquefied gas phase, or to a 2-propanol phase, and suggests that the phenomenon is more akin to a gas-in-liquid solubility than to stoichiometric binding. Since all of Wishnia's early data involve a nearly fixed molal ratio (5 moles/mole in the case of butane at 25°), no inference as to the existence of discrete sets of binding sites could be made.

The "solubilities" or "amounts bound" in proteins differ from protein to protein, and are much smaller ($\frac{1}{8}$ to $\frac{1}{2}$, or in the case of lysozyme almost nothing), than the solubilities in the largely hydrocarbon micellar model system, sodium dodecylsulfate (SDS). Wishnia suggests, therefore, that the binding by proteins is a measure of the extent to which the protein molecular volume is occupied by hydrocarbon (hydrophobic) clusters of the right size. However, the incremental solubility of butane relative to that of propane is only 0.7 of its value in SDS micelles; the micellar model cannot be pushed too far.

Wishnia does not give values for $\Delta F°$ and ΔS_u for the binding of butane to BSA. An attempt is made here to calculate rough values for 25° from Fig. 4-1. We define the reaction

$$\text{Butane (aqueous)} \overset{K}{\rightleftharpoons} \text{Butane (in protein)} \tag{4-1}$$

and define the concentration of butane as moles solute per 1000 gm solvent. The $[B_{\text{aqueous}}]$ is approximately 1.3×10^{-3} and $[B_p \cong 7.5 \times 10^{-2}]$ (20 times the solubility observed in a 5% solution of protein). K is 57 and $\Delta F°$ (1 molal) = -2420 cal. This is within the range of values reported by Kauzmann (1959) (Table 4-2), but less than the value for transfer to micelles of sodium dodecylsulfate (approx. 3500 cal). The entropy change is approximately 8.14 cal if we take $\Delta H = 0$; 8 cal ($R \ln X$ where X is 1/55) must be added to the experimentally determined ΔS to obtain the unitary entropy change, 16.14. It is not possible to calculate reliable figures for propane from the graphs in Wishnia's paper, but it is obvious that $\Delta F°$ for propane take-up would be smaller, approximately half as great as for butane. The unitary entropy change would also be smaller, by about 6 cal.

It should be noted that the numerical values given cannot be compared with others which are calculated for cases of binding in which definite stoichiometric relations exist. The figures merely refer to the transfer of 1 mole of hydrocarbon at infinite dilution in water to the protein phase. They do not depend on the amount "bound" and do not refer to the making of any particular number of hydrophobic bonds. The figures may only be compared with those given by Wishnia for solution in micelles of dodecylsulfate.

In a later paper, Wishnia and Pinder (1964) varied the gas pressure and

TABLE 4-2

THERMODYNAMIC CHANGES IN THE TRANSFER OF HYDROCARBONS FROM A NONPOLAR
SOLVENT TO WATER[a]

Process	Temp. (°K)	ΔS_u (eu)	ΔH (cal/ mole)	ΔF_u (cal/ mole)	$\frac{\Delta H}{\Delta S_u}$ (°K)
CH_4 in benzene → CH_4 in H_2O	298	−18	−2800	+2600	155
CH_4 in ether → CH_4 in H_2O	298	−19	−2400	+3300	126
CH_4 in CCl_4 → CH_4 in H_2O	298	−18	−2500	+2900	140
C_2H_6 in benzene → CH_2H_6 in H_2O	298	−20	−2200	+3800	110
C_2H_6 in CCl_4 → C_2H_6 in H_2O	298	−18	−1700	+3700	94
C_2H_4 in benzene → C_2H_4 in H_2O	298	−15	−1610	+2920	107
C_2H_2 in benzene → C_2H_2 in H_2O	298	−7	−190	+1870	27
Liquid propane → C_2H_8 in H_2O	298	−23	−1800	+5050	78
Liquid *n*-butane → C_4H_{10} in H_2O	298	−23	−1000	+5850	44
Liquid benzene → C_6H_6 in H_2O	291	−14	0	+4070	0
Liquid toluene → C_7H_8 in H_2O	291	−16	0	+4650	0
Liquid ethylbenzene → C_2H_{10} in H_2O	291	−19	0	+5500	0
Liquid *m*- or *p*-xylene → C_8H_{10} in H_2O	291	−20	0	+5800	0

[a] W. Kauzman, in *Advan. Protein Chem.* **14**, 1 (1959).

thus determined how the solubility ratio ($S_{protein}/S_{water}$) varied with the free butane concentration at a single temperature (Fig. 4-3). Remarkably this ratio appears to be practically constant (we have already seen that to a first approximation it is also independent of temperature). Wishnia estimates that the experimental error does not preclude saturation values (n) representing molal ratios greater than about 40. However, no values of $\bar{v}$ (average molal ratio) above about 8 were actually measured. It should be noted that the coordinates of Figs. 4-3 and 4-4 differ from those in Scatchard plots [Eq. (2-27)] only by constant factors in both abscissa and ordinate. A horizontal line on such a plot corresponds to values of n experimentally indistinguishable from infinity.

It may be noted in Figs. 4-3, 4-4, and 4-5 that there is a pronounced effect of pH on the binding of alkane by serum albumin—the binding increases as pH increases throughout the entire pH range investigated. This effect is at least partly due to the well-known reversible N ⇄ F conformational transition which occurs in the pH range 4.0–4.3 (Foster, 1960). In the presence of butane, the transition occurs at somewhat lower pH values (butane binding *stabilizes*) as shown by an acid shift in the characteristic viscosity increase and in other physical alterations which accompany the transition. In the same pH range, as the pH is lowered, a sharp reduction occurs in the ability of serum albumin to bind butane (to $\frac{1}{4}$) or pentane (to $\frac{1}{5}$). In molal ratios up to 5–8 both are

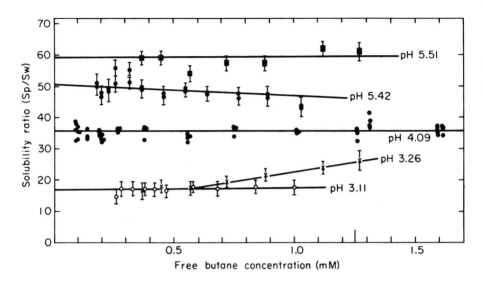

FIG. 4-3. Butane binding to BSA as a function of butane concentration; 25°, 0.15 M NaCl; pH as indicated. Ordinate, (S_p/S_w). Abscissa, calculated free butane concentration, mM. [A. Wishnia and T. Pinker (1964). *Biochemistry* **3**, 1377.]

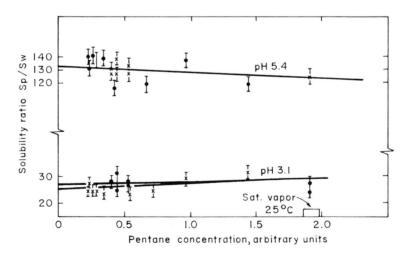

FIG. 4-4. Pentane binding as a function of pentane concentration. 25°, 0.15 M NaCl. Ordinate (S_p/S_p). Abscissa, free pentane concentration in arbitrary units (approximate concentration in equilibrium with saturated vapor is shown).

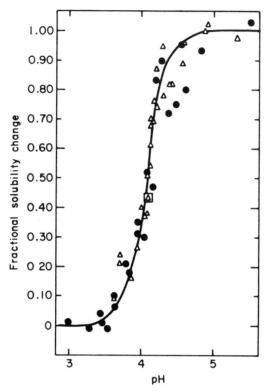

FIG. 4-5. Butane binding in the $N \rightarrow F$ transition, 25°, 0.15 M NaCl. Ordinate, fractional solubility change for butane: (S_p/S_w) pH-(S_p/S_w) pH 3/(S_p/S_w) pH 5.5-(S_p/S_w) pH 3 . Abscissa, pH. ● and △ represent runs, about eight months apart, using different samples of protein and gas. The data were normalized to minimize apparent systematic differences between the two runs: the values of (S_p/S_w) at pH 5.5 and 3.0 are, respectively, 50 and 13, and 61 and 16 for the two sets. [A. Wishnia and T. Pinder (1964). *Biochemistry* **3**, 1377.]

therefore stabilizers of the N form, as would be expected from the observed greater affinity of N to the alkanes. These effects (together with an additional prediction, that addition of hydrocarbon should cause a drop in pH) will be further elaborated in the discussion of the effects of binding on stability.

It appears, however, that the effect of pH on the binding of neutral molecules does not depend solely on the N ⇌ F transition and the difference between the binding of alkanes by the N and F forms. Additional measurements of the interaction of BSA with butane and certain other hydrocarbons at 1 atmosphere pressure have been made by Wetlaufer and Lovrien (1964) in the presence of salt (0.15 M KCl)[4] (Fig. 4-6). The molal ratio at atmospheric

[4] The presence of salt is stated to be without effect.

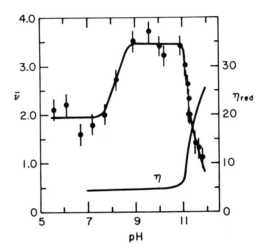

FIG. 4-6. Butane binding by BSA as a function of pH. Here $\bar{v}$ is the average number of butane molecules bound per BSA molecule, obtained from the "extra" solubility of butane (at 1 atmosphere of pressure) in BSA solutions compared with protein-free solvent. BSA concentration, 3% to 4%; 0.15 M KCl; 25.0°. The reduced viscosity curve for butane-saturated solutions of BSA is also included [D. Wetlaufer and R. Lovrien (1964). *J. Biol. Chem.* **239**, 596].

pressure is essentially constant at 2.0 from pH 5.6 to 7.4, rises to 3.4 and stays constant at pH values between 9 and 11, and then declines sharply to less than 1 at pH 11.8.[5] The decline is accompanied by changes in the ultraviolet spectrum in the tyrosine region (280–310 mμ) and a sharp, although small, increase in viscosity. Butane binding causes the pH at which the alkaline tyrosine "unmasking" normally occurs to shift to higher values. The red shift in the 280 mμ region which accompanies protonation of the unmasked tyrosines also occurs at a slightly higher pH. Small reversible viscosity changes occur at pH 11.22—the viscosity falls when butane is added, and rises again when the butane is removed by equilibrating the solution with nitrogen.

In similar measurements at high pH with both butane and butadiene, a fully reversible change in pH (rising by up to 0.07 unit) was shown to accompany butane binding. Such an increase need not indicate greater binding by the less protonated forms of the protein, it may be no more than a manifestation of an *increase* in the electrostatic factor w which, in part, governs the acid–base titration curve.

[5] With protein defatted by the method of Goodman (1957) the binding of butane by isoionic protein rises to 2.7. The fact that Wetlaufer and Lovrien obtain a lower value of $\bar{v}$ than Wishnia, by their extraction method, may indicate that one or two of the butane molecules may be very tightly bound.

Heptane has been used in the phase-distribution method of measuring the binding of fatty acids (Goodman, 1958) and of steroids (Alfsen, 1963), but it appears, incidental to the work of Alfsen on the binding of testosterone, that heptane itself causes a decrease in the levorotation of BSA as well as an alteration in the acidic titration curve. It is possible that heptane not only binds, but may cause a conformation change as well. The latter is quite different from one caused by binding testosterone. Both are discussed in the section on the stabilizing effects of ligands (p. 117).

Recent comprehensive papers (Mohammadzadeh-K *et al.*, 1967, 1969a) on the binding of higher hydrocarbons ($CH_2 > 5$) to BSA (and β-lactoglobulin) give results with pentane which appear to disagree with those of Wishnia and Pinder (1964), in that a definite mass-law binding on 3.8 sites was indicated by either reciprocal or Scatchard plots.

Isooctane has been used in the extraction of residual bound fatty acids from human serum albumin (Goodman, 1958). It is of particular interest, therefore, to determine to what extent it may be bound by the protein. It has been reported that isooctane is not solubilized by BSA (i.e., does not bind to the protein) (Strauss and Strauss, 1958) beyond 1–2 moles/mole. However, there is indirect evidence that BSA participates in isooctane interactions. This evidence results from an investigation of the solubilization in water of isooctane by BSA as a function of the amount of sodium dodecylsulfate bound by the protein (Breuer and Strauss, 1960). BSA itself is ineffective in solubilizing the hydrocarbon unless micelles of dodecylsulfate (critical micelle concentration = 0.0082) are present. When an average of more than about 24 molecules of the detergent are bound to each protein molecule, solubilization takes place. In itself, this information might be interpreted as indicating that the bound detergent constitutes a separate phase similar to the micelles which Wishnia has shown can dissolve hydrocarbons as in a Nernst isotherm (Wishnia, 1963), i.e., the protein–detergent complex constitutes a discrete liquid hydrocarbon phase. However, Breuer and Strauss conclude that the detergent bound to BSA is more effective in solubilizing isooctane than is the free detergent micelle phase, i.e., less of it is required for a given amount of solubilization than when only detergent is present. The amount of isooctane solubilized is always proportional to the number of *bound* SDS molecules. The solubilization phenomenon appears to be cooperative, i.e., the solubilization efficiency per bound detergent molecule is greater, the greater the amount of isooctane already solubilized. Other suggestions of pseudomicellar properties of bound detergent ions will be discussed in Chapter VII.

Wishnia seems to prefer to regard the solubilization as a manifestation of a lowering of the CMC (critical micelle concentration) of the dodecylsulfate by the protein, analogous to its lowering by dedecyl alcohol. However, the observation remains that these "micelles" are more effective per molecule of bound detergent than micelles of the detergent alone.

More direct evidence is available for *n-octane*: by using the solubility method with a radio-labeled sample of this soluble alkane, Ray *et al.* (1966) report a binding constant at pH 5.6 of approximately 3000, only slightly lower than the binding constant for *n*-octanol. The data on which this approximate value is based are meager, and the value itself is based on an assumption that the number of binding sites is the same as for *n*-octanol. Further work is needed. The important qualitative conclusion is that the longer-chain, straight-chain hydrocarbon is bound more strongly than the more soluble shorter-chain butane and pentane.

In the investigation of Mohammadzadeh *et al.* (1969a) other homologous hydrocarbons from heptane up to tridecane gave *decreasing* numbers of sites (molar ratios at saturation), from 2.80 for heptane down to 0.86 for tridecane. Branched chains reduced the apparent saturation values. The methyl esters of fatty acids are particularly good binders ($n = 18.5$ for methyl hexanoate). (The fractional numbers of sites may possibly relate to microheterogeneity.) All of the ligands just mentioned appear to bind in accordance with the simple law of mass action or Langmuir adsorption isotherm. Benzene and its derivatives, however, which bind on a very large number of sites ($n = 30$), seem to behave very similarly to the nonstoichiometric partition-law type of behavior described by Wishnia for the shorter-chain hydrocarbons. Partial digestion with proteolytic enzymes reduced the binding to BSA, but had the opposite effect with certain other proteins. Ligands which bind on a large number of sites will appear, within experimental error, to have a simple partition-law binding, when the experiments only cover a range of low $\bar{v}$ values.

No direct measurements of the binding of *toluene*, or of any other aromatic hydrocarbon have been made. However, it has been shown that toluene competes with an anionic azo dye for sites on serum albumin (Karush, 1950) and must therefore bind to the protein. Since the solubility of toluene, approximately 5×10^{-3} M, is about as high as that of octanol (see below) considerable binding may be expected. The fact that toluene *competes* with the anions, rather than *enhances* their binding, suggests that no conformation change is involved. Conformational changes appear to be involved in the binding of a number of anesthetic gases to BSA and β-lactoglobulin. Balasubramanian and Wetlaufer (1966) have reported that methoxyfluorene, chloroform, bromochlorotrifluoroethane, and ethyl ether produce large changes in the optical rotation at 5460 Å of solutions of these two proteins.

   (b) *Alcohols.* The binding of alcohols by proteins in aqueous solutions is least ambiguous, i.e., distinguishable from bulk or medium effects, in the case of those alcohols which are only very slightly soluble. The earliest demonstration that an alcohol, hexanol, was bound to serum albumin was based on its competition with the binding of anions (Karush, 1951); it can *decrease* the pH of isoionic solutions by dissociating anions, and thus leaving a positive charge (Steinhardt, unpublished). Recently, Ray *et al.* (1966) have measured the binding of the still less soluble *n*-octanol and *n*-dodecanol to deionized crystalline bovine serum albumin by both equilibrium dialysis and solubility techniques, making use of radio-labeled material. The results with octanol in phosphate buffers containing 1 % protein are shown in Fig. 4-7. These data and others may be summarized as follows:

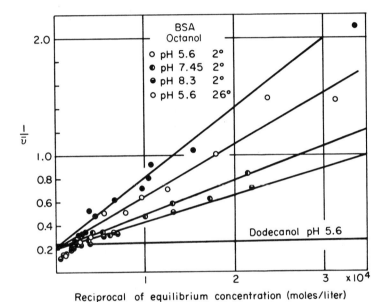

Fig. 4-7. Reciprocal plot of 1-octanol binding by BSA in 0.033 ionic strength phosphate buffers. The nearly horizontal line at the bottom of the figure represents the data for 1-dodecanol. [A. Ray *et al.* (1966). *Biochemistry* **5**, 2606.]

(1) Within the region of high-affinity binding, the *number* of available sites (five) is independent of both temperature and pH, except at the highest pH used, 8.3, where it may be as great as 7.

(2) The binding constants are pH-dependent; the association constant rises as the pH increases over most of the range shown from 3370 to 7140; this is discussed more fully in the next section.

(3) The binding constant also increases slightly as the temperature is raised at the same pH (5.6). Since ΔH is therefore positive and $\Delta F°$ is negative (-4460 to -5050 cal/mole, depending on temperature), there must be a

substantial positive ΔS. The actual value, which is greater than 17 eu, is quite consistent with hydrophobic interactions (Kauzmann, 1959).

(4) Phosphate ions do not appear to compete strongly with octanol. Almost the same binding constant is found with 0.1 M phosphate buffer as with 0.03 M at pH 5.6.

There is evidence of octanol binding in the observation by Schmid (1959), based on electrophoretic patterns, in that octanol stabilizes the N form in the pH region (4.0–4.3) of the N $\rightleftarrows$ F transformation.

There is no clear evidence that one or two of the five sites are characterized by a higher binding energy than the others, as Scatchard and others (see Chapter VII) have found for ionic ligands. There are, however, clearly a large number of sites of low affinity. It would be easy to attribute the absence of one or two sites of highest affinity to occupation of these sites by residual fatty acid. However, the finding of five sites in the high-affinity set is characteristic of many other binding experiments with BSA and suggests that fatty acid initially occupying one or two sites may be replaced by the ligand.

The well-known effect of a small amount of *decanol* in inducing the crystallization of serum albumin is probably a manifestation of its binding to the protein, but no analysis of this effect has been made. Since the alcohol is known to stabilize the protein against heating, its effect may be to reduce heterogeneity of conformation (Hughes *et al.*, 1947).

The longest-chain aliphatic alcohol for which data are available is *n-dodecanol*. Ray *et al.* (1966) determined that at 2° and pH 5.6 dodecanol bound on four to five sites with a very high binding constant, 150,000 ($\Delta F° = -6600$ cal/mole. This value was obtained with 0.1% protein. The binding constant appeared to depend on protein concentration when the latter exceeded 0.1%. There is reason to believe, however, that no concentration effect exists, and that equilibrium was not achieved when higher concentrations of protein were used (Cassel *et al.*, 1969).

As with octanol the extent of binding depends strongly on pH with the effect leveling off at pH values well over 8. If it is assumed that n does not change with pH, the fraction of the number of sites occupied rises from about 0.4 at pH 5.0 to over 0.9 at pH 8.3 when the concentration of free dodecanol is held constant (in equilibrium with solid phase) at $2.4 \times 10^{-5} M$.

(c) *Effects of pH on binding of Hydrocarbons and Aliphatic Alcohols to Serum Albumin.* An effect of pH on the binding of anions (or cations) to proteins has long been known, and would be expected, since interaction of the ions with the charged side chains of the protein, the number and distribution of which depend on pH, is clearly possible. Such effects are the subject of a later section of this book (Chapter VII, pp. 290–296). It will be shown that in addition to purely electrostatic effects, major complications occur as the result of conformation changes which occur in particular pH intervals as the protein is titrated. It is not surprising that such conformation changes should also affect the binding of neutral molecules. Such major effects were first demonstrated in the binding of butane and pentane to serum albumin (Wishnia, 1964), in the pH region of the much studied $N \rightleftarrows F$ transformation which occurs between pH 4.0 and 4.3 at 25° (see p. 91). Wishnia demonstrated that the binding of hydrocarbons is greatly reduced at low pH values, and that the reduction parallels the viscosity changes by means of which the transformation may be followed. He also showed that hydrocarbon binding shifts the transformation to lower pH values, i.e., the protein is stabilized by hydrocarbon binding. Rather unexpectedly the pH effect extends into regions considerably above those in which the $N \rightleftarrows F$ transformation has been believed to extend: the amount bound increases with pH up to 5.6, the highest employed by Wishnia, more than one pH unit higher than has been considered necessary in order for the protein to be entirely in the N form (see Chapter V, p. 185). The possibility exists, therefore, that when hydrocarbons are bound the transformation is less cooperative (with respect to hydrogen ions) than when the free protein is titrated and spreads over a wider interval of pH. Sogami and Foster (1968) have shown that the removal of tightly bound fatty acid sharpens the transition. We have seen that similar dependence on pH appears in the binding of higher alcohols already alluded to (Ray *et al.*, 1966; Reynolds *et al.*, 1968). The binding isotherm for *n*-octanol has been measured at pH values up to 8.3 (0.03 M phosphate). The extended range of investigation has revealed that there is a substantial although gradual increase in the amount bound at pH values up to 8.3, although the increase is small above pH 7.45. K seems to be proportional to the fifth root of $[H^+]$ between 5.6 and 7.45. The region of increased binding corresponds fairly well to that of a second conformation change discovered by Leonard *et al.*, 1963) on the basis of measurements of optical rotation. This change differs from the $N \rightleftarrows F$ transition at lower pH in that it is not accompanied by noticeable changes in the electrostatic interaction factor w employed in analysis of the titration curve (see Chapter II) although major changes in tertiary structure appear to occur, e.g., hydrogen–deuterium exchange is increased stepwise by this transition. The two conformation changes affect binding of neutral molecules in opposite directions; the change below the isoionic point $(N \rightleftarrows F)$ reducing binding of hydrocarbons and the change above the isoionic point, which is favored by high concentrations of ligand, and by ion binding (thiocyanate, perchlorate) increasing binding. The shifts brought about by ligands in the pH regions of the transitions are thermodynamically consistent with the effects of pH on binding. The binding of octanol and hexanol by BSA in unbuffered solutions reduces the pH (i.e., the protein becomes a slightly stronger acid). The initial change is followed by a slower reversed change with octanol but not with hexanol (Ray *et al.*, 1966).

(d) *Testosterone and Other Steroids.* An unusually detailed investigation by Alfsen (1963) reports the binding of testosterone to dissolved crystalline bovine serum albumin (not previously deionized). The results depend on temperature, and on the method of measurement [both equilibrium dialysis for 48 hours, and partition equilibrium with a heptane phase (24 hours) were employed]. It was possible to show that the differences given by the two methods were due to the binding of heptane in the partition experiment, and to a conformation change induced by this binding, discussed in Section 5) on the effects of ligands on protein conformation.

Alfsen's testosterone data followed the law of mass action, with no marked indications of the existence of sharp discontinuities in the binding constants of discrete sets of sites over a range of $\bar{v}$ from less than 0.2 to values of about 4 at 3° and 11.5 at 25°. Her results are expressed in terms of the parameter $n\langle K \rangle$ due to von Muralt (1930) and to Schellman *et al.* (1954), defined by the equation: $n\langle K \rangle = \sum_{i=1}^{n} K_i$ where the K_i are not necessarily a homogeneous set. Alfsen also gives an apparent dissociation constant $\bar{K}$ defined by

$$\sum_{i=1}^{n} K_i/n = \bar{K} \qquad (4\text{-}2)$$

At 25°, $n\bar{K} = 1.95 \times 10^4$ with $n = 4$; at 3°, $n\bar{K} = 1.82 \times 10^4$ and n increases to 20.[6] There is a much greater effect of temperature on n than on $\bar{K}$, implying that the accessibility of testosterone binding sites, and therefore the conformation of the protein, changes between 3° and 25°. More sites are available at the lower temperature. The standard free energy changes for binding 1 mole of testosterone to protein, derived from the values of $\bar{K}$, are -5.8 kcal/mole at 25° and -6.4 kcal/mole at 3°. The values would be -5.07 kcal/mole and -3.75 kcal/mole if based on $\bar{K}$ instead of $n\bar{K}$[7]. $\bar{K}$ itself varies widely with temperature although nK does not; the values are 5×10^4 at 25° and 1.1×10^5 at 3°. ΔH is thus negative; this reaction is not chiefly entropy driven. With heptane present, as in the partition equilibrium experiments, or on dissolving heptane in the aqueous solvent, the $\bar{K}$ and ΔF values were about the same as in its absence, but the values of n were smaller (13 at 3°). These will be discussed in a later section. Equilibrating the protein with heptane prior to

---

[6] Alfsen gives 1.95×10^{-4} etc., but this is an obvious error in the sign of the exponent. The value of $n = 20$ at 3° represents a large extrapolation. The dialysis data do not include values of molal ratio greater than about 4.

[7] K is the value of $\bar{K}$ if all the K's differ only by the usual combinatorial statistical factors.

measuring the binding by equilibrium dialysis at 3° increased n slightly to 22 rather than dropping it to 13, as in the partition equilibrium experiments with heptane. This treatment also increases the magnitude of the specific rotation change beyond that found when binding was measured in the continued presence of heptane. The effect suggests that the bound testosterone protects the protein from the denaturing action of heptane, and that the effect of heptane denaturation (possibly a phase-interface effect) is not readily reversible.

Alfsen's results may be compared with those obtained by an entirely different method (enhancement of solubility in protein solutions). In an earlier investigation (Bischoff and Pilhorn, 1948), it was found that the increment in solubility of testosterone in albumin solutions was proportional to the concentration of protein—the constant of proportionality at 37.5° indicated that the number of moles bound per mole of protein was 2.5 at pH 7.3 and 3.3 at pH 8.0. These figures represent a solubility in 3 % isoionic protein solutions 12–13 times as great as in isoionic solutions containing no protein. The same factor prevailed for progesterone, and an even higher factor, 22, characterized estradiol. However, the molal ratios for the latter two steroids were lower than for testosterone: 0.5 for estradiol and 0.7 to 1.5 for progesterone (depending on pH). The effect of temperature on the solubility in protein solutions was less than for water alone, except for estradiol, in which case it was much larger. It may be concluded, therefore, that the binding of testosterone and progesterone diminishes as the temperature is raised (ΔH negative), but that the binding of estradiol increases at higher temperatures, (ΔH positive).

The values given for testosterone represent much larger amounts bound than in Alfsen's experiments at 25° in which the most concentrated solutions at equilibrium were only one tenth-saturated, and resulted in molal ratios of about 1.25. A linear extrapolation on reciprocal plots [Fig. 4-8, curve B, from Alfsen (1963)] indicates that the values obtained by the solubility method are in fair agreement with those obtained by equilibrium dialysis.

Alfsen also reported that α-globulin showed little or no binding, but reported that β-globulin bound even more than albumin.

In another investigation of the binding of testosterone (Schellman *et al.*, 1954) (notable for emphasizing the fact that only the product $n\bar{K}$ rather than n or K can be obtained from either Klotz or Scatchard plots unless there is assurance that *all* the binding constants are identical), it was shown that the values of $n\bar{K}$ and the apparent free energy of binding increased as the protein was purified.[8] The finding of Bischoff and Pilhorn that the binding increased as the pH of equilibrium rose from 6.5 to 8.5 (as has already been shown to occur with aliphatic alcohols, and as will be demonstrated in Chapter VII, with detergents ions) was confirmed. Anions such as thiocyanate compete

---

[8] By assuming the $\bar{K}$ was equal to K, values of $\bar{v} = 10$ were obtained.

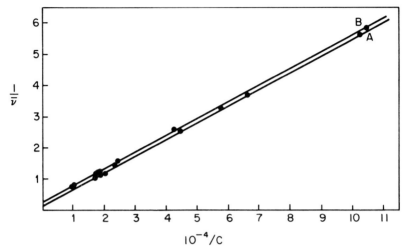

FIG. 4-8. Binding of testosterone by BSA in phosphate buffer pH 7.4 at 25°C. Curve A refers to data obtained by the partition method; curve B represents equilibrium dialysis data. [A. Alfsen (1963). *Compt. Rend. Trav. Lab. Carlsberg* **33**, 415.]

weakly with the steroid as they had earlier been shown to compete with aminoazobenzene (Klotz and Ayers, 1952). Methyl orange, a more strongly bound ligand, competed more strongly, as did divalent cations, known to combine with imidazole groups in the protein. On the basis of the data given, the conclusion was reached that the free energy of the binding of large organic ionic ligands to this protein depended only secondarily on coulomb forces, and that much of the free energy was due to an uninterpreted favorable entropy change.

Unfortunately, most of the earlier data on steroids were obtained by partition equilibrium, involving exposure to heptane; the data refer, therefore, to altered protein, and are superceded for native protein by the equilibrium dialysis measurements of Alfsen already described. It is noteworthy that the value of $n\bar{K}$ obtained for estradiol in the presence of toluene, 12,000, is in good agreement with another described below, obtained by means of solubility measurements; but the value obtained *for cortisone* in the presence of heptane, 30,000, does not agree with the value 2000 obtained by measurements of solubility.

An extensive investigation of the binding of testosterone and 14 other related steroids to BSA has been reported recently by Attallah and Lata (1968), who made use of the quenching of tryptophan fluorescence by bound steroid to obtain their isotherms. Unfortunately these investigators define their "formation constants" so that they are neither identical with nor simply related to, the association constants used by others. In addition, assumptions of direct proportionality between binding and quenching at a single frequency, the emission maximum, were made (the emission maximum commonly shifts to shorter wavelengths when ligands are bound). Thus, there is no direct basis for comparing their results or their conclusions with those already cited. Their general conclusions as to the hydrophobic forces involved, and the dependence of binding on conformation appear to be well supported although hardly novel.

Another recent study of the binding of testosterone to bovine and human serum albumins (Pearlman and Crepy, 1967) employed a gel filtration method (a batch method rather than the column method described in Chapter III) and gave nK approximately 26,000 for BSA and approximately 25,000 for HSA. A radioisotope assay was used. The results are in fair agreement with those obtained by Alfsen at 25°. No separate determinations of n or K were made.

Approximate values of the binding constants of other steroids have been obtained by the same method as that used by Bischoff and Pilhorn (1948); determining the increase in their apparent solubility when bovine serum albumin was added to solutions containing excess solid phase (Eik-Nes *et al.*, 1953). In Table 4-3 the steroids (except for anthraquinone) are arranged in descending order of solubility in water. The binding constants given are based on saturation values of $n = 10$, obtained with testosterone by partition analysis (Schellman *et al.*, 1954) and assumed, without experimental justification,

TABLE 4-3

BINDING OF STEROIDS TO BSA[a]

Ligand	$\bar{v}$	Solubility of steroids in water (μmoles/liter)	$K \times 10^{-4}$ $\left(K = \dfrac{\bar{v}}{\text{solubility}}\right)$	$\Delta F°$ kcal/mole ligand)
Cortisone	1.1	600	0.20 �️	−4.7
Androstanedione	4.1	220	3.22	−5.9
Androstenedione	3.17	200	2.34	−5.8
Deoxycorticosterone	1.17	180	0.74	−5.8
Testosterone	2.80	125	3.2	−6.2
Methyltestosterone	2.26	120	2.5	−6.1
Dehydroisoandrosterone	3.80	100	6.1	−6.5
Etiocholanolone	1.14	70	1.9	−5.8
Androsterone	1.85	43	5.3	−6.6
Estradiol	0.43	0.6	75	<(−8.0)
Δ^4-Androstene-3-one	0.68	<1.0	>73	<(−8.0)
Androstane-17-one	0.193	<0.2	>98	<(−8.0)
Anthraquinone	0.066	6.5	1.0	—

to apply to all other steroids. This value of n does not agree with the smaller value, 4, obtained by Alfsen with testosterone at 25°. The data given above are not strictly comparable, since they were obtained at two different temperatures, 25° and 37°, and in some cases with different concentrations of protein. Because of the methods used (exposure to heptane) and unverified assumptions as to the constancy of n, the values in the last two columns should be accepted only with reservations.

Curiously, Schellman et al., did not accept the inverse dependence of binding on the number of polar groups, and suggested that the finding was due to the choice of an incorrect standard reference concentration. When referred to the saturated concentration of a solution, the free energies of binding (all of them very small) showed a weak tendency to increase with the number of polar groups on the steroid; this finding led the authors to conclude that polar groups contributed to the binding forces!

It is clear that within the steroid group the binding tends to rise as the solubility in water goes down—affinity to protein goes up as affinity to water declines. The unitary standard free energies show the same trend, but, as would be expected, do not show great differences. In general, the least soluble steroids, and therefore those possessing the fewest polar groups, bind more strongly.

In these experiments testosterone showed no binding at all to three-times-crystallized beef hemoglobin, but a "modified" human globin (possibly denatured) did bind. Very little binding could be detected to insoluble collagen. Gueriguian and Pearlman (1968) have described a protein in human pregnancy serum that binds testosterone very tightly ($K = 3 \times 10^8$ at 25°) when measured by the batch method variant of the gel filtration method (Pearlman and Crepy, 1967).

Later investigations of cortisol binding to BSA and HSA (Brinkhorst and Hess, 1965) concluded that estimates of both the numbers of sites, and affinities were fraught with uncertainties which resulted not only from the difficulties of extrapolation but also from a reported dependence on the concentration of protein (as with dodecanol) and long-chain detergents (see pp. 47–48), and attribute these uncertainties to microheterogeneity and to competitive contaminants in the protein sample. Other recent work is reviewed by Westphal (1964).

(e) *Phosphatidylserine.* Phosphatidylserine, an ester of phosphatidic acid, binds to human serum albumin at two sets of sites which differ in apparent association constants. Therrault and Taylor (1964) report 2 sites with $K = 2 \times 10^5$ and 30 sites with $K = 1.3 \times 10^3$, determined by analysis of results with a turbidometric method.

(f) *Xanthine.* Xanthine and some of its derivatives, both neutral and ionic, have been studied by Gadzala (1964) and Guttman and Gadzala (1965) by equilibrium dialysis, as well as by analysis of the spectrophotometric changes produced by binding. The neutral compounds gave the same results by the two methods, but the ionic compounds (8-nitrotheophylline and 8-chlorotheophylline) produced discrepant results. Human serum albumin bound less than BSA. pH affected the binding of both neutral and ionic ligands similarly, with a decrease occurring in the pH range 9–10. Salicylic acid inhibited the binding of the ionic ligands as did acetylation of the protein. Gadzala therefore considers that the protonated form of the ε-amino groups of lysine are at the binding sites.

Four neutral caffeine derivatives differing only in the length of the substituent alkane behaved similarly, but an eight-carbon substituent increased the binding. ΔH appeared to be negative. Competitive binding studies were used to rank-order the various derivatives, all of which—charged or neutral—appeared to bind on the same site. Any agent which demonstrably altered the conformation resulted in decreased binding.

(g) *Sulfonamides and Antibiotics.* These substances are treated together here for convenience. Although many are capable of existing as ions, in most cases they are only weakly ionized at neutral pH.

The earliest work on *sulfonamide* binding to plasma protein was that of Davis (1943); the binding was first measured by equilibrium dialysis by Klotz and Urquhart (1948). Klotz and Walker (1948) and Wohler and Speckman (1960) have shown that BSA has a single binding site for a number of sulfonamides. Fischer and Jardetsky (1965) who also studied penicillin have shown that a different binding site is involved for the latter.

The binding to serum albumin of various sulfonamides and other antibiotics has been studied recently by observing the increment in the relaxation rate in nuclear magnetic resonance spectra (Jardetsky and Wade, 1965). A single mole of sulfonamide is bound. None of the substituted p-aminobenzenesulfonamides bind as strongly as the parent substance. Phenylpropanol, in less than stoichiometric equivalence to the ligand, completely inhibits the binding of the p-aminobenzenesulfonamides and is therefore presumably also bound. However, it enhances the binding of sulfaphenazole. The phenyl substituent appears to bind independently, and in the absence of phenylpropanol, the affinity is higher. Large differences in the binding tendencies of various derivatives of penicillin have been investigated by means of equilibrium dialysis and gel filtration against serum proteins (Acred *et al.*, 1963).

NMR studies are interpreted by the Jardetskys as showing that the p-aminobenzenesulfonamide " nucleus " is bound to the protein rather than any of the $N - 1$ substituents which may be added to it and which affect the binding constant. Sulfaphenazole is an exception—the phenyl portion of the substituent binds independently at a nearby site. The binding constants (approx. 200) are relatively low. There is an effect of pH which suggests that electrostatic forces can strengthen the binding. In the case of penicillin, the phenyl group was shown to be the effective ligand, by the effect of binding on the breadth of its peak (Fischer and Jardetsky, 1965).

There is a very extensive, less quantitative literature on the binding of sulfonamides by serum proteins. The most extensive series, by Scholtan, compares a large number of antibiotics and proteins at a number of pH values. Structural rules for varying the binding affinity have been deduced (Scholtan, 1964), and the relation has been deduced that binding to protein is proportional to the molecular refraction of the sulfonamides—an increase of one unit in the latter causes an increase in the affinity equivalent to an increase in free energy of 150 cal/mole (Scholtan, 1964). Most of the energy is due to hydrophobic forces, but electrostatic forces are also involved (Scholtan, 1964). The relation to molecular refraction is claimed to apply to the binding of other antibiotics such as penicillin and tetracycline. Scholtan's measure of affinity is not quantitatively relatable to those treated in Chapter II of this book, and has a strongly empirical character (Scholtan, 1964; Scholtan and Schmid, 1963). A very small sample of his very extensive data is shown in Fig. 4-9. Scholtan reports that the nonionizable antibiotic, amphenicol, is the only one of the two of this type tested which binds. The other was cycloserine.

A more conventional analysis of sulfonamide binding in terms of the Langmuir adsorption isotherm (BSA) was carried out by Nakagaki et al. (1964). A comparison of results obtained with ionic sulfamonomethoxine and sulfadimethoxine lead to the conclusion that electrostatic interactions are the most important. The standard free energy change was stated to be about 6 kcal/mole. Ruiz-Torres and Meinig (1965) have also discussed affinities and capacities of sulfonamide binding to serum albumin in terms of the Langmuir adsorption isotherm.

Conventional clinical " percents bound to serum proteins " or comparable measures are given for numerous antibiotics by the following, among others: Kamen and Yakovlev (1964); Woehler and Speckman (1960); Gione and Buogo (1965); Genazzani and Pagnini (1963); Berlin (1963); and Hasumura and Nakamura (1964). Kunin (1964) has examined over 250 antibiotics by equilibrium dialysis.

Sulfonamides are powerful inhibitors of carbonic anhydrase. The binding of a wide range of sulfonamides to the enzyme has been compared by determination of their inhibition constants [see Table 4-4, from Bonati and Sala (1959)]. The K values of the table are defined by $K = [E][I]/[EI]$, in which E represents active enzyme, I free inhibitor, and EI the enzyme-inhibitor complex. The ratio $[EI]/[E][I]$ was determined from the residual activity.

TABLE 4-4

$$\text{FORMULA BASE} \quad \begin{array}{c} X_2 \\ X_1 \end{array} \bigotimes \begin{array}{c} SO_3NHX_4 \\ X_3 \end{array}$$
$$N$$

Compound	X_1	X_2	X_3	X_4	K
I	Cl	H	H	H	5×10^{-8}
II	Cl	H	H	C_4H_9	2.3×10^{-4}
III	Cl	H	H	$CH_2-CH=CH_2$	8×10^{-6}
IV	NH_2	H	H	H	6.6×10^{-6}
V	H_5C_2NH	H	H	H	4.2×10^{-6}
VI	$CH_2=CHCH_2NH$	H	H	H	5.7×10^{-6}
VII	H_9C_4NH	H	H	H	7.3×10^{-7}
VIII	$\langle \rangle CH_2NH-$	H	H	H	1.9×10^{-7}
IX	$O\langle HN-$	H	H	H	1.9×10^{-6}
X	NH_2	H	H	$\langle \rangle SO_2NH_2$ (N=)	1.6×10^{-6}
XI	HO	H	H	H	1.7×10^{-6}
XII	HO	H	H	$\langle \rangle SO_2NH_2$ (N=)	1.7×10^{-6}
XIII	HO	H	H	$\langle \rangle SO_2NH_2$	9.5×10^{-7}
XIV	NH_2	SO_2NH_2	NH_2	H	3.9×10^{-6}
XV	Cl	SO_2NH_2	NH_2	H	1.3×10^{-6}
Acetazolamide					1.3×10^{-8}
Chlorothiazide					8.6×10^{-5}
Sulfanilamide					1.0×10^{-4}

(h) *Thyroxine.* Thyroxine is included in this chapter on neutral molecules, although it is a zwitterion, because its net charge is zero, and because Tabachnick and Giorgio (1964) have shown that neither the charged amino group nor the charged carboxylate group is required for expression of its characteristic high affinity for deionized human serum albumin. The largest K reported was 171,000; both the anionic phenolic group of tyrosine and the ε-amino group of lysine residues in the protein are required (Tabachnik, 1964). The binding of this potent pharmacologic agent was first studied by Lein (1952); and the association constant and free energy change were determined by equilibrium dialysis by Bezkorovainy and Doherty (1962). The latter report a

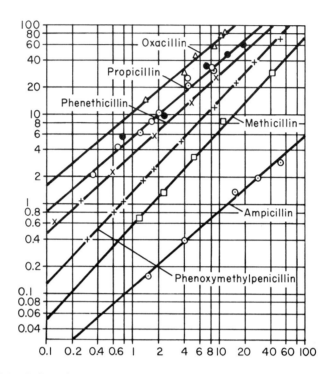

Fig. 4-9. Binding of penicillins by HSA. Ordinate is total antibiotic concentration in micromoles/liter. Abscissa is free antibiotic. *Die Bindungder Antibiotica an die EiweiBkorper des Serums Arzheim-Gersch (Drug Res.)* **13**, 347–360.]

set of six sites at 27° and five at 7°. The association constant is 4.0×10^4 at 27°, and 5.1×10^4 at 7°. ΔF is -6.3 and -6.0 kcal/mole, respectively; ΔH is -2.0 kcal/mole, and the entropy change is reported as 14.5 units. (ΔS_u would be 8 units larger.) Thus the reaction is largely but not entirely entropy-driven. Tabachnik (1964) distinguishes between two sets of sites ($n_1 = 2$, $K_1 = 2.75 \times 10^5$; and $n_2 = 6$, $K_2 = 2.5 \times 10^4$) at pH 7.4 and 30°. A review of determinations of the affinity prior to 1960 is given by Slaunwhite (1960).

The thorough investigations by Tabachnik and Giorgio (1964) of the binding of thyroxine derivatives to *human* serum albumin at 30° indicate about the same affinity (and about the same number of sites with about the same constant) as Lein reported, but in addition two other derivatives with K about 10 times as great were measured. These experiments are important because they show the relation of chemical constitution to binding affinity. With the replacement of the four iodine atoms of thyroxine by hydrogens, the affinity (*as judged by ability of the derivatives to compete with thyroxin*) is completely destroyed; and little remains if they are replaced by CH_3. Replacement of only one iodine atom has little effect unless it is ortho to the phenoxy group. Methylation of the phenoxy group reduces the affinity by 30%.[9] Removal of the charge pair on the alanine residue by acetylation and esterification *increases* the affinity by up to 40%; likewise complete removal of the amino groups has an enhancing effect. The diphenyl ether linkage is considered to be essential also, because diiodotyrosine itself is not a competitor. It is obvious, however, that the diiodotyrosine lacks two of the iodine atoms of thyroxine and is a considerably smaller molecule as well. Substitution of bromine or chlorine for the iodine gives a ligand with somewhat lower affinity for the protein. (See Table 4-5.) For tetraiodothyropropionic acid, the only substance besides thyroxine for which the binding was directly measured, K was 900,000, over 3 times as great as the indicated value, 275,000, for thyroxine.

It is also reported (Tabachnick, 1964) that a number of large organic anions depress the binding of thyroxine by competing with it. These anions, which differ greatly in effectiveness (association constants between 8×10^4 for dinitrophenolate and 1×10^6 for oleate[10]) include the long-chain fatty acids and a long-chain detergent ion, dodecylsulfate, as well as substituted phenols. Some of these results will be discussed in Chapter VII. Salicylate, which depresses the binding of thyroxine by some other serum proteins (Woeber and Longbar, 1963), is without effect on the binding by serum albumin. At this point attention is invited to the fact that the negative charge of salicylate may have only a small effect (positive or negative) on its competitive ability, since the charges on thyroxine appear to play no part in the binding to protein. The net charge on the protein is negative under the condition of these experiments.

Recent work (Steiner *et al.*, 1965) by the method of ultraviolet fluorescence quenching, appears to indicate fewer sites: a single high-energy site ($K = 1.6 \times 10^6$) and three or more others which are weaker. This finding is subject to the sources of uncertainty inherent in all "direct" methods (see Chapter III), which are seldom linear with number of occupied sites. This discrepancy does not necessarily cast doubt on the results obtained in Tabachnick's

---

[9] These relative affinities given by Tabachnik and Giorgio are not ratios of association constants. They are reductions in nK for the binding of L-thyroxine, expressed as a percentage of the reduction caused by equimolecular concentrations of D-thyroxine, which binds to the protein as readily as the L isomer. The difference between this criterion and the true affinity is illustrated by the data for tetraiodothyropropionic acid, stated to have 135% as great an affinity as D-thyroxine, but with an actual value of nK of 45×10^5 as compared to 7×10^5 for thyroxine.

[10] These constants and others were determined by analyzing the competitive effect. The values obtained are actually much smaller than those determined by direct measurement (see Chapter VII).

TABLE 4-5

RELATIVE AFFINITIES OF THYROXINE ANALOGS FOR ALBUMIN AT pH 7.4 AND 30°[a]

No.	Compound[a]	Substituents						Relative affinity
		4'	3'	5'	3	5	R	
1	D-Thyroxine	OH	I	I	I	I	$CH_2CHNH_2CO_2H$	100
2	O-Methyl-DL-thyroxine	CH_3O	I	I	I	I	$CH_2CHNH_2CO_2H$	30
3	3,3',5',-Triiodo-DL-thyronine	OH	I	I	I	H	$CH_2CHNH_2CO_2H$	100
4	3,5,3'-Triiodo-L-thyronine	OH	I	H	I	I	$CH_2CHNH_2CO_2H$	55
5	3',5'-Diiodo-DL-thyronine	OH	I	I	H	H	$CH_2CHNH_2CO_2H$	85
6	3'-Monoiodo-DL-thyronine	OH	I	H	H	H	$CH_2CHNH_2CO_2H$	15
7	3,5-Diiodo-DL-thyronine	OH	H	H	I	I	$CH_2CHNH_2CO_2H$	30
8	DL-Thyronine	OH	H	H	H	H	$CH_2CHNH_2CO_2H$	0
9	3,5-Diiodo-3',5'-di-methyl-D-thyronine	OH	CH_3	CH_3	I	I	$CH_2CHNH_2CO_2H$	15
10	N-Acetyl-L-thyroxine	OH	I	I	I	I	CH_2CHCO_2H | $NHCOCH_3$	110
11	N-Acetyl-L-thyroxine ethyl ester	OH	I	I	I	I	$CH_2CHCOOC_2H_5$ | $NHCOCH_3$	120
12	Tetraiodothyro-propionic acid	OH	I	I	I	I	$CH_2CH_2CO_2H$	135
13	Tetraiodothyroformic acid	OH	I	I	I	I	CO_2H	140
14	3,5,3'-Triiodothyro-propionic acid	OH	I	H	I	I	$CH_2CH_2CO_2H$	80
15	3,5,3',5'-Tetrabromo-L-thyronine	OH	Br	Br	Br	Br	$CH_2CHNH_2CO_2H$	85
16	3,5,3',5'-Tetrachloro-DL-thyronine	OH	Cl	Cl	Cl	Cl	$CH_2CHNH_2CO_2H$	65
17	3,5-Diiodo-L-tyrosine							

[a] M. Tabachnik and V. A. Giorgio, Jr. (1964). *Arch. Biochem. Biophys.* **105**, 563.

laboratory. Thus, Weber's measurements of the binding of certain dyes to human serum albumin by means of their induced fluorescence when bound, always gives a maximum of five sites, although other methods of measurements with similar dyes show that larger numbers may be bound (Daniel and Weber, 1966). The report of a single binding site is substantiated by a recent investigation by another method (Tritsch, 1967), which resulted in a report of a single site of high affinity (totally lost in 4 *M* urea) and a larger number of binding sites which first increased their binding and then decreased as the urea concentration was raised. The single site of high affinity, therefore, owes its free energy of binding to a particular local conformation, which possibly furnishes multiple contacts, as in the heme pocket of hemoglobin, or in the substrate "cavities" of enzymes.

(i) *Carbohydrates.* It has been reported (Giles and McKay, 1962) that certain carbohydrates form stoichiometric complexes with bovine serum albumin, as well as with gelatin and casein, while others do not. The evidence rests on discontinuities in the otherwise linear relationship between refractive index increment and volume fraction of ligand solutions in the mixtures tested. The ratio of carbohydrate to amino acid residues in the solutions to be mixed was close to unity, i.e., 2% to 4% protein was mixed with 0.05 *M* carbohydrate solution.

The results may be summarized as follows:

(1) All pentoses tested formed one or more definite complexes with ratios which varied discontinuously between 4 : 1 and 1 : 4.

(2) Among hexoses tried, complexes were formed with the D isomers of glucose, galactose, and mannose, but not fructose. The L forms did not form complexes, except in the case of L-sorbose. This stereospecificity varies from protein to protein, e.g., in gelatin the L isomers are favored.

(3) No complexes were formed with disaccharides.

The investigators postulate that hydrogen-bonded complexes are formed in water-free regions of the molecule (the sugar acting as donor) and that steric hindrance prevents some of the hexoses and all the disaccharides from entering these regions. Such an explanation is consistent with the expected absence of hydrophobic interactions with these highly soluble molecules.

Studies of the carbohydrate complexes of other proteins are given elsewhere in this chapter. A review of protein–polysaccharide complexes has recently appeared (Izumi, 1962). It includes complexes of nucleopolysaccharides and aminopolysaccharides.

(j) *Skatole, Tryptophan, and Tryptophan Derivatives.* These ligands are grouped for obvious reasons; although tryptophan is a dipolar ion, its net charge, like that of thyroxine, is zero over a wide range of pH. Indole derivatives appear to combine very tightly with BSA and the albumins of other chordate species at a single binding site (McMenamy and Lee, 1967). Thus skatole has an association constant of 4.2×10^5 at pH 6.3 and 0.1 M ionic strength at 40°, and 1.9×10^5 at 18° (Krasmer and McMenamy, 1966). This is near the value characteristic of L-tryptophan, to which it is related, of K (at pH 9 and 25°) equal to 1.9×10^5 (Fairclough and Fruton, 1966). The fact that the charges on tryptophan have a sum of zero seems to have little actual importance. Thus the investigators cited give for the negatively charged acetyl-L-tryptophan a K near 1×10^5 at pH values near 6. The binding is higher at pH 9 at which most of the measurements of Fairclough and Fruton were made. Other very much weaker binding sites are likely to exist ($K = 9.3 \times 10^3$ at pH 9).

D-Tryptophan has a much lower affinity than L-tryptophan. Although a residual negative charge on the acetyl derivative of the L amino acid lowers the affinity, removing it by amidation lowers the affinity drastically (K for acetyl-L-tryptophan amide is 2600). When incorporated into a peptide linkage as the center residue, the affinity is about the same as in glycyl dipeptide. The specificity of the optical isomers is greatly reduced in the lower affinity derivatives.

Of great interest is the large negative enthalpy found by Fairclough and Fruton for most of the tryptophan derivatives investigated—in most cases about double the free energy change. As a result large *negative* entropy changes accompany the binding.

The addition of urea or dioxane reduces K for neutral skatole and negative acetyl-L-tryptophan; glycine has no effect other than restoring the affinity when it has been reduced by urea. These effects are small, as are the effects of ionic strength at values above 0.02 (K at 0.02 is only 0.3 to 0.4 as great as it is at 0.005). The binding constants are maximal at pH 5–7 and fall off sharply outside these limits. Thus the data of Fruton and Fairclough are taken far outside the optimal limits (Krasner and McMenamy, 1966).

With both skatole and acetyl-L-tryptophan the effect of neutral salts on K is large at low ionic strength. The effectiveness of the 1–1 salts used appears to depend primarily on the anion. The order of ascending effectiveness at 18° is EDTA $< SO_4^- < Cl^- < I < SCN^-$. With skatole, ascending salt concentrations greatly increase the association constant, so competition cannot be involved; with the charged derivative the opposite effect is obtained (McMenamy *et al.*, 1968).

(k) *Undissociated Acids.* Large amounts of undissociated acids (up to several millimoles/gram) combine with insoluble wool keratin (Steinhardt *et al.*, 1943). The more insoluble acids, such as substituted phenols, bind more strongly. Thus the binding is not likely to be solely a simple solvation involving only the replacement of water by other polar molecules. Recent work has led to the conclusion that undissociated buffer acids (such as acetic acid) bind to serum albumin and modify its electrophoretic pattern (Cann, 1958; Cann and Phelps, 1959), and hence its conformation, presumably by stabilizing the N form. Undissociated acetic acid has also been postulated to mask a carboxymethylcellulose binding site on HSA (Cooke *et al.*, 1962). The effect of amino acids on the electrophoretic pattern has been interpreted as an inhibition of the effect of undissociated acid (Phelps and Cann, 1957) by the cationic form of the amino acid. No quantitative estimates of the binding and inhibition are offered. Similar results were obtained with ovalbumin and α-globulin. More recently similar data have been reported for zone electrophoresis of BSA and phosphate–borate buffers in a high range of pH (6.9–9.2) in which ions as well as neutral undissociated acids may be involved (Cann, 1966). A survey of many buffer-acids (Schmid, 1959; Schmid and Polis, 1960) indicates that the results reported by Cann are given to an even greater degree by longer-chain buffer acids, and by some aliphatic alcohols. Introduction of hydroxyl or amino groups, or double bonds, prevents the stabilization of the native conformation conferred by the undissociated acid, and possibly therefore the binding. The effects, which are reversible, indicate stronger binding by the longer-chain fatty acids.

There has been some disagreement as to whether the undissociated acid is responsible (Charlwood, 1958), but Schmid and Polis believe that both undissociated acid and anion are involved. Recently Cann and Goad (1965) have analyzed multiple boundary formation in zone electrophoresis in terms of a model involving association of *n* moles of undissociated buffer acid with 1 mole of protein.

Fatty acids in general (and a few other substances which bind to serum albumin) inhibit the action of hydrolytic enzymes, notably pepsin, on proteins. Electrophoretic evidence has been interpreted as showing that this inhibition is due to competition of fatty acid with substrate (protein) at a binding site (Cann, 1962).

(l) *Uncharged Polymers.* According to Noguchi (1956, 1960, 1961) only charged polymers—carboxymethylcellulose and dextrans—form complexes with human serum albumin.

(m) *Recent Reports of Interactions of Serum Albumins with Other Uncharged Molecules.* References to early measurements of the binding of other neutral molecules including aminoazobenzene, glycosides, steroids, chloroform, and naphthoquinones are listed by Klotz (1953). A few more recent references follow: Helmer *et al.* (1968) have recently given binding data for BSA and other proteins, with a large number of phenols (19), barbiturate- (4), and other miscellaneous neutral molecules. The results, obtained on furs ther unspecified "pure" protein, by means of gas–liquid partition chromatography (see Chapter III), were expressed in terms of empirical equations of uniform form which are given individually although all the results for a given class of ligand are also reduced to a single equation by means of a statistical fit. Both the individual equations and the aggregated ones make use of the measured "hydrophobicity" of the ligand, defined as its partition constant in octanol–water. The equations have nothing to say about numbers of sites—in fact they lose their empirical validity as an exact description of the data as more than two or three equivalents of ligand are bound. The individual equations do permit easy determination of the fraction of ligand bound. With 0.2% BSA these vary from a vanishingly small fraction when $\bar{v} = 1$, in the case of methoxyaniline, to about 0.3 in the case of azobenzene. Rough values of K may be calculated from the fractions bound if assumptions are made as to the number of binding sites. Considerable computation would be involved, and the results would be uncertain.

In the same paper, empirical efforts are made to correlate changes in optical rotation induced by ligands with their hydrophobicity, and a parallel is drawn with the denaturing effects of much higher concentrations of certain phenols and amides (Gordon and Jencks, 1963) on proteins and on DNA. The paper by Helmer et al. (1968) contains a great deal of data of problematical significance, and lies outside the main stream of recent work on binding by proteins.

Serum albumin appears to be capable of binding vitamin D_3 (Chen and Lane, 1965) and hematin (Sears and Huser, 1965) (other serum proteins bind the latter also). Starch gel has been reported to bind BSA when unfolded by acid, on the basis of its behavior in starch-gel electrophoresis (Lee and McInver, 1965). The carcinogen N-(2-fluorecyl)acetamide is also bound (Bahl and Gutmann, 1964). The ultracentrifugal method has been used to show that digitoxin, a cardiac glycoside, is much more strongly bound to serum albumin that is g-strophanthin, the pharmacological action of which is developed more rapidly and is of shorter duration (Scholtan et al., 1966).

Spectrophotometric analysis of shifts in the spectrum of tetrachloroquinone (chloranil) in 50% ethanol buffered at pH 8 when horse serum is added (an increase in absorption and a shift to higher wavelengths) have led to the conclusion that an $n \to \pi$ charge-transfer complex is formed with the protein, contributing electron pairs from one or more nitrogens of amino groups (Birks and Slifkin 1963). In alkaline solutions a precipitate is formed which behaves like a semiconductor with a conductivity of 10^{12} ohm-centimeters. No stoichiometric analysis of the formation of the complex has been published. Similar results are obtained with fibrinogen and with trypsin (see Klotz and Ayers, 1952).

4. The Numbers of Binding Sites on Serum Albumin

The data described in the foregoing pages do not easily lend themselves to consistent interpretation in terms of definite numbers of discrete binding sites for neutral molecules, possible differences between the sites for different ligands, or whether some of the sites are formed by the unfolding of the protein after initial binding has taken place on sites in the native molecule.

Wishnia's data on butane and pentane are adequately described by regarding the binding as a simple solution of the two gases in the hydrocarbon moieties of the protein, similar to their dissolving in micelles of such detergents as sodium dodecylsulfate. No saturation values are indicated—if they exist, they are large (Wishnia estimates the minimum n as well over 40). The same gases seem to bind on a limited number of definite sites in another protein (see Section II, B, on β-lactoglobulin). With numerous other ligands there are clear indications of a law of mass action binding on specific numbers of sites, with clear evidence from competition that many ligands compete for the same sites.

There are more data available for ionic ligands than for neutral ones. Among the latter, however, systematic information is available for BSA for some of the higher alcohols, for some steroids, and for thyroxine and thyroxine derivatives. These are summarized in Table 4-6. Most of the data were obtained with protein which retained one or two equivalents of tightly bound residual fatty acid of high-molecular-weight.

TABLE 4-6

BINDING OF NEUTRAL LIGANDS BY BSA

	pH	T	n_1	K	$-\Delta F°$ cals/mole	References
Butane (estimated)	—	25°	Very large	5.7×10^2	3800	Wishnia (1962) (our calculation)
Octanol	5.6	2°–4°	5	3.4×10^3	4500	Ray *et al.*, 1966
	5.6	26°	5	4.6×10^3	4100	
	7.45	2°–4°	5	7.1×10^3	4900	
	8.3	2°–4°	5	—	—	
Decanol	5.6	2°–4°	4–5	7×10^4	—	Reynolds *et al.*, 1968
Dodecanol	5.6	2°–4°	4–5	1.5×10^5	6600	Ray *et al.*, 1966 Cassel *et al.*, 1969
Testosterone	7.4	3°	20	—	6400	Alfsen, 1963
	7.4	25°	4	—	5800	
Thyroxine	7.4	30°	2	2.75×10^5	—	Tabachnik, 1964
			6	2.5×10^4	—	

Although up to about 10 equivalents of octanol may be bound by BSA at the saturation solubility of the ligand, insufficient data are at hand for estimating either the number or the binding constants of the more weakly binding sites. It is not certain that the work with the alcohols (results at 0.033 and 0.10 ionic strength did not differ) could have detected the presence of one or two sites which bound more tightly than the ones reported, since the protein was not exhaustively defatted by the method of Chen. However, recent unpublished work by Gallagher in Steinhardt's laboratory appears to indicate that residual fatty acid has only a very small effect on the binding of anions of high affinity, and none at all on the binding of uncharged ligands.

The results in the table are not easily reduced to any simple order. This is particularly true of Alfsen's values for testosterone—an additional value (10) for n given by Eik-Nes et al. (1953) only complicates the situation. Addition of data obtained with other ligands would make matters worse. Thus many antibiotics seem to bind on a single site. Simple sugars, which may form hydrogen bonds on binding, appear to form complexes with molal ratios that vary all the way from 4 to $\frac{1}{4}$.

Caution is required in interpreting these disparate results for the following reasons:

(a) The values of n obtained by the analytical methods used depend critically on the identity of the association constants within each set of groups, and on sufficient separation of these constants, so that they do not mutually interfere in the graphical analysis.

(b) The method of analysis does not take into account the existence of cooperative binding, nor of the possible binding of more than one protein molecule by a large molecule of ligand. The former effect is not in evidence in the octanol data (1% protein), but cannot be eliminated in all cases.

(c) Sites which bind one ligand do not necessarily bind others. There is evidence of this with ion binding, where competition between ligands is often selective, and where the number of sites appears to increase as the ligand size increases. (See Chapter VII.)

Subject to the above reservations, it may be tentatively concluded that there is evidence for the existence of discrete sets of sites, except when the ligands are small, completely apolar, hydrocarbon molecules. It will be seen when the binding of ions is considered, that there is a tendency for the numbers $n = 1$ or 2 and 5 to appear. Their appearance in Table 4-6 should not, however, be given any special significance since other small numbers appear. Insufficient data exist for characterizing n_2 and K_2 (or n_3 and K_3), although they undoubtedly exist.

All of the neutral ligands tested are characterized by negative free energies of binding which fall between 500 and 6800 cal; these are the sites of highest affinity or are possibly averages of the two classes of highest affinity. The effect of pH on the binding energy is appreciable (but not spectacular) between pH values of 4 and 8.3. The effect of temperature is quite small.

5. *Effects of Bound Neutral Molecules on The Stability of the Native Conformation*

Since most measurements of the binding of neutral molecules by serum albumin involve the achievement of equilibria over long periods of time, several hours to several days, no observations have been made of the time dependence of whatever conformation changes have accompanied the binding. Thus it is not yet possible to distinguish between slow conformation changes *following* a given extent of binding, as in some much-studied acidic or alkaline denaturations of proteins, and conformation changes which *accompany* binding. Neither is it possible to distinguish between stabilization of a native state resulting from binding and binding due to recovery of the native conformation. In the case of binding butane and pentane to BSA at pH < 4.5, the recovery of the native conformation is accompanied by an increase in the amount of butane dissolved, and it cannot be said which phenomenon precedes the other.

Spectroscopic observations can be completed soon after mixing. Difference spectra representing blue shifts on binding one or more long-chain alcohols have been reported by Ray *et al.* (1966), Polet and Steinhardt (1967), and by Mullin (1962). Polet and Steinhardt (1968) have shown that the blue shifts produced by neutral molecules are probably brought about by binding itself rather than by radical conformation changes. They are produced by binding as few as five (or fewer) equivalents and are not accompanied by measurable viscosity changes or by changes in optical rotation (Polet, unpublished), or by changes in the accessibility of chromophores to sucrose (Ray *et al.*, 1966). The major spectral effect is on tyrosine chromophores, but there is a weak effect on the two tryptophans also. In the deeper ultraviolet there is a larger *red* shift at 230 mμ which Polet and Steinhardt attribute to a third unidentified chromophore, demonstrably not the peptide bond. These optical effects will be discussed more fully when we have described the similar, but much more extensive, range of phenomena that are displayed in the binding of aliphatic anions. Thus, unlike the effect of butane on BSA, there is no definitive evidence that binding alcohols has any effect on the stability of this macromolecule.

A very general form of equation relating binding to conformation changes has been given in Chapter II [Eq. (2-63)]. It is important to realize that the addition of other equilibria to the Reynold's set of reactions will not change the result embodied in the final equilibrium equation. To make this clear we rewrite the reaction so that it refers to the binding of only a single molecule of ligand to either native or denatured protein:

$$
\begin{array}{c}
\quad\quad K \\
P + L \rightleftharpoons PL \\
U \updownarrow \quad\quad \updownarrow V \\
D + L \rightleftharpoons DL \\
\quad\quad J
\end{array}
\tag{4-3}
$$

where K and J are association constants, and U is a transformation constant. We are not free to arbitrarily assign an equilibrium constant V to a direct equilibrium between PL and DL, since V is demonstrably equal to UJ/K; likewise $[P]/[D] = U = VJ/K$. In either case the conformation change is favored if $J > K$; otherwise stabilization of the P form occurs.

The formation of PL and DL are not the only means by which L can affect the equilibrium between P and D. If L is a solvent (whether pure or mixed) it can effect the activities of P and D by virtue of their having different free energies of dissolving (i.e., they would dissolve to different extents); an effect on the equilibrium between P and D will follow (Tanford, 1964; Anson and Mirsky, 1933–34).

Because of the absence of kinetic data, the pages that follow will be limited to consideration of equilibria. There are indications that the dissociation of some protein–ligand complexes is itself time-dependent, so there is no early hope of following the time course of conformation changes independently of the time course of binding.[11]

Figure 4-10 (Wishnia, 1964) shows the shift in pH of the N → F transition, as measured by changes in viscosity, and the correlation of this shift with the

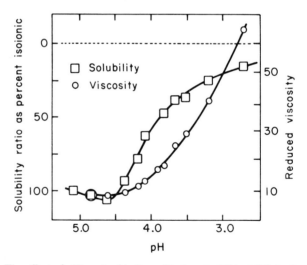

Fig. 4-10. The effect of pH on the binding of butane to BSA at 25°, in the absence of added salt: □, $100 \times (S_p/S_w)$pH/(S_p/S_w)pH5; O, reduced viscosity. [A. Wishnia and T. Pinder (1964). *Biochemistry* 3, 1377.]

[11] The fact that the dissociation of protein–detergent complexes is time-dependent has been deduced from the existence of a hysteresis loop in the binding isotherm when it is determined by analysis of electrophoretic patters (Hill and Briggs, 1956). Time dependence implies an energy of activation which suggests that a conformation change must *precede* dissociation of the complex.

amounts of butane bound. Wishnia and Pinder (1964) show that the results are consistent with a mechanism requiring the existence of either a few large hydrophobic clusters, or of more numerous smaller ones, which are disrupted when the $N \rightarrow F$ transition occurs. In terms of the scheme above, if L represents butane, $K > J$ and U is a function of pH. The native form $(P + PL)$ is more stable than the F form $(D + DL)$ because it removes more L from a saturated solution of ligand.

The results with pentane are very similar, except that the binding constant for pentane is much higher.

Wetlaufer and Lovrien (1964) have demonstrated that butane also stabilizes the native conformation of bovine serum albumin in the alkaline pH region. Saturation with butane at 1 atmosphere pressure raises the pH at which a given increase of viscosity occurs by about 0.15 unit (Fig. 4-11). This shift is considerably larger than the increases in pH produced when solutions of the protein are saturated with butane; the latter goes through a maximum of less than 0.09 unit at pH values near 11. The pH region in which these changes occur is characteristic of the ionization of tyrosine residues and is at the upper end of the unmasking of those phenoxy groups which are not accessible in the native protein. (See Chapter V.)[12] As would be expected,

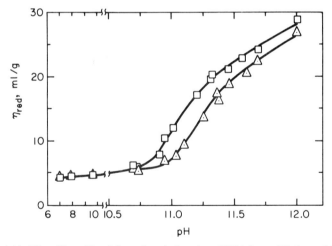

Fig. 4-11. The pH profile of the reduced viscosity of BSA in equilibrium with 1 atmosphere of N_2 (□) or 1 atmosphere of *n*-butane (△). Temperature, 25.00°; solvent, 0.15 *M* aqueous KCl. Protein concentrations varied from 3.4 % to 4.4%. The pH of each solution was measured in equilibrium with the gas indicated. [D. Wetlaufer and R. Lovrien (1964). *J. Biol. Chem.* **239**, 596.]

[12] Only 40% of the tyrosyls of either N or F forms of the protein are available to perturbation of the spectrum by a small perturbant, ethylene glycol (Herzskovits and Laskowski, 1962).

therefore, the ultraviolet spectra of the butane-containing solutions at pH slightly above 11 show slightly *less* absorption characteristic of the ionized phenoxy group than do solutions containing no butane. The evidence is paradoxical, however, in that the form of the difference spectra (Fig. 4-12) shows

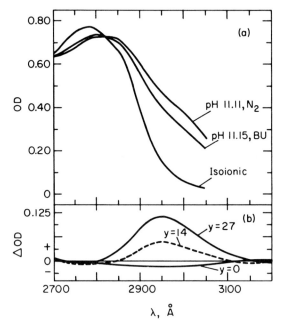

FIG. 4-12. (a) Depression by butane (BU) of ultraviolet spectrum characteristic of tyrosyl group ionization in BSA. The solutions with N_2 and butane were identical except for the dissolved gases. Optical path, 2 cm; BSA concentration, 0.059%; 0.15 M KCl; pH values as measured in equilibrium with 1 atmosphere of the indicated gas. (b) Difference spectra of BSA solutions containing N_2 compared with those containing butane. The quantity y is defined as (total molar concentration butane)/(total molar concentration of BSA). The solutions containing butane were in the reference beam; the solutions containing N_2 were in the sample beam. The solutions with N_2 and butane were identical except for the dissolved gases. BSA concentration 0.24%; pH 11.22 (N_2); 0.15 M KCl; 25.0°. [D. Wetlaufer and R. Lovrien (1964). *J. Biol. Chem.* **239**, 596.]

that butane produces no shift in absorption maximum—this may be interpreted as meaning that fewer groups are ionized when butane is bound, but that there is no conformation change such as would be expected from unmasking. Possibly such a change would be seen in measurements made at somewhat higher pH. In any case the experiment shows an unexpected influence of bound butane on phenoxy ionization (pK higher) and raises the possibility that the conformation change of serum albumin which occurs at high pH values, and which unmasks the inaccessible phenoxy groups, is triggered by the ionization of the normal tyrosine residues. Similar suggestions have been made by Herzskovits and Laskowski (1962).[13] Their conclusions, and ours, would apply only to protein that has not been degraded by reduction of disulfide bonds or by unfolding, in concentrated solutions of urea of guanidine salts. Wetlaufer and Lovrien (1964) show that butane binding drops drastically precisely at the pH values at which a sharp *fall* in viscosity begins. The reversibility of the viscosity effects produced in this region was demonstrated by alternate exposure to nitrogen and to butadiene (Fig. 4-13). The effects of butane on optical rotation were also shown to be reversible.

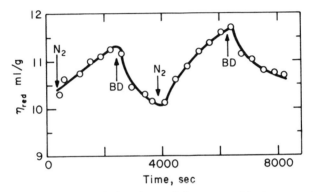

FIG. 4-13. Viscosity of BSA solution alternately in contact with nitrogen and butadiene (BD) atmospheres (4/3 atmospheres for each gas). Cumulative time is time after mixing protein solution and KOH. BSA concentration, 4.26%; pH 11.22 (N_2); 0.15 M KCl; 25.00°. [D. Wetlaufer and R. Lovrien (1964). *J. Biol. Chem.* **239**, 596.]

Since the viscosity increase at high pH indicated that removal of protons in this region causes the protein molecule to become less compact, Wetlaufer and Lovrien postulate that the effect of butane on tyrosyl ionization causes the loss of protons (and therefore the "swelling") to occur at slightly higher pH. The less compact molecules (whether larger, or more penetrable to solvent) are characterized by a smaller value of w in the Linderström-Lang equation

$$\text{pH} = \text{p}K_{int} + \log \frac{h}{n-h} - 0.868\, wZ \qquad (4\text{-}4)$$

[13] Tanford and Roberts (1952) have shown that all of the tyrosyl residues of BSA are reversibly ionizable at alkaline pH values, although the pK is high and the heat of ionization anomalously high. These results, coupled with the finding that 60% of the tyrosyls in native, neutral serum albumins are inaccessible to solvent contact, suggest one (or both) of the following explanations: (a) Structural transition takes place above pH 7.5 in which some or all of the tyrosyls become exposed before they are actually ionized. (b) Solvent-inaccessible tyrosyls may still be reversibly ionizable; the high heats of ionization reflecting the rupture; tyrosyls would become exposed only as tyrosylate ions.

which describes the ionization of many discrete sets of prototropic groups in proteins (see Chapter V). Any decrease in w will therefore lower the pH if it is high since the positive third term on the right-hand side of Eq. (4-4) becomes smaller. Butane, by preventing the expansion of the molecule, therefore raises the pH. By the same mechanism it also raises the pH at which any given fraction of the tyrosyls ionize. A maximum ΔpH occurs at a well-marked pH of 11 instead of persisting throughout the entire tyrosyl range, so that neither an effect on pK_{int} nor an effect on w suffices to explain the shifts.

The existence of a maximum in the amounts of butane bound between pH 8.6 and 11 points to another conformation change at pH values between 7.4 and 8.6, *unaccompanied by change in compactness of the molecule* [no viscosity changes have been found here (Tanford and Buzzell, 1956)]; evidence obtained by Leonard and Foster for a conformation change in this region has already been cited; additional support for its existence comes from studies of dye binding (Klotz and Ayers, 1952), ultraviolet fluorescence (Steiner and Edelhoch, 1963), and hydrogen–deuterium exchange (Benson *et al.*, 1964)].

Wetlaufer and Lovrien suggest that hydrocarbons may bind either to (a) clusters of hydrocarbon side chains at the protein " surface " or to (b) similar clusters in the interior (see below, for similar conclusions by Wishnia and Pinder for β-lactoglobulin). They state " a protein which binds hydrocarbon when it is *not* involved in a pH-controlled structural transition should show evidence (optical rotation, ultraviolet difference spectra, etc.) of structural change if (b), but not if (a), is true." These alternatives do not appear to be exhaustive. The recent findings of Schoenborn (1965) that xenon, and even $HgI_3{}^-$ ions can fit into a *hole* in the intact metmyoglobin molecule, without producing large changes in the positions of other atoms, as measured by X-ray methods, requires qualifications to this conclusion.

The experiments of both Wishnia and of Wetlaufer and Lovrien describe only stabilizing effects when hydrocarbons are bound. Alfsen's work with heptane (1963) describes only destabilizing effects, i.e., heptane induces a conformation change instead of repressing one as butane and pentane do. It is possible that the difference lies in the difference in conditions rather than in the hydrocarbons; Alfsen's experiments were done at pH 7.4 rather than 4.0, and with pure liquid in contact with the aqueous solution instead of gas at atmospheric pressure. Conformation change was judged by changes in optical rotation rather than in viscosity. It is curious, in this connection, that when serum albumin was saturated with heptane before exposure to testosterone a greater effect was produced than when the protein was exposed to the two ligands simultaneously; since the effects of the two ligands oppose one another, it may be that the effect of heptane is not fully reversible and takes its full effect when testosterone is present. In that case the stabilizing effect of the testosterone is either exercised by means of its effect on heptane rather than by an effect on the protein, or enables the protein to resist irreversible attack by the heptane. The binding of alcohols sometimes *destabilizes*: octanol, for example, makes the acid denaturation of ferrihemoglobin occur at a higher pH than in its absence (Steinhardt and Moezie, unpublished). Partial unfolding may enhance binding in some cases. Scatchard (1954) found that more Cl⁻ was bound at pH values at which F was formed.

It has been reported that low concentrations of ethanol (2–4 %) stabilize human serum albumin against denaturation at high temperatures (Milar *et al.*, 1962) although higher concentrations reduce the denaturation temperature. The usual ionic stabilizers, such as caprylate, add their effectiveness to that of ethanol (1963).

Understanding the changes brought about by binding testosterone may be complicated by the fact that in Alfsen's experiments, at concentrations over $3 \times 10^{-4} M$, the ligand liberated fatty acid from the protein, even when the latter had been defatted by Goodman's drastic procedure. Testosterone also reacts with the protein to produce a modified, unidentified, more highly polar steroid.

Although data have been obtained on the binding of numerous other steroids in the presence of heptane, no conclusions are possible as to conformation changes. The same is true for the binding of the other neutral molecules discussed earlier. We summarize the facts just enumerated in Table 4-7.

The judgements made with alcohols are based on the characteristic blue shifts described by Ray *et al.* (1966), Polet and Steinhardt (1968), Reynolds *et al.* (1968), and Polet and Steinhardt (1968); as well as the absence of changes in solvent perturbation spectra. It would be desirable to have accurate viscosity data as well as observations of changes in optical properties.

TABLE 4-7

EFFECT OF BINDING NEUTRAL LIGANDS ON CONFORMATION[a]

Ligand	Region of $N \rightleftharpoons F$	pH 5.6	pH 7.4–8.6	pH 11
Butane ⎱ Pentane ⎰	S[b]	S[b]	—	S[b]
Heptane	—	—	Destabilizes[c]	—
n-Octanol	No demonstrated effect on BSA to $\bar{v} = 17$			
n-Dodecanol	No demonstrated effect on BSA to $\bar{v} = 3$			
Undissociated acids	S	S	—	—
Testosterone	—	—	S	—

[a] S signifies stabilization.

[b] No data at high values of $\bar{v}$.

[c] No data at low values of $\bar{v}$; pH titrations by Alfsen suggest a partial stabilization against acid, less than that of testosterone.

The entries in this table are too meager to support any firm conclusions. All the low-molecular-weight hydrocarbons appear to stabilize, and testosterone does in the case of one transition region, which is the only one studied. No cases of stabilization by alcohols have been observed, but data for this protein are missing with alcohols of lower molecular weight than octanol (in the case of ribonuclease—see below—lower molecular-weight alcohols destabilize). Before considering the effects of neutral ligands on other proteins, it can only be said that binding can either stabilize or help disrupt the native form of the protein, depending on what is bound, and perhaps how much. The smaller apolar molecules have never been demonstrated to produce destabilizing effects with $1 < \bar{v} \leq 4$. We may anticipate our discussion of ion binding by saying that the largest anions which contain large apolar residues stabilize when small amounts are bound, and destabilize beyond certain small values of $\bar{v}$.

In all discussion of stability in BSA it must be recalled that Sogami and Foster (1968) have clearly shown that the protein owes much of its normal remarkable stability to the one or two residual molecules of fatty acid of high molecular weight that it so avidly retains during most purification and crystallization procedures. Removal of this material by the mild acid–charcoal method of Chen leaves the protein in a less stable state than the lipid-associated material. There is no doubt that some materials of high affinity, particularly anions, can replace the fatty acid, but it is possible that since they *replace* it rather than leaving a hole this change can have no strong effect on the tendency to be denatured.

It has recently been demonstrated by Gallagher and Steinhardt (1969) that completely defatted BSA gives the same difference spectrum against material containing a single fatty acid residue as material containing more fatty acid residues gives against the original residually fatted BSA. More important, every aliphatic *anion* containing over five carbon atoms gives the same difference spectrum when it is added to and measured against totally defatted BSA in up to two to three equivalents. *Such neutral molecules as aliphatic alcohols* (C_6 *to* C_{10}) *do not give this spectrum.* Their binding is therefore demonstrably different than that of stabilizing anions; as will be explained in Chapter VII the latter may give spectra of two different classes, depending on their type, if residual fatty acid is present. They yield spectra of only one type, the type normally given only by carboxyl ions, when the first two equivalents are added to totally defatted BSA.

B. β-LACTOGLOBULIN

Discussion of β-lactoglobulin has been selected to follow that of serum albumin although far less work has been done on it than with the transport proteins hemoglobin and myoglobin, primarily because binding of many of the substances which were subjects for study with serum albumin were also studied with β-lactoglobulin. The contrasts and similarities should be revealing; at least they are untouched by the highly specialized functional adaptations of the respiratory proteins.

The problem of heterogeneity arises here, as it did with serum albumin, but somewhat less drastically and in a better understood way: there are two distinct genetic variants present in the milk obtained from most herds, and most of the work on binding has been done on mixtures of the two variants, which differ in a pair of amino acid residues (Aschaffenborg and Drewry, 1955, 1957).

In view of the work of Anderson (1966), further microheterogeneity with respect to unfolding by a detergent anion, octylbenzenesulfonate, similar to that found with BSA by Foster and his collaborators, cannot be ruled out.

1. *Binding*

(a) *Butane, Pentane, and Iodobutane.* In his first work with this protein Wishnia reported that the binding of butane by β-lactoglobulin at pressures between 0.1 and 1 atmosphere differs drastically from its binding to bovine serum albumin. Instead of a Henry's law "solubility" in the protein, with no indications of maximal molal ratios, analysis of the data was consistent with the existence of a small number of discrete binding sites, five for the normal dimer at pH 5, and three for the monomeric form (molecular weight approximately 18,000) which predominates at pH 2. The free energy of binding in either case is -4 kcal/mole, slightly lower than with BSA. (Wishnia, 1964). The behavior is thus similar to that shown by BSA when it binds alcohols rather than alkanes. Wishnia interpreted the values of n in the dimer and monomer as indicating that one of the monomer binding sites was located at the juncture of two monomer units when dimer is formed. Another possibility must be borne in mind: that deep-seated conformation changes accompany dimerization. The formation of dimer may result in the adoption of conformations which in each separated monomer unit do not represent free energy minima, but which do so when the surface sites involved in dimerization are engaged.

Wishnia and Pinder (1965) have also investigated the binding of 1-iodobutane, using a tritium marker. The binding constant reported was close to that of pentane (K (25°) $\simeq 3300$) but only one site in the monomer, and two in the dimer, were found. The reduction in the number of sites was attributed to the large dipole moment (2.1 Debye units) of the iodinated hydrocarbon; this moment is responsible for an unfavorable free energy for its removal from contact with water. Thus binding was postulated to be restricted to a single surface site, which does not require removal from solvent contact. The other sites at which butane binds, including the site at the dimer "joint," are not on the surface, i.e., do not permit ligand contact with solvent. Wishnia and

Pinder propose that the differential binding of iodobutane and pentane may be used to distinguish between surface and interior hydrophobic regions.

In a later paper the two genetic forms A and B of the protein were investigated separately, and significantly different results were obtained. The binding of butane, pentane, and iodobutane to monomer, dimer and, in the case of the A, for the octamer were determined (Wishnia and Pinder, 1966). In contradiction to the earlier findings, both A and B forms bind the same number of molecules per monomer unit whether in monomer or dimer. Therefore the "joint" in the dimer is not a site, nor does the process of dimerization involve a conformation change in the monomers that alters the binding sites. The A form binds both *butanes* equally strongly ($K_1 = 102,000$, $K_2 = 26,000$, corresponding to an intrinsic K_0 of 52,000, $\Delta F = -6.44$ kcal, $\Delta H = 1.1$ kcal, $\Delta S = -17.8$ cal/degree). However the second *pentane* is bound only one-tenth as strongly as the first and separate ΔF and K values must therefore be given ($K_1 = 330,000$, $K_2 = 34,000$; $\Delta F_1 = -7.54$ kcal/mole, $\Delta F_2 = -6.19$ kcal/mole; $\Delta H_1 = +2.1$ kcal/mole, $\Delta H_2 = 0.9$ kcal/mole, $\Delta S_1 = -18.3$ cal/degree, $\Delta S_2 = -17.7$ cal/degree). The single iodobutane molecule bound per monomer unit has $K = 140,000$, $\Delta F = -7.03$ kcal/mole, $\Delta H = 4.0$ kcal/mole, and $\Delta S = -10.2$ cal/degree.

The B isoprotein has somewhat higher affinities, and a more stable dimer, and forms an octamer as well. A largely steric explanation for these phenomena is favored, i.e., there is a single region in each B monomer which can accommodate at least 200 ml/mole but not more than 230 ml/mole protein. Molecules which are accommodated are removed from contact with water. Each butane accounts for about 100 ml; but pentane occupies 116 ml/mole. Thus one of the two pentanes either strains the native structure, or, more likely, is not entirely engulfed in the cavity (remains to a small extent in contact with water). Iodobutane occupies only 115 ml/mole, but since work required to transfer its large dipole from a medium of high dielectric constant to one of low dielectric constant offsets a large part of the free energy of hydrophobic (entropic) origin, it tends to stay near the surface of the cavity, and thus prevents the entry of a second molecule. Xenon, which has a large molal volume, is bound only about 1% as strongly as butane, even when it is "salted out" of water by high concentrations of ammonium sulfate.

A single dodecylsulfate ion was reported by McMeekin (1949) to be bound very tightly to this protein. Wishnia and Pinder suggest that its molal volume, 210 ml, would fit very well into the same cavity as two butane molecules. The binding of another ion to β-lactoglobulin (more than one equivalent binds to the native protein) has been investigated by Hill and Briggs (1956) and is discussed at some length in Chapter VII.

It is noteworthy that butane and pentane, although bound only in small amounts by β-lactoglobulin, are bound much more tightly than they appear to be to BSA, and fully as tightly as is dodecanol to that protein. If the cavity principle is a general one, affinities should not rise with molecular weight of ligand indefinitely, but there are some indications with a number of proteins, including BSA, or albumin, and wool keratin, that they tend to do so up to fairly high molecular weights. The interpretation of "equivalent sites" (e.g., the five sites found with BSA for the aliphatic alcohols of low solubility) appears to be incapable of general application. In the case of BSA, for example, it will be shown that there are more numerous equivalent sites for dodecyl- and myristylsulfates than for the much smaller hexyl- and octyl-sulfates.

Extensive data on the binding of higher hydrocarbons to β-lactoglobulin are reported by Mohammadzadeh-K, *et al.* (1969a). This protein has about half as many sites for pentane and heptane as are found by the same investigators for BSA, but with all other hydrocarbons and methyl esters the ratio is lower—between one-half and less than one-quarter (a good deal less than one-twentieth with tridecane). Thus, the diminution with aliphatic chain length is even sharper than with BSA. With the cyclic hydrocarbons the ratios cover a very similar range. Reduced and alkylated β-lactoglobulin binds only 70% as much as the native material. The amount bound is also reduced by about 20% by increasing the ionic strength to 0.3, but it becomes independent of ionic strength beyond this point.

(b) *Vitamin B_{12}.* When present in excess this vitamin binds to all the milk proteins including β-lactoglobulin (Gizis *et al.*, 1965). The caseins and proteose-peptose fractions bind more strongly. 6 M Urea increases the binding by β-lactoglobulin by about 20%.

2. Stability

Wetlaufer and Lovrien (1964) have shown that butane at pH 7.8 at atmospheric pressure induces a small reversible rise in the pH (about 0.04 units) of β-lactoglobulin solutions. The effect is slightly less than half of the maximum effect produced in BSA at pH 11. Reversible changes in optical rotation also occur, and have been followed over the pH range 6.1 to 8.5— the change at 546 mμ is approximately the same over the entire region, a decrease in specific levorotation of about 20% (0.022° for a 3% solution in a 2-cm path length at 25°). Cyclopropane produces the same effect on optical rotation as butane, but the effect with isobutane is only half as great. The direction of the change in [α] at 546 mμ prevails over the wavelength region studied, 330–670 mμ. Changes in KCl concentration from 0.02 M to 0.15 M reduce the steepness of the pH dependence of [α] but not its maximum size.

Wetlaufer and Lovrien interpret the pH profile of the changes in rotation as a shift to higher pH in the pH profile of the conformation change (Fig. 4-14). Evidence has been presented for such a change at pH values between

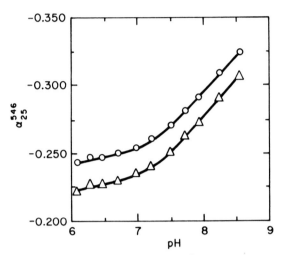

FIG. 4-14. The pH profile of optical rotation of β-lactoglobulin with N_2 and with butane. The protein concentration was the same at all pH values (approximately 3%). The optical path was 2.00 cm; the solvent, 0.02 M KCl; and the temperature, 25.0°. Sequence of measurements: O, 1 atmosphere of N_2; $\triangle$, 1 atmosphere of butane. [D. Wetlaufer and R. Lovrien (1964). *J. Biol. Chem.* **239**, 596.]

7 and 8 on the basis of analysis of the titration curve and measurements of optical rotation and sedimentation velocity (Tanford *et al.*, 1959); it has also been reported that dissociation into subunits occurs here (Georges *et al.*, 1961, cited by Wetlaufer and Lovrien, 1964); a conformational change incident to dissociation is not unexpected. However, the pH profiles (Fig. 4-14) cannot be superimposed solely by a shift along the pH axis as would be the case if *only* a change in the pH–stability relations were affected by hydrocarbon binding. The near constancy of the change in rotation at all pH values suggests that a different explanation should be sought.

C. MYOGLOBIN AND HEMOGLOBIN

Myoglobin adds only one new feature to the phenomena of complexing with neutral molecules already described: its combination with O_2 and CO and a few other neutral substances such as alkyl isocyanides is at a single known site of which the iron atom of heme forms an essential part. No *multiple* equilibria are involved. However, a great deal is now known about the relative affinities of the various ligands (Banerjee, 1962), the related affinities of the heme itself to the apoproteins of a number of different species, and—almost uniquely among proteins—the atomic displacements involved in binding [X-ray diffraction measurements with both bound molecules and ions; see, for an instructive example, the case of methyl isocyanide, Nobbs (1965)].

It has been argued from the enhancement of the urea denaturation of myoglobin by aromatic compounds (Cann, 1967) that the protein–ligand complexes involve both hydrophobic and charge-transfer interactions. The aromatic ligands are believed to disrupt the π-bonds between two phenylalanine residues CD1 and 15H and the heme. It is well established that stabilization of the entire protein is strongly dependent on the presence of the prosthetic group in both myoglobin and hemoglobin.

Two unexpected complexes are found with myoglobin and seem to be formed similarly although one of the ligands is neutral, monatomic, and apolar, and the other polyatomic and negatively charged. The neutral ligand is xenon (Schoenborn, 1965). Its high electron density allows it to be located in a deep cavity close to the heme; in the tetrameric hemoglobin, however, it lies near the surface but in different locations in the α and β chains. The second ligand, HgI_3^-, an ion, is similarly bound.

The subunit structure of hemoglobin, now known to play an important role in the oxygen-binding isotherm (Guidotti, 1967), adds an additional complication, made more portentous by the fact that mammalian hemoglobins are heterotetramers of the type $\alpha_1\beta_1\alpha_2\beta_2$. Recent knowledge of the part played by subunit interactions makes much of the earlier speculation as to how the "cooperative" nature of the isotherm, and the Bohr effect (a dependence of O_2 binding on pH) were to be explained wholly irrelevant. An abbreviated discussion of this enormous literature, which has affected the entire field of multiple equilibria, is deferred until simpler equilibria have been described.

Wishnia (1962) has measured the solubility of butane and propane in 5% solutions of human oxyhemoglobin. The protein was not altered as a result of the experiments (see Fig. 4-1 on p. 88). Only slightly more than half as much alkane is bound to this protein as to BSA at any temperature. The ratio of "solubility" in protein to solubility in water is practically independent of temperature. The enthalpy of transfer from water to the protein at 25° is slightly endothermic ($\Delta H = +0.8$ kcal), whereas the enthalpy change in the transfer from water to BSA was zero. The ratio of "solubilities" of butane to propane in hemoglobin to their solubilities in SDS micelles is 0.5 rather than 0.7, as it was in BSA. Thus the affinity to the micelles goes up with increasing chain length more slowly than does the affinity to proteins.

K and $\Delta F°$, calculated as in the case of BSA, are about 265 and 3300 cal. ΔS_u is 16.4 cal. As in the similar calculations for BSA these figures refer only to the transfer of 1 mole of butane from aqueous solution to the protein phase. By themselves they give no information as to the energy or entropy involved in a single hydrophobic bond.

Murayama has shown that propane, ethane, and methane, can inhibit the phenomenon of sickling in whole erythrocytes containing hemoglobin-S.

The mechanism postulated is the hydrophobic binding of these hydrocarbons to a valine residue in the β-chain (present only in Hb S), thus preventing cyclization from valine one to valine six (the mutant) by hydrogen bonding. Gel formation at 38° by deoxyhemoglobin S is also prevented (Murayama, 1964). Structural details are proposed.

No data are available for the effects of butane binding on the conformation of normal hemoglobin, other than Wishnia's statement that at the end of the measurements no changes were observed in the spectra of oxygenated or reduced protein. Since hemoglobin lacks the unusual conformational adaptability of serum albumin, it is unlikely that it *returned* to its native form at the end of any experiment in which it had undergone changes. The heptane-binding measurements of Mohammadzadeh-K *et al.* (1969b), appear to have been made on *denatured* bovine hemoglobin. The number of sites found (2.48) is close to the number of sites reported by the same authors for native BSA (2.80).

Wishnia has reported (1964) that the ferri forms of human hemoglobin and sperm whale myoglobin behave differently in binding butane or pentane than the reduced or carbonyl forms, and concludes, as others have done (e.g., Lumry, 1964; Steinhardt *et al.*, 1966) that the conformations of ferri species differ from those of the reduced species. Comprehensive reviews cover the subjects of the binding of CO and O_2 by heme proteins, the relations between the equilibrium constants for the successive binding of up to four ligand molecules, the dependence of binding on pH (the Bohr effect), the binding of other ions, and the relations of these phenomena to protein conformation (Wyman, 1948, 1965; Rossi-Fanelli *et al.*, 1964; Antonini, 1965). Many of these phenomena have their counterparts in the binding of other ligands, including ions, by the oxidized form, methemoglobin, and many of the ligands are powerful stabilizers of the native form (Steinhardt *et al.*, 1963).

These phenomena are so intimately related to the prosthetic group, and particularly to the iron atom of the latter, that they are not usually included in general discussions of binding to protein. Nevertheless, they are probably closer to a complete *mechanistic* rather than formal explanation of the binding of neutral molecules involving the phenomena of conformation changes or of allostery (Wyman, 1965) than are most other binding phenomena. Success in the understanding of this group of systems is partly due to clear ideas as to the identity and number of sites involved in gas binding, which has reduced the problem of determining the K's to an algebraic one, once the form of the S-shaped binding isotherm was clearly established experimentally. Nevertheless, there was until recently incomplete agreement as to how the K_i are related to one another or to such factors as temperature, pH, and the binding of such other substances as Bromthymol blue.

The analytical development of the subject took an essential step forward with the equation of Adair (1925), which stated rigorously and generally the isotherm for a reversible quadrivalent oxygen molecule acceptor in terms of four completely arbitrary dissociation constants K_i. The simplest case, and one possessing an inherent logic, would be to find that all the intrinsic constants were the same. The isotherm would then be the same as that for myoglobin, which is obviously not the case. The next simplest case would be one in which four arbitrary selected values of the constants would yield the data. It has been maintained by a number of careful experimenters that this case actually applies (Roughton *et al.*, 1955), but differences of opinion persist as to how many different values are required, and the ratios of these values. Thus, there has been discussion of a "square" hemoglobin molecule (interactions by two nearest neighbors only); a four-value model, or a two-value model (Margaria *et al.*, 1963). The earlier models are discussed by Wyman (1948). The most recent comprehensive references are by Antonini (1965),[14] by Rossi-Fanelli *et al.* (1964), and by Wyman (1964).

Recently, Weber and Anderson (1965) have formulated analytical tests of Adair's equation readily applicable to the experimental data. They conclude that the equation does not truly apply, at least in certain molecularly dissociated hemoglobin systems. In a formal sense some of the K's have to be allowed to depend on the degree of saturation, as in several protein–ligand systems described in Chapter VII. This is most likely to mean that at least two different protein conformations are involved, that binding at certain sites favors the transition from one to the other, and that each conformation has its own number of sites and its own binding constants. Such a system could obey Adair's equation only out of sheer coincidence and because of low experimental accuracy. The recent work of Guidotti has furnished a mechanism involving dissociation into $\alpha\beta$-dimers, which fits this description, on the basis of imaginative experiments published in four different papers in 1967. We refer specifically to the summary paper (Guidotti, 1967) which contains references to the other three papers and to the key monographs of the reactions of hemoglobin with ligands which have appeared in the last decade. It is, however, instructive to quote from the introduction to the first paper (1967), in slightly abridged form.

The principal concepts which arise from the work presented here and from the data in the literature are embodied in the following propositions:

Proposition 1. The tetrameric molecule of human hemoglobin, $\alpha_2\beta_2$,

---

[14] Unfortunately this excellent review perpetuates the incorrect reports in the literature to the effect that there are no "heme–heme interactions" in the ferric hemoglobins. Cyanide has the same Hill constant in combining with Hb^+ as O_2 on combining with Hb^0 (Steinhardt *et al.*, 1963).

is in rapid equilibrium with its subunits according to the equation

$$\alpha_2\beta_2 \rightleftharpoons 2\alpha\beta \qquad\qquad [4\text{-}5]$$

under all solvent conditions. . . .

Proposition 2. As a consequence of this rapid equilibrium, there exist tetrameric molecules of hemoglobin in which one $\alpha\beta$ dimer is of one type and the other $\alpha\beta$ dimer is of another type. These forms are called hybrid molecules, $(\alpha\beta)_j (\alpha\beta)_k$, and they can arise either by mixing of the two parent species, $(\alpha_2\beta_2)_j$ and $(\alpha_2\beta_2)_k$, or directly as intermediates in the combination of hemoglobin with ligand, $(\alpha\beta)_{\text{deoxy}} (\alpha\beta)_{\text{ligand}} \cdots$.

Proposition 3. The stability of the tetramers depends very strongly on the presence or absence of ligands on the heme groups. The order of decreasing stability of the tetramers is deoxytetramers $>$ hybrid tetramers $[(\alpha\beta)_{\text{deoxy}} (\alpha\beta)_{\text{ligand}}] >$ liganded tetramers.

Proposition 4. The conformation of dimers free in solution as compared to that of dimers in a tetrameric molecule depends on the presence or absence of ligand on the heme groups. Thus, the conformation of deoxy-dimers free in solution is markedly different from that of deoxy-dimers in a deoxy-tetramer; indeed, the conformation of free deoxy-dimers resembles that of liganded dimers. . . .

Proposition 5. The combination of ligand, L, with hemoglobin is dominated by the reaction of the $\alpha\beta$ subunits, whether they are free in solution or part of a tetrameric molecule, according to the equation

$$\alpha\beta + 2L \rightleftharpoons \alpha^*\beta^* \qquad\qquad [4\text{-}6]$$

where $\alpha^*\beta^*$ represents chains combined with ligand.

Proposition 6. In any solution of hemoglobin which is partially combined with ligand, there are only five types of hemoglobin molecule: liganded tetramers and dimers, nonliganded tetramers and dimers, and hybrid tetramers, consisting of one liganded and one nonliganded dimer. This is a direct consequence of Propositions 1, 2, and 5.

Proposition 7. Propositions 1 through 6 lead to the scheme for the combination of ligand, L, with hemoglobin given on p. 135.

Propositions 5, 6, and 7 follow simply from the preceding ones.

Guidotti's experiments were designed to test the validity of Propositions 2, 3, and 4 since Proposition 1 is generally accepted. Although the results of experiments were compatible with these concepts, they do not unequivocally prove them.

However Guidotti demonstrates that the propositions can explain many of the phenomena attending the reaction of hemoglobin with ligand although he does not claim that the scheme is necessarily correct or complete in every detail.

The summary description of the system to which Guidotti's work leads, and which is consistent with many of the kinetic and equilibrium data in the literature, cannot be given better than in Guidotti's words (slightly abridged):

The sequence of events in the reaction of hemoglobin with ligands is the following:

Step A. When one chain (α or β) of a dimer, be it free or associated into a tetramer, combines with ligand, the conformation of the chain is changed ... and this conformation change is transmitted to its partner (β or α), the affinity of which for ligand increases enormously. Thus, for all practical purposes, 2 molecules of ligand combine with the $\alpha\beta$ dimer at one time over most of the intermediate range of saturation with ligand. This is the fundamental step which governs these reactions.

Step B. If the $\alpha\beta$ dimer that reacts with ligand is free in solution, the now liganded dimer, $\alpha^*\beta^*$, can associate with another liganded dimer to produce a liganded tetramer, $\alpha_2^*\beta_2^*$, it can associate with a deoxygenated dimer to produce a hybrid molecule, $\alpha\beta\alpha^*\beta^*$, or it can remain free in solution.

Step C. If the $\alpha\beta$ dimer that reacts with ligand is already part of a tetramer, $\alpha_2\beta_2$, the resulting molecule is the hybrid $\alpha\beta\alpha^*\beta^*$. This hybrid may either persist in solution or dissociate into the dimers, $\alpha\beta$ and $\alpha^*\beta^*$.

Step D. The hybrid molecule $\alpha\beta\alpha^*\beta^*$ can react with ligand to produce the liganded tetramer $\alpha_2^*\beta_2^*$.

Steps A to D described above embody three important and critical points:

1. The complete sequence of events is described by three ligand-binding reactions and three tetramer to dimer dissociation reactions.

2. The term "hybrid molecules," $\alpha\beta\alpha^*\beta^*$, refers only to tetramers composed of different $\alpha\beta$ subunits (here, one liganded and one deoxy-dimer) ... and does not refer to the mechanism by which these molecules are produced. Thus, the molecule composed of one deoxy- and one liganded dimer, $\alpha\beta\alpha^*\beta^*$, can arise either by association of the two $\alpha\beta$ dimers or directly, by combination of two ligand molecules with a deoxy-tetramer.

3. The existence of hybrid molecules of the type $\alpha\beta\alpha^*\beta^*$ is a key event in the combination of hemoglobin with ligand ... once the first $\alpha\beta$ unit in a tetramer has combined with ligand, its conformation is altered and it forces the associated $\alpha\beta$ unit into a new conformation. The new conformation of the uncombined $\alpha\beta$ unit in the hybrid tetramer may be one

in which the affinity for ligand is greater or smaller than that predicted on statistical grounds, depending on the solvent conditions. Thus, the solvent, by its effect on the stability of deoxy tetramers, hybrid tetramers, and liganded tetramers, necessarily determines the affinity of the two sets of dimers in the tetramer for ligand.

Guidotti arrives at the value of the Hill interaction coefficient, n, as follows:

> Since two molecules of ligand are presumed to combine with the $\alpha\beta$ dimer at one time over most of the saturation curve, the value of n is close to but less than 2. The value of n cannot be 2 because Wyman (1964) has shown that a plot of log $y/(1 - y)$ with respect to log pO_2 tends to a limiting slope of 1 as $pO_2 \to 0$. If simultaneous combination with two oxygen molecules were obligatory, the limiting slope should be 2. Now, if the affinity for ligand of the uncombined dimer in the hybrid molecule, $\alpha\beta\alpha^*\beta^*$, is greater than that predicted on statistical grounds, the value of n is greater than 2, while n is less than 2 for the opposite situation.
>
> Thus, the conformational change which takes place in going from deoxygenated $\alpha\beta$ units to liganded $\alpha^*\beta^*$ units always has a large positive effect on the affinity of the heme groups in each chain of the $\alpha\beta$ unit, and is fairly insensitive to solvent conditions. On the other hand, the effect of a liganded dimer on the affinity of the deoxy-dimer in a hybrid tetramer may be positive or negative, is small, and is very sensitive to solvent conditions.

The model Guidotti proposed (next paragraph) is sufficient to explain fairly simply many of the phenomena observed in the reaction of hemoglobin with ligands; it is consistent with Guidotti's own data, and does not differ widely from the model proposed by Wyman in 1948 and reelaborated by him in 1967, and with the hypotheses presented by Benesch et al. (1965, 1966) or Benesch et al. for the reaction of hemoglobin with ligands.

If the combination of the fundamental unit of function, the $\alpha\beta$ dimer, with ligand L is written as follows:

$$\alpha\beta + L \underset{k_2}{\overset{k_1}{\rightleftarrows}} (\alpha^*\beta \text{ or } \alpha\beta^*) \qquad K_3'$$

$$(\alpha^*\beta \text{ or } \alpha\beta^*) + L \underset{k_4}{\overset{k_3}{\rightleftarrows}} \alpha^*\beta^* \qquad K_3'' \tag{4-7}$$

so that

$$K_3 = K_3' K_3'' = \frac{k_1 k_3}{k_2 k_4}$$

Guidotti proposes (a) that $K_3'' \gg K_3'$, (b) that the rate-limiting step for combination with ligand is determined by the condition $(K_3 \gg K_1)$ and that the rate-limiting step for dissociation of ligand at zero ligand activity[15] is determined by the condition ($k_2 \gg k_4$). The species $\alpha^*\beta$ or $\alpha\beta^*$ are thus very unstable and are converted rapidly to either $\alpha\beta$ or $\alpha^*\beta^*$.

Thus the simplification $\alpha\beta + 2L \rightleftharpoons \alpha^*\beta^*$ will apply over most of the saturation curve of hemoglobin but will break down at very low and very high values of the fractional saturation.

Within the limits of the rate-limiting conditions the combination of ligand with hemoglobin can be described by the following reactions:

$$A_2 + 2L \overset{K_1}{\rightleftharpoons} AB \tag{4-8}$$

$$AB + 2L \overset{K_2}{\rightleftharpoons} B_2 \tag{4-9}$$

$$A + 2L \overset{K_3}{\rightleftharpoons} B \tag{4-10}$$

$$A_2 \overset{K_{deo}}{\rightleftharpoons} 2A \tag{4-11}$$

$$AB \overset{K_H}{\rightleftharpoons} A + B \tag{4-12}$$

$$B_2 \overset{K_O}{\rightleftharpoons} 2B \tag{4-13}$$

where A_2 represents deoxygenated tetramer, $\alpha_2\beta_2$; AB, the "hybrid" $\alpha\beta\alpha^*\beta^*$; A, the dimer $\alpha\beta$; and B, the dimer $\alpha^*\beta^*$ (the asterisks indicate chains combined with ligand). The constants are defined by the reactions as written [i.e., binding constants for Eqs. (4-8) to (4-10) and tetramer-to-dimer dissociation constants for Eqs. (4-11) to (4-13)].

They are related by

$$K_1 = K_3 \frac{K_{deo}}{K_H} \tag{4-14}$$

$$K_2 = K_3 \frac{K_H}{K_O} \tag{4-15}$$

Thus there are only four independent constants, for example, K_3, K_{deo}, K_H, and K_O, which completely specify the system.

$$[A] = \frac{\frac{1}{2}(1 + K_3 p^2) + \left\{\frac{1}{4}(1 + K_3 p^2)^2 + 4[\text{Hb}]_{\text{tot}}\left[\frac{1}{K_{deo}} + \frac{K_3 p^2}{K_H}(1 + K_2 p^2)\right]\right\}^{1/2}}{2\left[\frac{1}{K_{deo}} + \frac{K_3 p^2}{K_H}(1 + K_2 p^2)\right]} \tag{4-16}$$

[15] This condition is necessary because if the rate constant for the forward reaction is given by k_1 ($k_f = k_1$), then the rate constant for the reverse reaction must be $k_r = k_2 k_4/k_3$.

The fractional saturation of hemoglobin with ligand, y, is given by

$$y = \frac{K_1 p^2 \left(1 + \dfrac{K_H}{[A]}\right) + 2K_1 K_2 p^4}{2\left[\left(1 + \dfrac{1}{2}\dfrac{K_{deo}}{[A]}\right) + K_1 p^2 \left(1 + \dfrac{1}{2}\dfrac{K_H}{[A]}\right) + K_1 K_2 p^4\right]} \tag{4-17}$$

in which $[A]$ is related to the total hemoglobin concentration, $[Hb]_{tot}$, and the activity of ligand, p, by the expression shown in Eq. (4-16). Equation (4-17), with the accompanying Eq. (4-16), is the fundamental equation of this model of the hemoglobin system.

Equation (4-17) is distinguished from other models in that the presence of a term dependent on total hemoglobin concentration allows its application to ligand saturation curves obtained under a wide range of conditions. When the total hemoglobin concentration is very small relative to the values of the tetramer-to-dimer dissociation constants, Eq. (4-11) becomes

$$y = \frac{K_3 p^2}{1 + K_3 p^2} \tag{4-18}$$

for which the value of n is close to 2. Thus, all the saturation curves should approach this form as the concentration of hemoglobin decreases (Roughton et al., 1955; Rossi-Fanelli et al., 1961).

Equation (4-11) should apply when the concentration of hemoglobin is approximately equal to the values of the dissociation constants, i.e., in strong salt solutions (Rossi-Fanelli et al., 1961). Figure 4-15 shows an oxygen saturation curve for human hemoglobin in 2 M NaCl, at pH 7 and 20°, calculated with Eq. (4-11).[16] The values of K_{deo}, K_H, and K_O are those determined experimentally by Guidotti for hemoglobin in 2 M NaCl. The values used for the total hemoglobin concentration and for ligand activity at 50% saturation, P_{50}, are those reported by Antonini et al. (1962), for the same solvent conditions (5 × $10^{-5} M$ and 16.4 mm of Hg, respectively). The value of n, the interaction coefficient, for the curve shown in Fig. 4-15 is 2.7, in good agreement with the value 2.8 determined by Antonini et al. (1962). The fit of the data to Eq. (4-11) under these solvent conditions is good.

Guidotti then develops an approximate form of the complete equation [Eq. (4-17)] and shows that it can simulate the Adair equation, or, for that

[16] The calculated value of y at $p = 4$ mm of Hg is 0.04. From this point the curve was extrapolated to $y = 0$ in a completely *arbitrary* fashion. This was done because Eq. (4-11) is expected to break down at very low values of the activity of ligand; no attempt was made to correct for this inaccuracy of the model. However, down to a value of $y = 0.104$ the model appears to fit the experimental data, as shown in Fig. 4-15.

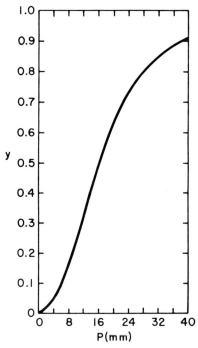

FIG. 4-15. Calculated curve for the saturation of hemoglobin with O_2 in 2 M NaCl, at pH 7 and 20°; Eqs. (4-13) and (4-16) were used in the calculation, with the following parameters: $[Hb]_{tot} = 5 \times 10^{-5}$ M; $K_{deo} = 0.5 \times 10^{-5}$ M; $K_H = 3 \times 10^{-5}$ M; $K_O = 12 \times 10^{5-}$ M; and $K_3 = 1.165 \times 10^{-2}$ mm^{-2}. The values of the dissociation constants are those experimentally determined and reported in Papers II (46) and III (32). [G. Guidotti (1966). *J. Biol. Chem.* **242**, 3704.]

matter, some of the various modifications that have been proposed. The Hill constant, n, in the time-honored approximate Hill equation

$$Y = \frac{K_p{}^n}{1 + K_p{}^n} \quad \text{is simply} \quad \frac{8}{2 + (K_1/K_2)^{1/2}} \tag{4-19}$$

The availability of Guidotti's hypothesis and the substantial experimental underpinning on which it rests has made it possible to omit from this chapter a vast body of very ingenious investigation and speculation such as the relations of the induced conformations to "unfolding" or denaturation [it is well known that heme stabilizes the protein (Watson, 1966)]. There are cases which will not fit Guidotti's model. Thus, Antonini *et al.* (1966) have produced and studied hybrid NO-ligand dimers which behave similarly to fully un-liganded hemoglobin. Likewise Gibson and Parkhurst (1968) have shown that the rate of production of "rapid" hemoglobin by flash photolysis of

COHb in the presence of deoxyhemoglobin cannot be made to conform to a dimer subunit, but requires that the change in reactivity associated with the appearance of " rapid " hemoglobin occur after at least three ligand molecules have combined. A tetrameric functional limit therefore appears to be required. Another unanswered question is, To what structural features are the wide differences in the affinities of various hemoglobins for oxygen due? There are indications that the affinities are lower the larger the number of reactive cysteines—see, e.g., Taketa *et al.* (1967)—but there is also conflicting evidence (Nagel *et al.*, 1967). The list could be greatly extended.

It is important to classify the Guidotti model with respect to the two models for reversible binding-induced conformation changes we have already encountered. These may be called (a) the purely thermodynamic model (Foster and Aoki, 1958; and Reynolds *et al.*, 1967), which have been applied to BSA, and which depend solely on the relationship between the numbers of sites and their association constants for both native and unfolded forms, and (b) the simple mechanistic model (e.g., the accumulation of a sufficiently great electrostatic repulsive charge may overcome the small net balance of cohesive forces over disruptive forces). In principle, model (a) will always apply, if it is not " forestalled " by the occurrence of the events postulated in model (b) at lower concentrations of ligand than are required to induce a transition.

The class (b) includes all mechanistic as opposed to thermodynamic models and is not confined only to the simple case of electrostatic repulsion for disruptive conformation change. Neutral ligands cannot participate in such a simple electrostatic mechanism, unless we postulate that by being bound they can greatly change the balance of an internal state of ionization, involving the movement of protons from previously uncharged and undissociated acidic groups to previously uncharged basic groups. It is not easy to see how such an effect can be produced solely by binding uncharged molecules.

We will see that the "disruptive pH-induced conformation change" in the case of BSA may actually increase the amount of ligand bound over at least a portion of the total concentration range. Models (a) and (b) become undistinguishable when this is so. Attention has been directed to this feature of the simple models, because it is sometimes averred by those who are familiar with hemoglobin and certain isozymes that the cooperative features of the reaction with ligand which indubitably depend upon conformation transitions, somehow also depend on the possession of subunit structure, or even of a "symmetrical" subunit structure.

Guidotti's model is a mixed case of both class (a) and class (b). It is a complicated combination, so far removed from the simplest cases that its kinship to (a) and (b) is difficult to perceive. A skeletonized sequence of events would show (1) tetramer dissociating to dimer; (2) two molecules of ligand binding very tightly to the dimer; (3) reassociation into tetramers; (4) facilitated oxygen binding on unoccupied $\alpha\beta$ of tetramer. This skeleton omits all the events at each step which do not proceed to a new state. We learn that $\alpha\beta$ has a high affinity for ligand, but that $\alpha\beta$ $(L)_2\alpha\beta$ has a still higher affinity. It is important that $\alpha\beta$ have a high affinity primarily so that all other dimers but $\alpha\beta(L)_2$ be very rare. It is important for $\alpha\beta(L)_2$ to have a still higher affinity so that the binding will be cooperative, i.e., change by a large amount over a relatively narrow range of [L]. The latter requirement bears a clear resemblance to class (a), the "thermodynamic" model. The case bears a certain degree of formal resemblance to Koshland's concept of induced fit of substrate to protein.

The analysis above is rather instructive, because it shows that the basic binding reaction is $\alpha\beta + L_2 \rightleftharpoons \alpha\beta(L_2)$ and that the unfolding transition of case (a) is in the compound step

$$L_2 + 2\alpha\beta \rightleftharpoons \alpha\beta(L_2)\alpha\beta$$
$$\alpha\beta(L_2)\alpha\beta + L_2 \rightleftharpoons \alpha_2\beta_2 L_4 \tag{4-20}$$

Since the new sites of high K are created in the first of these two reactions, this is the "unfolding" step.

The "hemoglobin problem" now becomes, at least in part, to determine all the forces involved in the dimer–tetramer equilibria (pure or mixed) and in the endowment of $\alpha\beta$ and $\alpha\beta L_2 \alpha\beta$ with the required relative velocities of binding. Some of the latest work to this end is concerned with the interaction between α- and β-chains in human hemoglobin (Neer *et al.*, 1968) and shows that chemical modification of either chain of the dimer changes the reactivity of widely separated groups, so that it must be concluded that a general conformational change occurs; further evidence is given that the $\alpha\beta$ dimer is the fundamental unit of both structure and function. Substitution of dinitrophenol at a single location, the NH_2 terminus of the α-chain, gives a higher oxygen affinity, a value of 1 in the Hill equation, and abolishes the Bohr effect, as well as producing a more tightly associated tetramer.

Some of the work concerned with the properties of the tetramer has for some years taken the form of isolating or preparing mixed tetramers of various mutant-containing chains, or even of tetramers consisting only of α- or of β-chains but not of the two together (Bookchin *et al.*, 1963).

In the preceding paragraphs the general expression "ligands" has been used, rather than specifying oxygen or carbon monoxide. Hemoglobins and myoglobins combine with other ligands when their iron is in both oxidized and reduced states. We confine the discussion to those with which it reacts in the ferrous form. One of these is the indicator bromthymol blue (Antonini *et al.*, 1963). Although this substance is ionic we include it here because of its strong effect on the oxygen equilibrium. Since the oxygen equilibrium is strongly affected when this dye is bound, it must be expected that some or all of the partial reactions entering into oxygenation affect the binding of the dye. This is demonstrably the case: the affinity of the dye is much greater for the deoxy than for the oxy form, and the difference is visible in the *rates* of oxygenation as well as in the equilibria. On binding, the pK_H of the dye rises from 7.1 to above 8. Over 10 equivalents of dye are bound per heme with an affinity that rises at acid pH where the dye is largely unionized. The stoichiometry differs very obviously from that in oxygenation. The maximum K is about 3000.

It is noteworthy that the *rate* of binding of hemoglobin with the dye is measurable by stop-flow methods, i.e., it is not a diffusion-limited rate. The half-period for binding the first dye molecule at pH 7 is about 200 milliseconds in the case of deoxyhemoglobin and about 450 milliseconds with oxyhemoglobin, both at about 1% protein concentration. These periods are very much longer than those which have been found in kinetic binding studies with BSA or in the first constituent step in the binding of CO heme by globin (Gibson and Antonini, 1966), the half-period of which is almost at the limit of a diffusion-limited reaction.

Alkyl isocyanides combine with hemoglobin, at least up to the butyl derivative (St. George and Pauling, 1951). A recent study of exchange reactions shows that ethyl isocyanide combines reversibly with hemoglobin in the same manner as oxygen in spite of the substantial difference in molecular size (Sumita *et al.*, 1964). A monophenyl diimide coordination compound of bovine ferrihemoglobin has been reported (Itano and Robinson, 1961).

Other gases combine with the heme proteins, although they do not link to the prosthetic group. Thus, Murayama (1964) has demonstrated that propane or isobutane can be bound by hemoglobin-S, the protein of sickle-cell anemia. There is a strong presumption that in binding, one or more valyl residues which interact in this mutant protein are separated, and a more normal conformation results. The interpretation is supported by optical rotatory dispersion data, and by changes in other physical properties.

The binding of heme itself to the apoprotein is a subject with a growing literature. Heme will exchange between human ferrihemoglobin and any apoglobin having a higher affinity for heme, such as apomyglobin (Banerjee, 1962). The migration is blocked by the complexing with ligands or by binding to haptoglobin. The exchange between α-chains is slower than with non-α chains. Primate albumins in excess can strip hemes from ferrihemoglobin (Bunn and Jandl, 1968); but the albumins of other mammalian orders are ineffective.

Herzskovits and Jaillet (1969) have shown that in a group of 31 neutral aqueous solutes, including alcohols, ureas, and amides, all of which denature myoglobin when sufficiently concentrated, each is effective within each group, in proportion to its hydrocarbon chain-length.

D. Lysozyme

According to Wishnia (1962), lysozyme shows negligible binding of the same hydrocarbons that bound effectively to BSA and hemoglobin. Since lysozyme has a higher surface-to-volume ratio than the other proteins he studied, Wishnia concluded that the binding observed with the other proteins is unlikely to be a nonspecific surface phenomenon.

Wishnia's finding of negligible hydrocarbon binding by lysozyme has been confirmed by Mohammadzadeh-K *et al.* (1969b) with heptane. Gradually increasing amounts are bound at progressively lower pH values down to about 3, where the binding levels off at a value which is still low compared with those found with BSA or β-lactoglobulin ($\bar{v} \simeq 0.4$). This effect of acid pH is common to other proteins which bind only small quantities of heptane (ovalbumin, ovotransferrin, α-chymotrypsin, and α-chymotrypsinogen). Partial acid hydrolysis of the protein first increases and then decreases the amounts bound. Reduction and alkylation increases the binding by a factor of about 10 at neutral pH and by a factor of about 1000 at pH 10.3 ($n = 2.67$). Partial hydrolysis of this material increases the binding, and the progressively reduces it to a low figure.

Rupley *et. al.* (1967) has recently determined the binding of various substrates (disaccharides) and substrate analogs to the enzyme. The reaction follows the law of mass action. The binding constant increases by a factor of about 100 for each saccharide unit in a polysaccharide from monomer to trimer but not beyond (tetramer, and hexamer, and pentamer). The hexamer is nevertheless cleaved more rapidly than the trimer. The monomer acts as a competitive inhibitor and is therefore bound. There is no pH dependence between pH 4 and 5.5, but in strongly acid solutions the activity diminishes. There is an additional step in pH dependence of activity at 5 to 8 although the binding to substrate does not change in this range. Values of n, K, and $\Delta F°$, and relative enzyme activity have been calculated for the trimer. It appears that an amide group on the substrate is essential for binding and activity. Rupley and Gates (1967) have shown that the binding of saccharides displaces protons. Butler and Rupley (1967) have used X-ray analysis to study formation of the enzyme-substrate complex.

In a nuclear magnetic resonance study the α and β anomeric forms of 2-acetamido-2-deoxy-D-glucopyranose give different chemical shifts of their acetamido methyl protons when bound to lysozyme, and are therefore either bound with different affinities, or their methyl protons when bound are in different magnetic environments. The anomeric forms compete in binding with methyl glycosides. In the case of methyl glycosides, it was possible to show that the affinities differ slightly but that the magnetic environments do not (Raftery *et al.*, 1968).

In a study of difference spectra produced by substrate binding, Imoto and Rupley (1968) have shown that although three tryptophans (62, 63, and 108) are perturbed, 108 is perturbed the most, and draw the important conclusion that the effect depends on the close proximity of Try 108 to Glu 35. Ionization of the latter (pK 6.3) also perturbs Try 108. The most exposed trytophan, 62, shows only slight substrate perturbations. An NMR study of the effect of temperature and pH on lysozyme–inhibitor interactions yields practically the same aberrant value for the pK of Glu 35 (Dahlquist and Raftery, 1968). The same study shows that ΔH for binding to the enzyme is -5.5 kcal. The binding constant is 10 at pH $>$ 7, and about 30 at pH $<$ 5.5. Interactions with substrate and with inhibitor are also evident in the 280 mμ CD bands (Glazer and Simmons, 1966).

E. OTHER ENZYMES

Lysozyme has been separated from other enzymes because of its inclusion in the proteins studied by Wishnia. Few measurements of the binding by other enzymes of substances other than substrates or inhibitors are to be found in the literature.

All enzymes are believed to act by combining with their substrates to form enzyme–substrate complexes. Many of the substrates of the familiar well-studied enzymes are neutral molecules or zwitterions having no net charge (e.g., catalase, peroxidase, esterases including some of the proteolytic enzymes, saccharases, among many others). Enzyme mechanisms are usually formulated in terms of various modifications of the Michaelis-Menten theory which contains an explicit enzyme–substrate binding constant and explicit enzyme–inhibitor binding constants, among others, all derived primarily from kinetic data (Alberty, 1956; Friedenwald and Maengwyn-Davis in McElroy and Glass, 1954). The binding constants of inhibitors, more or less chemically homologous to the normal substrate, have been widely determined by investigators whose principal interest was understanding the molecular basis of enzyme specificity.

As a result of these studies binding constants can be tabulated for many proteins (enzymes) with at least one substance, the substrate; and, for numerous proteins, with a number of closely related chemical substances which inhibit. The inhibitors are not always closely related to the substrate, and in a few cases it has been possible to show that the inhibition is an "allosteric" effect, and noncompetitive; they may, for example, inhibit by bringing about a conformation change in the enzyme by combining with it at a different binding site than that occupied by the substrate. Aspartic trans-carbamylase is an example of such a system, inhibited by a substance which is formed in reactions several steps removed from the reaction it catalyzes

(Gerhart and Schachman, 1965). The information, although copious, is fragmentary and lacking in generality; the proteins are widely different, the substrates have little or nothing in common, the inhibitors belong to a very restricted class peculiar to each enzyme, and above all, the special nature of the binding is illustrated by the fairly general occurrence of a molal ratio of 1 (which might appear to exclude them from the province of a treatise on multiple equilibria) and a very high degree of specificity, which is in the highest degree unlike the binding by proteins of such neutral molecules as the hydrocarbons, alcohols, steroids, and undissociated acids which have been discussed here. The situation resembles that of antibodies and antigens, and is too individual to be reviewed in detail. Nevertheless, these two examples, enzymes and antibodies, in spite of their specialized diversified characteristics, constitute the most practically important examples of binding by proteins. If any inferences on the nature of highly specific binding could be drawn from the mass of enzyme data, they would make a most important contribution not only to the subject of this treatise, but to all protein chemistry, and to biology.

In the absence of such generalizations, only a few of the most recent data on enzyme binding studies will be presented, giving preference to those in which the system is well characterized and the experiments are unambiguous from the standpoint of the chemistry involved.

1. *Chymotrypsin*

Ultraviolet difference spectroscopy has been used to detect the formation of intermediates between *chymotrypsin* and certain un-ionized substrates, e.g., acetyl-L-phenylalanine ethyl ester (James and Trowbridge, 1965). The difference spectra differ with the substrate. The enzyme is inhibited by aromatic hydrocarbons (benzene, toluene, chlorobenzene, nitrobenzene, ethylbenzene, naphthalene, azulene, and anthracene). The free energy of binding at pH 7.05, 25°, rises with size of inhibitor from just under 3.0 kcal/mole to 7 kcal/mole, and appears to be directly proportional to the surface area of the inhibitor, which extends, in this series from 60.03 to 100.5 Å^2 (Miles *et al.*, 1963). The constants given are inhibition constants in the presence of ionized substrate (methyl hippurate) which has a K of 407 at the ionic strengths used. The K values for the hydrocarbons rise from 121 for benzene to 177,500 for anthracene—the substrate fits between toluene (351) and ethylbenzene (55). It has been assumed that the molal ratio is 1, but the work of Mohammadzadeh-K *et al.* (1969b), with heptane indicates that only 0.07 moles are bound at saturation at pH 6.8 (the amount bound increases at low pH). All the association constants are linearly related to increasing ionic strength (a salting-out effect, to be expected). The decomposition (catalytic) constants are not affected by salt. The association constants for the substrates (methyl hippurate has been cited) rise as the alkyl group increases in size, but branched chains are less effective in raising the affinity than straight chains. The investigators consider that the effect of salt (KCl) is in effect a "salting-out" of inhibitor from water onto the active site, and consider that the enzyme may extract the substrate from aqueous solution as a nonelectrolyte is extracted from water by an organic solvent.

Of 36 aromatic inhibitors tested with acetyl L-valine as the substrate, including mono-, di-, and tricyclic compounds, benzo [f]quinoline is the most effective (Wallace et al., 1963). When acetonitrile, acetone, and dioxane are the inhibitors, part of the effect is due to changes in dielectric constant as well as to binding (Clement and Bender, 1963). When α-chymotrypsin binds certain neutral inhibitors such as anisole or coumarin, protons may be released (pH ~6) or taken up (pH ~ 8). Calculations indicate that two prototropic groups at the active site undergo a change in pK when substrate binds. The original pKs are 6.7 and 8.7—the former drops and the latter rises on binding. The association constant of the inhibitor may be correctly inferred from the pH changes observed, but not all inhibitors give the effect (Glick, 1968).

Chymotrypsin adsorbs to emulsified n-octadecane in phosphate buffer (Ghosh and Bull, 1962).

2. Trypsin and Trypsin Inhibitor

The formation of complexes between trypsin and certain un-ionized substrates (as well as with some trypsin-inhibitor proteins) has been demonstrated by ultraviolet difference spectroscopy by James and Trowbridge (1965). Unlike many enzymes, trypsin is active when dissolved in aqueous dimethyl sulfoxide or dioxane and exhibits enzymatic activity in both mixed solvents (Inagami and Sturtevant, 1960). When p-nitrophenyl acetate is used as substrate, spectrophotometric analysis and acylation experiments indicate that it combines with the protein (Bettleheim and Lukton, 1963) prior to the appearance of hydrolytic products. Combination of the enzyme with dimethyl sulfoxide is also postulated on the basis of discontinuities in the mixing curve at a molal ratio of 2:1 for water/dimethyl sulfoxide for such properties as heat of mixing, viscosity, and dielectric constant (Bettleheim and Senatore, 1964).

The transient nature of the complex with the substrate (it does not survive precipitation by ethyl ether, or long standing) is cited as evidence that no covalent bonds are formed, but that a hydrophobic linkage is involved. Similar bonds were found with α-chymotrypsin, chymotrypsinogen, pepsin, and ribonuclease. Trypsinogen and "albumin" were insufficiently soluble to yield information.

Soybean trypsin inhibitor and certain other trypsin inhibitors differ from other trypsin substrates in that after undergoing cleavage, the modified protein is not released from the enzyme (Finkenstadt and Laskowski, 1965). Removal of the new terminal group (not present in the original protein) abolishes its capacity to complex (Ozawa and Laskowski, 1966). It has been found in Laskowski's laboratory that all trypsin inhibitors examined involve the splitting by the enzyme of an arginine–leucine, lysine–alanine, or similar peptide bond which forms part of an intramolecular cystine loop. It has proved possible to reverse the hydrolysis and even to replace the C-terminal arginine by a lysine or *vice versa* by a proper sequence of steps.

Comparison of rates of hydrolysis of normal substrates with others in which the lysine and arginine positive charges had been removed, by conversion of these residues to citrulline and heptyline, gives evidence for the existence of a ternary complex consisting of enzyme, positively charged molecule, and neutral molecule, (Sanborn and Hein, 1968). The existence of both competitive and noncompetitive inhibition is attributed to the existence of an auxiliary binding site to which neutral molecules bind.

3. *Carboxypeptidase A*

Apocarboxypeptidase can be prevented from combining with Zn^{2+} by prior combination with synthetic dipeptide substrates; nonsubstrate peptides do not have this effect. Proteins which are hydrolyzed by this enzyme also bind to the apoprotein even more strongly than peptide substrates (Combs and Wacker, 1965).

4. *Acetylcholinesterase*

Although the substrate of this enzyme is cationic and the most potent inhibitors are also cationic, the uncharged homologue of one such substrate (isoamyl alcohol) is a weak inhibitor (Wilson, 1952). There is indirect evidence that the enzyme forms a reversible complex with sulfonyl fluorides prior to sulfonylation, and becomes inactive (Fahrney and Gold, 1963). Similar evidence for the existence of such noncovalent intermediates exists for other esterases such as α-chymotrypsin and trypsin. Organophosphorus inhibitors of the type $CH_3(RO)P(O)SR'$, where R and R' are normal alkyls of varying chain lengths, show a sharp increase in effectiveness as the alkyl chains increase up to six carbons in length, but not beyond. The increase is much greater when the R chain is increased than when R' is lengthened. From $R = 2$ to $R = 7$ the effect in this case increases 18,000 fold. It is the R portion of the molecule that is not split off by the enzyme, and which may account for binding to a hydrophobic patch on the enzyme surface (Rozengart *et al.*, 1967).

5. *Pepsin*

Indirect evidence of a statistical nature, based on examination of the sequences of amino acid residues near cleaved peptide bonds in insulin, α-corticotropin, ribonuclease, and the α-chain of hemoglobin, points to reversible combinations of pepsin with "hydrophobic sites" containing phenylalanine near the cleaved bonds in these proteins (Tang, 1963). Higher aliphatic alcohols reversibly inhibit the enzyme, presumably by competing for the hydrophobic site. However, carboxylic acids also inhibit, including formic acid, which would not be expected to compete for a hydrophobic site (Yoon and Shin, 1967). Pepsin solubilizes benzene, with a maximum effect near pH 4 (Pehelin *et al.*, 1962). The substrates are, of course, cationic, and the enzyme anionic at the pH at which the enzyme is active, but the hydrophobic nature of the postulated bond has led to inclusion of this case in the present chapter.

The gel filtration method of determining binding isotherms has been used ingeniously by Humphreys and Fruton (1968) to show that a small synthetic substrate of pepsin is bound at multiple sites, only one of which is the enzymatically active site. Acetyl pepsin has fewer strongly binding sites, but these include the active site; pepsinogen has very little if any tendency to bind the substrate and thus has no sites at all.

Schlamowitz *et al.* (1968) give inhibition constants for 43 competitive inhibitors of pepsin, including numerous uncharged molecules. Either 1 or 2 molecules per mole are bound.

6. β-Amylase, Invertase, Luciferase, and Kidney Mutarotase

A recent analysis of the inhibition of β-amylase by urea has led to the conclusion that urea inhibits the enzyme when the latter binds at least two molecules competitively with substrate (Weintraub *et al.*, 1964). The dissociation constants obtained ($K_1 = 2.1$ and $K_2 = 1.0$) indicate exceedingly weak binding. Similar calculations on data in the literature for invertase ($K_1 = 2.6$ and $K_2 = 5$ to 10) and luciferase ($K_1 = 1.4$ and $K_2 = 0.4$) also indicate weak binding. There were indications that additional molecules bound still more weakly. The binding is so weak, and the inhibiting concentrations so high, that medium effects rather than stoichiometric binding cannot be excluded. The substantially greater effectiveness of tetramethylurea has been interpreted to indicate that a hydrogen bond is responsible for complex formation—it is postulated that the enzyme is the donor (Chase *et al.*, 1964).

Chase *et al.* (1963) have also concluded that "about four molecules of urea and guanidine hydrochloride combined per catalytic site to produce inhibition."

7. Ribonuclease

Ribonuclease has practically no tendency to bind hydrocarbons at neutral pH (Mahammadzadeh-K *et al.*, 1969b). The lowering by a series of alcohols of the temperature of thermal transition of pancreatic ribonuclease to the unfolded form has been attributed to hydrophobic interactions between the nonpolar side chains of the denatured enzyme and the bound alcohol molecules (Schrier *et al.*, 1965). The transition temperature is a linear function of the molarity of added alcohol over a wide range. The slope is steeper the greater the chain-length, but branched chains are less effective than straight chains. The following binding constants correspond to calculated free energy changes $\Delta F°_B$, defined as the free energy contribution from the formation of hydrophobic bonds between the alcohols and the denatured protein [obtained from the theory of Nemethy and Scheraga, (1962)] minus the absolute temperature times the entropy change, -11 eu, calculated from the entropy of dimerization of small model compounds in aqueous solutions.

Side chains	K_B
CH_3	131
CH_3CH_2	222
$CH_3CH_2CH_2$	406
$CH_3CH_2CH_2CH_2$	740

From these values predictions were made of the extent of lowering of the transition temperature which were in fair agreement with the observed effect. No values of numbers of sites result from these calculations, since all the calculations are based on the amounts of alcohol bound rather than on molal ratios. The Peller theory (1959) on which the calculations are based did, however, assume two binding sites per amino acid residue. In the modification employed, which considered binding to nonpolar groups which help stabilize the helix (rather than to helix-forming elements), the number of moles per protein molecule would be lower, but still very large. It should be noted that the values of K are small compared to those found for bovine serum albumin with the higher alcohol octanol; with the latter, however, a small value of n was found. The low values of K are not unreasonable for the large n involved. Even with octanol (BSA), molecules bound in excess of five have much lower K values.

The regions involved in the thermal transition in propyl alcohol at 35° have been shown by partial tryptic digestion to be from Lys 3 to Asp(NH_2) 34. The same regions are affected in the absence of alcohol at 60°.

One of the most extraordinary interactions between an enzyme and a large molecule is the reaction between ribonuclease S-protein and its S-peptide. The latter is a long peptide sequence formed by the cleavage of a single peptide bond in ribonuclease by the proteolytic enzyme subtilisin. S-peptide is tightly bound to S-protein even without the peptide bond, and the complex has normal enzymatic activity. Richards and Logue (1962) have shown that formation of the complex is accompanied by changes in the light absorption of one or more phenylalanine and two of the six tyrosine residues. The changes are pH-dependent and occur at 0.8 pH unit higher if the tetramethyl ester of the S-peptide is substituted for the S-peptide (Richards and Logue, 1962). Complexing is very rapid, but is followed by a slow conformation change with a half-period of about 1 minute. pH changes alone cause similar changes with about the same half-period. Numerous studies in depth of the S-protein– S-peptide system, in both crystals and solution, have continued to appear from Richard's laboratory, but are not directly related to multiple equilibria [see also a study of stabilization by S-peptide by Kato and Anfinsen (1969)].

The action of subtilisin in forming the S-peptide is greatly retarded when a competitive inhibitor 2′-cytidylate is bound to the active site of ribonuclease, although the active site and the cleaved bond are far apart. The action of the inhibitor is therefore ascribed by Markus et al. (1967) to a conformation change which it induces. The same inhibitor and 3′-cytidylate also protect against the action of trypsin and chymotrypsin, and against the temperature induced transition which reduces the helical content of the protein.

8. *Carbonic Anhydrase*

The extent of inhibition of activity caused by sulfonamides is affected by *N*-substitutions in the sulfonamide group (Bonati and Sala, 1959). There is an extensive chemical and pharmacological literature on this inhibition. Zn(II) and Co(II) ions are involved in the binding of azosulfonamides (Coleman, 1968).

9. *Lipases*

Microbial lipases are reported to be inhibited by antibiotics, including pimiricin and penicillin even when the latter do not slow down cell growth (Chandan et al., 1962).

10. *Lipooxygenase*

In addition to irreversible inhibition brought about by various oxidizing agents and photooxidizers, lipooxygenase undergoes reversible inhibition by saturated monohydric alcohols which are more effective, the longer their chain length. The inhibition is only partially competitive, and the inhibitors do not protect the active site from attack by oxidizing agents. It is concluded that the binding site and the active site are separate (Mitsuda et al., 1967).

11. *Papain*

Methanol competes with a number of synthetic substrates, according to Sluyterman (1964), but the effect is so weak that it is difficult to distinguish competitive binding from a solvent effect. About 50 vol % is required to abolish activity toward benzoylglycine ethyl ester; the value depends on the substrate used. Urea is stated to be a competitive inhibitor also, but even at 8 *M* urea activity remains.

12. Δ5 → Δ4,3 – Oxosteroid Isomerases

An effort has been made by Alfsen (1966) to account for the specificities and relative rates of reaction of the various substrates of mammalian and bacterial isomerases on the basis of the effects of their substituent side chains on the order of the water envelope on the enzyme and hence on the association constant of each for the enzyme.

13. Horseradish Peroxidase

There are few available rate measurements of protein-binding reactions except with heme proteins. Wittenberg *et al.* (1967a,b) have measured the velocity of both " on " and " off " reaction between ferro-horseradish peroxidase and carbon monoxide. The second-order " on " constant with oxygen at $20°$ is 5.8×10^{-4} mole^{-1} sec^{-1} and only about 5% as great with CO. These rates are extremely slow compared with combination with myoglobin. The first-order " off " rate with CO is 1.6×10^{-5} mole^{-1} sec^{-1}, equivalent to a half-period of about 13 hours (care must be taken to assure that no ferric heme protein is formed during the measurement, as when dithionite is used, or the reaction appears to be much faster). There are indications in the effects of pH that an equilibrium between ferrous HRP and CO may be oversimplified. If it is not, K is about 2×10^4 at $20°$. The activation energy for the dissociation is 33 kcal/mole.

14. Liver Alcohol Dehydrogenase (LADH)

The kinetics of both association and dissociation of the coenzyme NADH and its analog 3-acetylpyridine NADH to LADH have been measured by both spectrofluorometry and stopped-flow spectrophotometry (Shore and Gilleland, 1968). Thus the equilibrium binding constants have been determined indirectly. The " on " velocities for both are the same, but the " off " velocity of the coenzyme analog is 20 times greater than that of NADH. It is proposed, therefore, that the amide group of the nicotinamide ring binds *after* the binding of the ring itself.

G. GLOBULINS

Globulins are the most heterogeneous class of proteins; not only with respect to molecular size and conformation, but especially with regard to their binding processes. A close examination of the great diversity of specificity expressed through antigen–antibody reactions can only be attempted by one who is thoroughly familiar with immunochemistry, and would be impractical here (Kabat, 1968).

Mammalian globulins are reported to bind corticosteroids more strongly than albumin (Westphal and Devenuto, 1966). The binding constant for cortisol, determined by the ultracentrifugation method, is reported to be very high, 4.7×10^7 (Beisel et al., 1964), but slightly more is bound by albumin than by globulin in whole serum. Various carcinogenic hydrocarbons are bound; they are stated to have affinities parallel to their carcinogenicity (Gemant, 1964). Cholesterol and trilaurin were bound less efficiently.

The corticosteriod binding globulin isolated and purified by Muldoon and Westphal (1967) from human plasma (molecular weight 51,700) has a single binding site of very high affinity for cortisol. K is 5.2×10^8 at 4° and 2.4×10^7 at 37°. Thus ΔH is negative and relatively large, and the binding process is not primarily entropy-driven. It is noteworthy that dialysis against water destroys the binding site, but exhaustive removal of sialic acid is without effect.

The corticosteroid binding globulin of rabbits has also been purified (Chader and Westphal, 1968). Although the amino acid and carbohydrate composition resembles that of human protein, the molecular weight is less (40,700). The binding constants are slightly higher at both 4° and 37°. (See Table 4-8.)

It will be observed that a large negative enthalpy is found with the globulins, but not with glycoprotein or serum albumin.

β-Globulin, as well as serum albumin, binds hematin (Sears and Huser, 1965). α_2-macroglobulin, but not other globulins, binds a human growth hormone (Hadden and Prout, 1964). The binding by antibodies of certain dye haptens and their determinant groups [4,5-dihydroxy-3-(p-nitrophenyl) azo-2,7-naphthalene disulfonate, and p-nitrobenzene] causes a change in their absorption spectra (Froese and Sehon, 1964).

A globulin containing carbohydrates and sialic acid which binds corticosteroids reversibly has been isolated and purified from the sera of eight species including man (Seal and Doe, 1963). The stoichiometric molal ratio is apparently 1 (Seal and Doe, 1962). Although the affinity decreases as the temperature is raised from 2° to 37°, at 2° the binding constant is estimated to have the enormous value 6×10^8.

α-Globulin (bovine) is reported to have less than one binding site for n-heptane per 169,000 molecular weight unit at pH 6.8 (Mohammadzadeh-K et al., 1969b). Glycoproteins (mucoids) bind even less.

The binding of thyroxine by a globulin (and by a "prealbumin") have been reviewed by Ingbar (1960). The binding to globulin at pH 7.4 is not inhibited by salicylate, as is the binding to prealbumin and albumin (Woeber and Ingbar, 1963). The binding of thyroxine to bovine M-2 glycoprotein (a

TABLE 4-8

BINDING PARAMETERS OF STEROID–PROTEIN COMPLEXES

Complex	n	K (M^{-1})		ΔF° (kcal/mole)		ΔH° (kcal/mole)	ΔS° (cal mole^{-1} deg^{-1})
		4°	37°	4°	37°		
Rabbit CBG–cortisol	1	9.0×10^8	4.7×10^7	-11.3	-10.9	-15.0	-13
Human CBG–cortisol	1	5.2×10^8	2.4×10^7	-11.0	-10.5	-15.7	-17
Human α_1–acid glycoprotein–progesterone	1	11.0×10^5	4.9×10^4	-7.7	-8.1	-4.1	$+13$
Human serum albumin–progesterone	2	1.0×10^5	4.6×10^5	-6.3	-6.6	-4.0	$+9$

globulin) has been determined by equilibrium dialysis (Bezkorovainy and Doherty, 1962). Removal of the sialic acid component was without effect on the binding. Scatchard plots for both proteins indicated a single set of binding sites: six at 27°, slightly fewer at 7°; the binding constant was 3.2×10^4 at 27° and 6.1×10^4 at 7°. The negative ΔH is relatively large, -5.4 kcal/mole; ΔF was only slightly higher, about -6.1 kcal/mole; only 2 or 3 eu were therefore involved. This is in sharp contrast to the binding by BSA, which is only slightly tighter, $K = 4.0 \times 10^4$, and which has approximately the same $\Delta F°$, but a low $\Delta H°(-2.0$ kcal), and an entropy change of 14.5 units. Eight entropy units must be added to each of the values given to correct them to ΔS_u, the unitary entropy change. A thyroxine-binding globulin isolated from human plasma has a molecular weight of 58,000, and an extremely high association constant, 10^9, at a single site. (Giorgio and Tabachnik, 1968.)

The above adds to the rare instances cited in this chapter of strong binding of a neutral molecule by a protein where the binding force is not primarily entropic. There have been numerous other reports of thyroxine binding by globulins, e.g., by Guerin and Tubiana (1965), Imarisio and Greco (1964), and Osario (1963). The last of these investigations demonstrated inhibition of binding by salicylate, as already described for thyroxine binding by serum albumin.

Cyanocobalamin (Vitamin B_{12}) is bound to different extents by different globulin fractions in different animal species, as shown by equilibrium dialysis (Rosenthal et al., 1962). The binding by the mammalian globulins is abolished by 8 M urea, but urea does not affect the binding by the globulins of frog or chick. Reduction of disulfide bonds does not abolish the binding, which involves multiple sites.

H. Acid Glycoprotein (Human)

This protein binds progesterone with values of n and K that depend on pH, temperature, and history of the preparation (Gangurly et al., 1967). When initially precipitated lipid-free with alcohol-acetone, the protein appears to have a single high affinity site ($K = 10.8 \times 10^5$). Fractional numbers of sites appear to be indicated when lipid is restored. Binding is at a maximum at pH 8 and falls away steeply, especially on the acid side. ΔH is positive in the range measured (10° to 50°).

I. Concanavalin A

This protein, the phytohemagglutenin of the jack bean, is included to represent protein–carbohydrate interactions. Its ability to bind sophorose and sophorose derivatives can be studied, as Goldstein et al. (1965) have shown, by inhibition of the precipitation of dextrans by this protein. The data shown in Fig. 4-16 have been used to determine the structural features that are responsible for the affinity but no thermodynamic parameters have been calculated. The results are stated to indicate that the C-3, C-4, and C-6 hydroxyl groups of the reducing D-glucopyranose moiety of sophorose are the units with which the protein reacts (Goldstein *et al.*, 1967). More recently evidence has been presented that the combining sites of the protein may be more diverse (So and Goldstein, 1968).

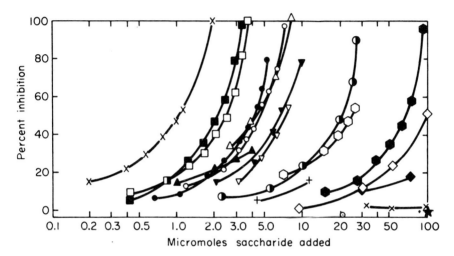

FIG. 4-16. Inhibition by saccharides of dextran–concanavalin A precipitation. Each tube contained concanavalin A (300 μg), dextran NRRLB-1355-S (200 μg), and inhibitor as noted in a total volume of 1.0 ml. ×, α-Methylsophoroside; ■, isomaltose; □, methyl-α-D-glucopyranoside; ●, maltose; ○, maltitol; △, α-methylsophoroside 2′, 3′, 4′, 6′-tetraacetat; ▲, *p*-nitrophenyl-β-sophoroside; ▼, sophorose; ▽, 2-O-β-D-galactopyranosyl-D-glucose; ◑, D-glucose; ⌀, β-methylsophoroside; +, sophorotriose; ⬡, methyl-β-D-glucopyranoside; ◇, gentiobiose; ◆, β-methylsophoroside-2′, 3′, 4′, 6′-tetraacetate; ⊙, sophoritol; X, cellobiose; (·), cellobiitol; and ★, laminaribiose. [I. J. Goldstein, I. N. Iyer, E. E. Smith, and L. L. So (1967). *Biochemistry* **6**, 2373.]

A protein which complexes sugars and saccharin has been isolated from bovine taste buds; the affinities parallel the degrees of sweetness. Values of K ranged from 10 for galactose to 1030 for fructose (Dastoli and Price, 1966).

J. MYOSIN

Myosin from beef skeletal or heart muscle binds the glycoside lanatoside ($K = 4 \times 10^5$) and K-strophanoside ($K = 1.2 \times 10^5$); $n = 1$ for skeletal muscle myosin, but $n = 2$ with heart muscle myosin. Complexing with K^+ is increased about eightfold when the protein binds the glycosides.

III. The Hydration of Proteins

The concept of hydration as the stoichiometric binding of water by proteins in aqueous solution is fraught with difficulties. To begin with, unequivocal measurements can only be made with dried proteins, i.e., one can measure their weight loss on drying *in vacuo* after exposure to water vapor at various partial pressures (relative humidites) (Bull, 1944; Mellon *et al.*, 1947, 1948, 1949; McMeekin, 1952). However, it is no longer believed that the native configuration of proteins is stable when dried at any but very low temperatures. Furthermore, the weight loss *in vacuo*, even after prior exposure to the lowest available relative humidity (0.05), is so large, of the order of 3% with many proteins, that it corresponds to the combination of over 100 moles of water per mole of such proteins as serum albumin or β-lactoglobulin, or to about 1 mole for every six amino acid residues. With higher relative humidities, up to 0.95, values over ten times as great are found. Thus the binding of water would appear to exceed an average of two molecules per amino acid residue (Fig. 4-17).

With such high values there is no prospect of applying the usual forms of binding analysis: the lower observed binding must represent binding to more than one identifiable set of "sites." The heat of adsorption is higher for the most tightly bound water than for the water that combines at somewhat higher relative humidities, but the lowest values represent such large amounts bound that there can be no assurance that still greater enthalpies would not be found at lower partial pressures.[17]

It if is desired to apply the results obtained with dried protein to native proteins in solution, it might appear most appropriate to use the values at the highest relative humidities, rather than the low values stressed above. This procedure would probably grossly exaggerate the hydration, since the escaping tendency of water in the protein phase of the experiments just described would always be less than that in a water-saturated atmosphere, even after saturation of all water binding sites on the protein, provided there were any tendency at all for the proteins to "dissolve"—the problem would be analogous to that of attempting to measure the hydration of calcium chloride in a similar manner; the hydration would appear to be infinite because the salt dissolves; nevertheless, its constituent ions have finite hydration shells.

An excellent discussion of the difficulties of measuring, or even of defining, protein hydration has been given by Edsall (1953). The still greater difficulty

---

[17] This may be the case, even though ΔH does not change by large amounts until the hydration increases by about 50% of the lowest observed values (Bull, 1944). At very low amounts bound (under 4%) ΔF is smaller than at slightly higher values. There is an apparent gain in affinity for water as a little more water is added; this is a sign of "cooperative" interactions.

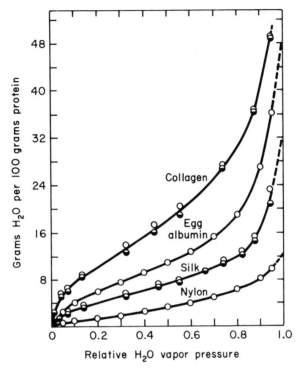

Fig. 4-17. Water adsorption curves for unstretched nylon, for wet (○) and dry (◑) silk, for unlyophilized egg albumin, and for wet (○) and dry (◑) collagen at 25°. [H. B. Boll (1944). *J. Am. Chem. Soc.* **66**, 1500.]

of defining "bound water" in hydrodynamic experiments (diffusion, sedimentation, electrophoresis, viscosity) is analyzed by Tanford (1961).

The values on which the widest degree of agreement has been attained have been measured in a number of different manners, which include:

(1) Comparison of the x-ray cell dimensions with the cell volume which would correspond to the pycnometric partial specific volume calculated on a dry-weight basis. Alternatively, the actual volume may be calculated from electron microscopy for comparison with the dry-weight partial specific volume.

(2) Comparison of the frictional ratio (ratio of the frictional coefficient determined by any one of a number of hydrodynamic measurements compared with the calculated frictional coefficient for a sphere the dimensions of which are based on molecular weight and the partial specific volume of dry protein) with the calculated frictional ratio of an unhydrated ellipsoid of specified eccentricity. This method cannot always be used, in practice, since

the eccentricities are not known independently of the hydrodynamic measurements, except when X-ray data are available or when asymmetry has been measured by double refraction of flow.

(3) The actual density of the protein in solution may be determined by changing the density of the solvent until no sedimentation occurs in a strong centrifugal field. The use of this method requires assurance that the substance used to change the solvent density does not affect the solvation properties of the protein, e.g., does not dehydrate it by osmotic effects or by replacing water (or induce conformation changes of any kind). It is difficult to assure that these conditions can be met; in fact, different values of the hydration of a number of viruses, including tobacco mosaic virus, have been obtained when the solvent density has been controlled by another protein, BSA, or by sucrose (large molecules have been favored in order to render less likely complications due to osmotic effects). Schachman and Lauffer (1949) found that the sedimentation rate for TMV became zero at a solvent density of 1.13 when BSA was used to increase the density, but required a density of 1.27 when sucrose was used. The hydrations corresponding to these two figures would be 190% and 37%, respectively, of the dry weight of the protein. This paradox illustrates one of the inherent difficulties in formulating the concept of hydration: since the average distance of closest approach of BSA to TMV is 47 Å and only 6 to 7 Å in sucrose, a "hydration" shell of these two different thicknesses is measured by the two density perturbants. Schachman and Lauffer conclude that the smaller of these two thicknesses corresponds fortuitously to the true hydration shell; it yields a value of 0.15 gm water/gm dry protein. This may correspond to about five layers of water. Larger and presumably more organized viruses, such as influenza and rabbit papilloma, have yielded much higher values by this method, in excess of 1 gm water/gm protein (Sharp et al., 1945, 1946). There are numerous recent studies which indicate that in multicomponent systems it may seldom be assumed that some preferential adsorption or interaction between pairs of components does not occur (see, among others, Timasheff and Inoue, 1968; Noelkin and Timasheff, 1967; Hade and Tanford, 1967). However there are indications that in sucrose–water systems used to create density gradients, no preferential adsorption exists (Kupke and Senter, 1966). Proteins interact preferentially with water in solutions of dextrose or tetramethylurea up to 20–30% of their anhydrous weight. In solutions of urea or thiourea they interact preferentially with the solute—the extent of interaction parallels the ability of the solute to denature (Gordon and Warren, 1968).

(4) The hydrated protein may be driven by an ultracentrifugal field into an underlying solvent of higher density than the protein solution; the amount of *upward* displacement of the boundary of the lower (high-density) layer then measures the total volume of the sedimenting particles (Lauffer and Taylor,

1952). This is then compared with the dry-weight partial volume. This method has been shown to give consistent results, independent of the density of the underlying layer, provided the density of the latter does not exceed the density of the hydrated protein, and provided the two layers are immiscible, as when bromobenzene–kerosene mixtures are used (Bendet *et al.*, 1960). *E. coli* has been shown by this method to contain 3.29 gm of water for every gram of dry weight bacteria. A spherical virus, Southern Bean mosaic, gave a value of 0.98 gm water/gm dry weight, close to the value 1.07 gm obtained by combining the frictional ratio derived from specific viscosity measurements with dry-weight partial specific volume (Lauffer *et al.*, 1952). If the frictional ratio determined from sedimentation, diffusion, and partial specific volume is used, a figure of only 0.78 gm water/gm dry virus is obtained, but the values of the diffusion coefficient used in obtaining the latter figure are considered to be less accurate than the parameters used in the alternative calculations.

(5) The possibility has recently arisen of comparing the volume of exclusion of protein, obtained by infrared difference spectrophotometry, with its partial specific volume on a dry-weight basis. The method consists of estimating the size of the *negative* water spectrum which is obtained when a protein solution is compared with a water blank. A value of 0.77 cc/gm has been obtained for BSA in 0.05 NaCl in this manner and compared with the dry-weight partial specific volume which is 0.734 (McCabe and Fischer, 1965). The difference is too small to be interpreted simply as a change in volume due to hydration; information is lacking as to the ir absorption spectrum of bound water. There is evidence that at some frequencies bound water is a better absorber than free water.

A little reflection leads to two questions: (a) Is the hydration of a protein entirely a " shell " or surface effect, or is there internal water? (b) If the former is true, do the larger proteins have a lower degree of hydration, consistent with their lower surface volume ratio? How many layers are involved? Are the surfaces of all proteins hydrated to the same extent?

The two questions may be answered piecemeal. The x-ray analysis of the structure of sperm whale metmyoglobin shows that there is little or no " room " " inside " the structure for water (Kendrew, *et al.*, 1961),[18] although other evidence (a combination of asymmetry obtained by x-ray low-angle scattering,[19] and the frictional ratio) indicates that hemoglobin is a prolate ellipsoid, probably hydrated in solution to the extent of 25–30% (Ritland *et al.*, 1950). This figure is not far from that calculated for a number of other proteins,

---

[18] There is, however, a single space, just large enough to be filled by a xenon atom or by the HgI_3^- ion. Both of these substances enter the space readily (Schoenborn, 1965).

[19] Low-angle x-ray scattering always gives dimensions that include internal water of hydration.

which have very nearly the same partial specific volumes. Most, if not all, of this water must be external.

It is only with the larger proteins that electron microscope dimensions for the dry protein [which usually agree closely with the radii for the dissolved protein calculated from hydrodynamic properties (Miller and Price, 1946)] can be compared with the dimensions given by small-angle x-ray scattering. This comparison yields a value of 55% "internal" hydration and an "external" hydration of 28% for both tobacco necrosis virus and Southern bean mosaic virus; the latter is equivalent to a layer of water 7 Å thick. A comparison of x-ray diffraction spacings for wet and dry edestin crystals yields a total hydration figure of 64% on dry weight (Hall, 1950). This is a rather high value, especially for so large a molecule (molecular weight, 300,000) for which one would expect much lower hydration values if all the water is "external," unless, of course, it is external to the eight subunits rather than to the molecule as a whole. As we have seen, even higher values have been obtained with the still larger viruses (see also, Leonard et al., 1951). With the latter at least some of the water is demonstrably internal. In these large structures, however, a higher degree of organization (and nonprotein components such as lipids) must occur.

In summary, the hydration of dissolved proteins may vary between a lower limit of 15% and an upper limit, excluding the larger viruses such as vaccinia and influenza, of up to 65%. As will become apparent in the next section, even the lower of these figures may include some water which is practically indistinguishable by NMR techniques from bulk solvent. While some proteins (e.g., metmyoglobin) appear to lack internal water of hydration, many of the larger ones, which are constructed of subunits, must have some internal water. The external water of hydration appears to correspond to a layer about 7 Å thick, i.e., possibly four to five molecules in thickness, in excess of an average of one water per amino acid residue. There is no reason, however, to suppose that the layer is uniform. The representative figure of approximately 30% would correspond to a single molecule of water on every ionized group or amide or hydroxyl group in the molecule plus an additional water molecule for each peptide bond. It is clear, however, from x-rays, hydrogen-ion titration curves, and difference spectra, that not all of these are accessible to solvent, so more than a single water molecule must be associated with the groups which are available. Of these, some (over 100 molecules per 65,000 molecular weight units) are bound very much more energetically than the others. It has been shown by Bull (1944) that the water vapor adsorption isotherm fits the equation of Brunauer, Emmettt, and Teller. A theoretical treatment of the hydration of TMV protein in solution has been given by Lauffer (1966) and applied to the changes in hydration which accompany its depolymerization (Banerjee and Lauffer, 1966).

A. THE STATE OF COMBINED WATER

Some of the impetus for current review of the structure of water bound to proteins was provided by a striking and significant experiment reported by Klotz (1958), who covalently bonded an azomercurial dye to cysteine and to serum albumin. The pK of the acid form of the dye when bound to cysteine was the same as that of other para-substituted azobenzenes, about 3.4. When coupled to serum albumin, the apparent pK shifted downward about 2 pH units. Subsequent experiments by Klotz and Fiess (1960), designed to test the effect of electrostatic interactions on the apparent pK, utilized a different dye which can couple to a lysine (or, perhaps, serine) residue in a protein form. The dye can also be coupled to a simple amino acid such as glycine.

Figure 4-18 shows the experimental titration curves and calculations of the

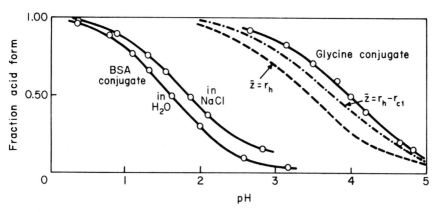

FIG. 4-18. Optical titrations of 5-dimethylaminonaphthalenesulfonyl conjugates of bovine serum albumin and glycine, respectively. Circles represent experimental points; – – – represents curve computed theoretically for the $-N(CH_3)_2$ group on serum albumin whose net charge $\bar{Z}$ equals r_H, the number of protons bound from the isoionic point to the given pH; —·—·— represents theoretical curve correcting $\bar{Z}$ for the moles of anion, r_{Cl}, bound by the protein at the given pH. The theoretical curves are for protein in solutions of 0.1 ionic strength. [I. M. Klotz and H. A. Fiess (1960). *Biochim. Biophys. Acta* **38**, 57.]

electrostatic effect on an isolated group in serum albumin. It is clear that the effect of the protein environment is not simply the anticipated electrostatic effect which was described in Section IV. In fact, the latter would displace the curve of the model compound only slightly, relative to the enormous shift actually observed for the BSA–dye complex.

Table 4-9 lists the observed values for the pK's of the glycine–dye and BSA–dye complexes in water and urea. In water, the observed ΔpK between the glycine complex and the BSA complex is 2.32 units. This figure is unaffected by alteration of the dye/protein ratio from 4.1:1 to 10.9:1. Urea has

TABLE 4-9

ACIDITY CONSTANTS OF

$$\underset{\underset{SO_2-R}{}}{\overset{\overset{+}{HN(CH_3)_2}}{}}$$ AT 25°

R	Solution	pK_a
—NHCH$_2$COOH	Water	3.99
	8 M urea	4.18
—OH	Water	4.27
—Bovine serum albumin $(5.9/1)^a$	Water	1.67
	0.1 M NaCl	1.86
	0.1 M NaSCN	2.05
	8 M urea	3.27

^{a} The number within the parentheses refers to the (average) number of dye molecules attached to each protein molecule.

the dramatic effect of reducing the anomalous value although not eliminating it entirely. This anomalous pK is also observed when the dyes are coupled to ovalbumin, β-lactoglobulin, and lysozyme. Urea reduces or eliminates the anomaly in all cases.

Klotz suggested (1960) that the effect on the dye of coupling to the protein is similar to the masking of some groups in proteins. The basis of the Klotz model for the effect observed is the behavior of certain small molecules in inducing the formation of crystalline hydrates in water (Frank and Wen, 1957). For example, the apparent molal heat capacity, and hence the total heat capacity, of aqueous solutions of tetra-n-butylammonium bromide is much higher than anticipated from additivity rules for unsolvated hydrocarbon molecules. Behavior of this kind may be explained if the large cation causes a "freezing" of the water in its neighborhood, for extra heat is necessary to disorder this ordered structure when the temperature of the system is raised. There are a substantial number of simple molecules, such as methane, methyl mercaptan, ethylene, ethane, isobutane, methyl chloride, and the inert gases, which, when dissolved in water at sufficiently high concentrations, form crystalline hydrates with melting points well above 0°C. The heats of hydration, furthermore, are essentially the same for all these compounds, indicating that the drop in internal energy characterizing the formation of these inclusion compounds is due to the crystallization of the water. Klotz suggests that in protein molecules, the *apolar* side-chain residues (leucine, alanine, cysteine, etc.) are capable of forming such hydrates around them, and further, when several such residues are close to one another, an icelike lattice (iceberg) is formed. The rates of diffusion of most substances (but not protons) in such a sheath would be reduced relative to diffusion rates in the bulk solvent; this, in Klotz's view, might explain, for example, why silver ion reacts slowly with –SH in many proteins.

The explanation of the anomalous pK of the dye cation, according to Klotz, is that the charged $(CH_3)_2NH^+$ group tends to rupture the water structure, whereas the possibility of maintenance of the cooperative icelike sheath favors the un-ionized $(CH_3)_2N^\circ$, thereby depressing the pK_A. Urea is pictured as disrupting the hydration lattice, by hydrogen-bonding to water molecules.

Klotz and Luborsky (1959) have discussed the binding of many small ions and neutral molecules to proteins on the basis of this model, which largely attributes the stability of such complexes to the cooperative formation of an icelike hydration lattice between the complexing species. From this point of view, the small molecule becomes attached to the protein not because of any strong direct attraction nor because of indirect effects on other ionizations but because of the energetic stabilization accompanying the formation of a bigger hydration lattice. Differences among different proteins in their ability to bind small ions or molecules are explained in terms of the ability of the ligands to couple or extend the hydration sheath which depends on the distribution of apolar residues in the peptide chain.

Kauzmann (1959) has questioned the applicability here of the results of studies on small molecules to proteins. He does not believe that the structural water around an apolar residue of a protein has " anything approaching the stability of crystalline hydrates." It will be shown (Chapter V) that most ionizing groups in proteins have quite reasonable hydrogen-ion dissociation constants, although among those must be many that are located in the vicinity of clusters of apolar residues.

Laskowski and Finkenstadt (1965) have used the solvent perturbation technique to demonstrate that the hydrophobic conjugate introduced into BSA by Klotz was "engulfed" by the protein (its absorption could not be changed by changes in the refractive index of the solvent), but that other proteins to which it was attached did not "engulf" it. In keeping with this observation the pK of the dye was entirely normal in proteins other than BSA.

Other experiments which bear on the thickness of the hydration shell, and with its organization, deal with the volume increase (reversal of electrostriction) when the protonated amino groups of proteins are deprotonated by titration with hydroxyl ion. It was shown by Rasper and Kauzmann (1962) that the volume increase with proteins is only 16 ml/mole while it is about 25 ml/mole when other protonated amines, including long-chain polypeptides, are deprotonated. Krausz and Kauzmann (1965) have recently succeeded in determining the distance from the surface of the protein that an ammonium group must be in order to have a normal volume increase on reaction with hydroxyl ion; their method was to couple polypeptides of various chain lengths to all the free amino groups of ribonuclease before titrating with hydroxyl. The volume change for the titration of the terminal polypeptidyl ammonium groups was characterized by the same abnormality as that of the normal native protein unless the polypeptide chain consisted of more than three residues—beyond that length the volume change approached a normal value as the chain length was further increased. The effect of the protein environment thus extends to this distance, somewhat larger than the 7-Å thickness of the hydration shell which has already been referred to. It would appear that within this shell, the relaxation from electrostriction when the charge is removed is not complete.

Considerable light on the state of the bound water may be shed by studies of the dielectric properties of dry and wet protein crystals (Takashima, 1962). Lyophilized crystals of both ovalbumin and BSA have dielectric constants no greater than 1, over a wide frequency range, and this value shows little if any increase until the water content of the former exceeds 10% and of the latter 20% of the weight of dry protein. Beyond these values the dielectric constant increases very rapidly, eventually levelling off at 20% and 30% hydrations, respectively, values considerably higher than that of free water and even higher than that of ice. It has been concluded that the more tightly bound water, 0.13 to 0.20 gm/gm dry protein, present even in the lyophilized crystals, is too immobile to exhibit dielectric dispersion and is far from icelike, i.e., the water molecules are firmly held individually and are too far apart for hydrogen bonding to one another, or for the consequent proton jump in the hydrogen bonds of ice which are responsible for the high dielectric increment of ice. When more water is added an icelike first hydration shell may be completed, but additional hydration beyond this point has little effect on the dielectric constant.

It may be concluded that up to 0.13 gm/gm of water is strongly bound to definite sites in ovalbumin crystals and that about 0.20 gm/gm is similarly bound in crystals of BSA. These figures are only slightly larger than the amounts of water which resist removal by lyophilization of crystals. The molal ratios (in excess of 700 for both proteins) are 3–4 times higher than can be accounted for by the number of charged groups, unless the number bound to each charged group is of this magnitude. Completion of the first hydration shell by binding to other polar groups (such as amides and hydroxyls), or by water–water hydrogen bonding, gives a layer with a higher dielectric increment than ice.

Recent elegant measurements of the appearance of the water lines in the nuclear magnetic resonance spectrum of vacuum-dried BSA which has been allowed to resorb water vapor in measured amounts have added considerable information about the state of bound water (Fuller and Brey, 1967). The first NMR water lines are observed at about 0.037 gm water/gm BSA. When less water is bound it is considered to be immobilized by the existence of *two* hydrogen bonds to the protein. At larger amounts bound, some of the water is held by only one bond, and is therefore relatively motile. At about 0.080 gm/gm bound all of the water is in this condition. This amount corresponds roughly with the binding of a single water molecule to every exposed polar group in the protein. When 0.090 gm/gm is exceeded there is an abrupt change in the NMR spectrum: water is now bonded to water and a second layer of bound water is built up.

These conclusions are reinforced by the way in which the activation energy of water dissociation varies with extent of hydration. The energy is very high at 0.050 gm/gm bound at low temperature, and declines sharply until it reaches a minimum at 0.090–0.10 gm bound, where it then rises until about 0.15 gm is bound. However, at 30° the activation is essentially featureless— the activation energy at this temperature is below that of liquid water! At lower temperatures there is slight decrease in activation energy at more than 0.165 gm/gm bound. This decrease appears to mark the maximum quantity of "primary" and "secondary" water which can be bound.

The quantity of 0.15 to 0.17 gm/gm, is in fair agreement with other estimates for this protein in solution, e.g., 20% by Klotz (1958); 18 ± 1% from self-diffusion data for ovalbumin (Wang *et al.*, 1954); and 20% from dielectric dispersion measurements of human serum albumin (Oncley *et al.*, 1947). Estimates from light-scattering and small angle x-ray scattering give much larger results, and the interpretation is therefore suspect. The much larger values given for larger proteins in preceding pages must be definitely the result of organized structure in these large molecules. The extremely small values for native ovalbumin given by Daszkeiwicz *et al.* (1964), obtained by proton magnetic relaxation measurements, remain unexplained unless they refer to the doubly bound water of Fuller and Brey (1962).

Since there is every indication that alcohols, phenols, and undissociated acids bind to proteins in larger amounts than the other ligands discussed in this chapter (see Section II, A, 3k, on the binding of undissociated acids), it seems possible that they are associated in a manner similar to that of water. At least one-tenth as much undissociated acid as water is bound under some of the conditions of Steinhardt's experiments; this amount is *preferentially* bound—it is about 3000 times more concentrated (relative to water) in the protein than outside (Steinhardt *et al.*, 1943).

IV. Interactions with Other Solvents

Dissolved proteins are greatly affected by a variety of substances when they are present in high concentrations. It is evident that these interactions are quite different from those considered in the preceding pages, and elsewhere in this book. Thus if multiple equilibria of the kind we have been describing were involved, the high concentrations required would indicate that the association constants are quite small. Most or these substances, such as urea and its derivatives, guanidine salts, and even ordinary neutral salts when present in very high concentrations, produce effects which are either manifested only when certain threshold concentrations are exceeded, or the effects may be expressed as depending on a high power of the concentration. The amounts "bound" are not known, and need not vary directly as the effects referred to. Thus these effects are quite different from those which can be described by Eqs. (2-63) in Chapter II.

Without making an effort to describe this phenomenon of solvent-induced "conformation change" or "denaturation" at all exhaustively, a few of the general features will be indicated by selected references to recent work.

A. DEPENDENCE ON HIGH POWERS OF CONCENTRATION

Tanford and De have shown that formamide changes the equilibrium between native and unfolded β-lactoglobulin in proportion to the 20th power of its concentration, and urea by its 22nd. Data are also given for β-lactoglobulin in a number of mixed solvents (Tanford and De, 1961). An earlier estimate for urea gave the 10th power (Kauzmann and Simpson, 1953). Caution is required in the interpretation of these high powers in terms of the binding of a given number of equivalents as a condition for the conformation change, since the change is produced at high mole fractions of the denaturant where many of the bulk properties of the solvent) such as dielectric constant, internal hydrogen-bond structure of the water) are greatly altered. In general, "denaturants" of this kind, although they include such classical modifiers of conformation as urea and guanidine salts, differ from those already treated in requiring high mole fractions, and therefore extremely high molal ratios relative to the protein, for production of effects measurable at room temperature. A number of reports have appeared attributing high n values to urea in the denaturation of other proteins [e.g., 9 in the case of hemoglobin (Simko, 1962)]. Detailed comparisons have been made of the effectiveness of many such reagents against BSA and ovalbumin as measured by changes in optical rotation without distinguishing between unfolding and unfolding followed by refolding into helices (Gordon and Jenks, 1963).

Guanidine salts, urea, a few derivatives of urea, and certain other amides are far more effective than the other substances tried. Some substances, such as amino acids, appear to stabilize. Urea and the molecules studied in this monograph may denature by different mechanisms than the one described in Eq. (2-63). Urea lowers the critical micelle concentration (CMC) of ionic detergents; the CMC is also lowered by proteins with which they combine (see Chapter VII). The "structure-breaking" effect of urea on water is weakened, as Gordon and Jenks have shown, by loading its derivatives with "structure-making," i.e., apolar, groups (Krespeck and Benjamin, 1964). In contrast the effect of surfactants (water structure makers), and other conformation changers, which are effective at low concentrations, is directly on the protein, and is mediated by binding, even when the initial result of binding in small amounts is a stabilization of the protein. These conclusions are supported by the effects of the "bulk" denaturants on the solubilities and heat capacities of amino acids (Tanford, 1962; Nozaki and Tanford, 1963; Kresbeck and Benjamin, 1963) and by theoretical studies of the hydrophobic bond in proteins (Scheraga *et al.*, 1962; Wetlaufer *et al.*, 1964). The transfer of hydrophobic residues from water to the interior of protein molecules is driven by changes in entropy (at the water interface) rather than by changes in enthalpy (hydrophobic bonds are largely entropic in origin) (Kauzmann, 1959). The transfer in the reverse direction to solutions of urea, indicated by Tanford's solubility data, is also entropy-driven (Nemethy and Scheraga, 1962).

Tanford (1968) has provided a review in depth of several of these topics.

V. Mechanism of Binding of Neutral Molecules

This chapter on the binding of uncharged molecules to proteins has preceded consideration of binding of ions, not only because in so doing it is possible to exclude the rather poorly known corrections for electrostatic effects which are involved in the binding of ions to proteins, but also because of a further complication in the binding of ions. Whatever effects may be due to their charges (coulombic effects), they also differ in affinity because of parameters such as size, polarity, propensity to hydrogen bonding, tendencies to associate hydrophobically, etc., which have nothing to do with their ionic nature. We can concentrate upon the latter parameters, uncomplicated by coulombic forces, when we deal with uncharged molecules.

Even when we confine attention to neutral ligands and survey the results with a single, much-studied protein, serum albumin, we are confronted with a confusing array of data. The situation becomes even more complex when we contrast the behavior of one protein with another. At one extreme, with BSA some small hydrocarbons appear to show a limitless Henry's law solubility; with β-lactoglobulin a sharply limited stoichiometric binding; with lysozyme no binding of small hydrocarbons at all. At the other extreme, a vast array of enzymes and antibodies show a very limited, highly specific binding, at molal ratios of unity or slightly above unity, toward highly diverse, narrowly homologous, classes of substances. We may anticipate the results of the next chapters slightly by stating that with ions all proteins show some degree of binding although they differ widely among themselves in affinity and saturation values, and in the conformational consequences of ion binding.

An attempt to draw some limited, useful conclusions from the array of details in this chapter is made in the following paragraphs:

(1) At least one protein appears to show, within the experimental range, a "limitless" capacity to dissolve small apolar hydrocarbons. All proteins, within an even more extended range, show a capacity to combine with the highly polar water molecule which shades away from a few percent by weight of water on definite sites, to an almost limitless amount of slightly organized water. The fact that an actual limit is observed in the case of water and not with butane is due to the circumstances that the affinity for water is so much higher than for butane that huge amounts (molal ratios over 700) are bound at partial pressures at which only a few molecules of butane are bound per mole. The free energy involved in the transfer of 1 mole of water to 100 gm of dry serum albumin can be calculated from Bull's data, and from the free energy change in condensing water vapor to liquid water at $25°$ (-2 kcal/mole), to be about -16.5 kcal/mole; the figure for butane transferred to dissolved protein is less than one-third as great—the difference corresponds to a ratio of partition constants of the order of 10^8! The protein in which the "limitless" hydrocarbon binding occurs is widely recognized as having unusual "conformational adaptability."

(2) In some other proteins the hydrocarbon binding is sharply limited, although the water binding is approximately the same as in BSA. The difference seems to derive from the existence of only a few binding sites into which butane can fit rather than from differences in the free energy of binding. It would appear, therefore, that compared with most other proteins the surface of native BSA contains many hydrophobic patches or sites, and it follows that fewer or smaller stabilizing hydrophobic clusters will be found in the interior of this protein. The same conclusion has been drawn by Tanford on the basis of a comparison of the acid limits of the pH-stability range of serum albumin and ribonuclease (Tanford, 1961).

(3) The binding of polar hydrocarbon derivatives such as the large-chain alcohols is sharply limited to a few strong binding sites and a somewhat larger number of weak sites. Although the free energy of binding appears to increase with hydrocarbon tail length, the number of sites does not; in fact it almost certainly diminishes (Mohammadzadeh-K et al., 1969a) except when ions are involved (Chapter VII). The number is, however, affected by the nature of the polar head (e.g., alcohol or carboxylic acid; also, as we shall see in Chapter

VII, sulfonate and sulfate). Alcohols are restricted to fewer sites than carboxyl groups—a carbonyl oxygen seems to have some of the properties of a water oxygen and may bind like water rather than like an alcohol—on the other hand, its binding affinity is enhanced by a large hydrocarbon moiety.

(4) The number of binding sites for any type of molecule is fixed at any particular temperature and pH, but may vary slightly with both of these parameters, or very widely when major conformation changes occur. The latter change may be positive or negative, and may involve changes in affinity as well. In the case of ligands containing hydrocarbon moieties, it seems plausible to identify the binding with the formation of hydrophobic bonds involving apolar groups on clusters of groups in the accessible parts of the protein (surface or crevices).

(5) The binding in small molal ratios of some other molecules seems to depend on the availability of spaces or crevices of more or less exactly the right size. The binding of xenon by myoglobin is a case in point; the binding of thyroxine may be another. In the case of antibiotics, enzymes, and antibodies, the "spaces" may also involve configurations of groups favorable to a large free energy of binding. With xenon it is unlikely that anything more than an entropic effect (relaxation of the ordered array of water molecules on its surface, when it escapes to the protein "hole") is involved.

(6) The binding of lipids is probably largely hydrophobic, but may partake of a carboxylic function as well. The binding of polyhydric substances such as glycol and sugars may be largely waterlike but limited by steric factors such as the space occupied by each molecule. It seems unlikely that substances of this kind are ever bound internally. We will return to this question in Chapter VII.

(7) It is difficult to draw definite conclusions about the binding of the larger aliphatic or cyclic hydrocarbons, including the steroids, beyond the fact that very powerful hydrophobic factors are involved. The variation in the apparent number of available sites in the case of these substances is particularly puzzling. The possibility of a correlation between high affinity and *multiple contacts* has already arisen with a number of enzymes, and such conjugated proteins as hemoglobin. Its bearing on this problem is further considered in Chapter VII.

(8) With most of the neutral molecules investigated which bind in molal ratios above 1 the solubility has limited the range of investigation to fairly low molal ratios, far lower than those which have been investigated for ions. Rarely has definite information been obtained about "second" or "third" sets of weaker binding sites. It is, therefore, not possible to answer the question whether sets of binding sites for neutral molecules other than the first are preformed, or whether they only come into being as the result of conformation changes incident to the initial binding. This question will engage us in

Chapter VII. The methods used in measuring binding have also precluded observation of rapid time-dependent effects which would aid in the recognition of groups that require unmasking. It is established, however, that conformation changes sometimes occur at very low molal ratios. The ligand concentrations at which they occur exclude any possibility of their being due to medium effects. These conformation changes may occur in pH regions remote from H^+-dependent conformation transitions. They also may occur within or close to the latter regions and affect the H^+-dependent equilibria involved, since the two conformations do not have the same binding properties. In this latter case, ligands act as either conformational stabilizers or destabilizers where H^+-dependent transitions occur.

(9) Discussions of the kinetics of binding and dissociation are reserved for Chapter VII.

(10) It is obvious that much of the foregoing leans heavily on experiments performed with that much-studied protein, serum albumin. That protein, however, is undoubtedly quite unique, since it is specialized for a very general transport function. The meager data available for other proteins show that their binding properties bear little detailed resemblance to those of serum albumin. It is a matter of the greatest importance, therefore, that the great range of binding measurements that have been carried out with serum albumin be applied to a number of other proteins which differ radically in structure and function. Such proteins will have fewer disulfide groups, more sulfhydryls, different helical content, or alternative secondary ordering, a quarternary structure, different contents of aromatic amino acids, and will differ in their propensity to combine with positive and negative ions.

REFERENCES

Acred, P., Brown, D. M., Hardy, T. L., and Mansford, K. R. C. (1963). *Nature* **199**, 758.
Adair, G. S. (1925). *J. Biol. Chem.* **63**, 529.
Alberty, R. A. (1956). *Advan. Enzymol.* **17**, 1.
Alfsen, A. (1963). *Compt. Rend. Trav. Lab. Carlsberg* **33** (11), 415.
Alfsen, A. (1966). *Proc. Intern. Cong. Hormonal Steroids, 2nd, Milan*, p. 508.
Anderson, D. G. (1966). Univ. Microfilms, Xerox Co., Ann Arbor, Michigan, order no. 67-3.
Anson, M. R., and Mirsky, A. E. (1933–34). *J. Gen. Physiol.* **17**, 399.
Antonini, E. (1965). *Science* **158**, 1417.
Antonini, E., Wyman, J., Rossi-Fanelli, A., and Caputo, A. (1962). *J. Biol. Chem.* **237**, 2773.
Antonini, E., Wyman, J., Mosetti, R., and Rossi-Fanelli, A. (1963). *Biochem. Biophys. Acta* **71**, 124.
Antonini, E., Brunori, M., Wyman, J., and Noble, R. (1966). *J. Biol. Chem.* **241**, 3236.

Aschaffenburg, R., and Drewry, J. (1955). *Nature* **176**, 218.

Aschaffenburg, R., and Drewry, J. (1957). *Nature* **180**, 376.

Attallah, N. A., and Lata, G. F. (1968). *Biochim. Biophys. Acta.* **168**, 321.

Bahl, O. P., and Gutmann, H. R. (1964). *Biochim. Biophys. Acta* **90**, 391.

Balasubramanian, D., and Wetlaufer, D. B. (1966). *Proc. Natl. Acad. Sci.* **56**, 762

Banerjee, R. (1962). *Biochim. Biophys. Res. Comm.* **8**, 114.

Banerjee, K., and Lauffer, U. A. (1966). *Biochemistry* **5**, 1952.

Beisel, W. R., Diraimondo, V. C., Chao, P. Y., Rosner, J. M., and Forsham, P. H. (1964). *Metab. Clin. Exptl.* **13**, 942.

Bendet, I. J., Smith, D. E., and Lauffer, M. A. (1960). *Arch. Biochem. Biophys* **88**, 280.

Benesch, R. E., Benesch, R., and Macduff, G. (1965). *Proc. Natl. Acad. Sci. USA* **54**, 535.

Benesch, R., Benesch, R. E., and Tyuma, I. (1966). *Proc. Natl. Acad. Sci. USA* **56**, 1268.

Benson, E. S., Halloway, B. E., and Lumry, P. W. (1964). *J. Biol. Chem.* **239**, 122.

Berlin, H. (1963), *Intern. Cong. Chemotherapy, Proc.* 3rd, Stuttgart, 1720.

Bettelheim, F. A., and Lukton, A. (1963). *Nature* **198**, 357.

Bettelheim, F. A., and Senatore, J. (1964). *J. Chim. Phys.* **61**, 105.

Bezkorovainy, A., and Doherty, D. G. (1962). *Biochim. Biophys. Acta* **58**, 124.

Birks, J. B., and Slifkin, M. S. (1963). *Nature* **197**, 4862.

Bischoff, F., and Pilhorn, H. R. (1948). *J. Biol. Chem.* **174**, 663.

Bonati, F., and Sala, R. (1959). *Bull. Soc. Ital. Biol. Sper.* **35**, 1749.

Bookshin, R. M., Nagel, R. L., and Ranney, H. M. (1967). *Biochim. Biophys. Acta* **140**, 243.

Breuer, M., and Strauss, U. P. (1960). *J. Phys. Chem.* **64**, 228.

Brinkhorst, W. K., and Hess, E. L. (1965). *Arch. Biochem. Biophys.* **111**, 54.

Bull, H. B. (1944). *J. Am. Chem. Soc.* **66**, 1500.

Bunn, H. F., and Jandl, J. H. (1968). *J. Biol. Chem.* **243**, 465.

Butler, L. G., and Rupley, J. A. (1967). *J. Biol. Chem.* **242**, 1077.

Cann, J. R. (1958). *J. Am. Chem. Soc.* **60**, 4263.

Cann, J. R. (1962). *J. Biol. Chem.* **237**, 707.

Cann, J. R. (1966). *Biochemistry* **5**, 1108.

Cann, J. R. (1967). *Biochemistry* **6**, 3427.

Cann, J. R., and Phelps, R. A. (1959). *J. Am. Chem. Soc.* **81**, 4378.

Cann, J. R., and Goad, W. B. (1965). *J. Biol. Chem.* **240**, 148.

Cassel, J. (1969). *Biochemistry* **8**, 2603.

Chader, G. J., and Westphal, U. (1968). *J. Biol. Chem.* **243**, 928.

Chandon, R. C., Carrancedo, M. G., and Shahani, K. M. (1962). *J. Dairy Sci.* **45**, 1312.

Charlwood, P. A. (1958). *Biochem. J.* **69**, 627.

Chase, A. M., Lopedes, S. L., and von Meier, H. C. (1963). *J. Cellular Comp. Physiol.* **61**, 181.

Chase, A. M., Weintraub, B. D., and Henshaw, C. (1964). *Abst. Intern. Cong. Biochem. 6th.*

Chen, P. S. (1967). *J. Biol. Chem.* **242**, 173.

Chen, P. S., and Lane, L. (1965). *Arch. Biochem. Biophys.* **112**, 70.

Clement, G. K., and Bender, M. L. (1963). *Biochemistry* **2**, 836.

Coleman, J. E. (1968). *J. Biol. Chem.* **243**, 4574.

Combs, T. L., and Wacker, W. E. C. (1965). *Fed. Proc. Abst.* 1553.

Cooke, K. B., Tombs, M. P., and Maclagan, M. G. (1962). *Protides Biol. Fluids, Proc. 9th Colloq.*, Bruges, Belgium 1961, 90.

Dahlquist, F. W., and Raftery, M. A. (1968). *Biochemistry* **7**, 3277.

Daniel, I., and Weber, G. (1966). *Biochemistry* **5**, 1893.

Dastoli, F. R., and Price, S. (1966). *Science*, **154**, 905.

Daszkiewicz, O. K., Hennel, J. W., Lubas, B., and Szczopkowski, T. W. (1964). *Intern. Cong. Biochemistry 6th.*

Davis, B. D. (1943). *J. Clin. Invest.* **22**, 753.

Edsall, J. T. (1953). *In* "The Proteins" (H. Neurath and K. Bailey, eds.), Vol. IB, 1st ed., Chapter 7, p. 549.

Eik-Nes, K., Schellman, J., Lumry, R., and Samuels, L. T. (1953). *J. Biol. Chem.* **206**, 411.

Evans, R. J., Bandemer, S. L., Heinlein, K., and Davidson, J. A. (1968). *Biochemistry,* **7**, 3095.

Fahrney, D. E., and Gold, A. M. (1963). *J. Am. Chem. Soc.* **85**, 997.

Fairclough, G. F., Jr., and Fruton, J. S. (1966). *Biochemistry* **5**, 673.

Finkenstadt, W. R., and Laskowski, M., Jr. (1965). *J. Biol. Chem.* **240**, 962.

Fischer, J. J., and Jardetsky, O. J. (1965). *J. Am. Chem. Soc.* **87**, 3237.

Foster, J. F. (1960). *In* "The Plasma Proteins" (Putnam, F. W., ed.), Vol. 1. Academic Press, New York.

Foster, J. F., and Aoki, K. (1958). *J. Am. Chem. Soc.* **80**, 5215.

Frank, H. S., and Wen, W. (1957). *Disc. Faraday Soc.* **24**, 133.

Friedenwald, J. S., and Maengwyn-Davis, C. D. (1954). *in* "Mechanisms of Enzyme-Action" (W. W. McElroy and B. Glass, eds.), p. 154. Johns Hopkins Press, Baltimore, Maryland.

Froese, A., and Sehon, A. H. (1964). *Proc. Intern. Biochem. Cong. 6th* N.Y.

Fuller, M. E., and Brey, W. S., Jr. (1962).

Fuller, M. E., and Brey, W. S., Jr. (1967). *J. Biol. Chem.* **243**, 274.

Gadzala, A. E. (1964). Ph.D. Thesis, Univ. Microfilms Service, Order No. 65-1176.

Gallagher, J., and Steinhardt, J. (1969). *Fed. Proc.* **28**, No. 2, Abst. No. 3325, 853.

Gangurly, M., Carnighan, R. H., and Westphal, U. (1967). *Biochemistry* **6**, 2803.

Gemant, A. (1964). *Grace Hosp. Bull.* **42**, 17.

Genazzani, E., and Pagnini, G. (1963). *Am. J. Vet. Res.* **24**, 1212.

Georges, C., Guinand, S., and Tonnelat, J. (1961). Abst. of the Intern. Biophys. Congr. Stockholm, August, p. 63.

Gerhart, J. C., and Schachman, H. K. (1965). *Biochemistry* **4**, 1054.

Ghosh, S., and Bull, N. B. (1962). *Arch. Biochem. Biophys.* **99**, 121.

Gibson, Q. H., and Antonini, E. (1966). *In* "Hemes and Hemoproteins" (B. Chance, R. Estabrook, and T. Yonetani, eds.), p. 67. Academic Press, New York.

Gibson, Q. H., and Parkhurst, L. J. (1968). *J. Biol. Chem.* **243**, 5521.

Giles, C. H., and McKay, R. B. (1962). *J. Biol. Chem.* **237**, 3388.

Gione, M., and Buogo, A. (1965). *Minerva Med.* **56**, 3608.

Giorgio, N. A., Jr., and Tabachnik, U. (1968). *J. Biol. Chem.* **243**, 2247.

Gizis, E., Kim, U. P., Brunnes, J. R., and Schuergert, B. S. (1965). *J. Nutr.* **87**, 349.

Glazer, A. N., and Simmons, N. S. (1966). *J. Am. Chem. Soc.* **88**, 2335.

Glick, D. M. (1968). *Biochemistry* **7**, 3391.

Goldstein, I. J., Hollerman, C. T., and Smith, E. E. (1965). *Biochemistry* **4**, 876.

Goldstein, I. J., Iyer, I. N., Smith, E. E., and So, L. L. (1967). *Biochemistry* **6**, 2373.

Goodman, D. S. (1957). *Science* **125**, 1296.

Goodman, D. S. (1958). *J. Am. Chem. Soc.* **80**, 3892.

Gordon, J. A., and Jenks, W. P. (1963). *Biochemistry* **2**, 47.

Gordon, J. A., and Warren, J. R. (1968). *J. Biol. Chem.* **243**, 5663.

Gueriguian, J. L., and Pearlman, W. H. (1968). *J. Biol. Chem.* **243**, 5226.

Guerin, M. T., and Tubiane, M. (1965). *Strahlentherapie, Sonderbaende* **60**, 378.

Guidotti, G. (1967). *J. Biol. Chem.* **242**, 3673, 3685, 3694, 3704.

Guttman, D. E., and Gadzala, A. E. (1965). *J. Pharm. Sci.,* **54**, 742.

Hadden, D. R., and Prout, T. E. (1964). *Nature* **202**, 1342.

Hade, E. P. K., and Tanford, C. (1967). *J. Am. Chem. Soc.* **89**, 5034.
Hall, C. E. (1950). *J. Biol. Chem.* **185**, 45.
Hasumura, N., and Nakamura, K. (1964). *Sogo Igaku* **19**, 911.
Helmer, F., Kiehs, K., and Hansch, C. (1968). *Biochemistry* **7**, 2858.
Herzskovits, T. T., and Jaillett, H. (1969). *Science* **163**, 282.
Herzskovits, T. T., and Laskowski, M., Jr. (1962). *J. Biol. Chem.* **237**, 2431.
Hill, R. M., and Briggs, D. R. (1956). *J. Am. Chem. Soc.* **78**, 1590.
Hughes, W. L., Jr., Cohn, E. J., and Weare, J. R. (1947). *J. Am. Chem. Soc.* **69**, 1753.
Humphreys, R. E., and Fruton, J. S. (1968). *Proc. Natl. Acad. Sci.* **59**, 519.
Imarisio, J. J., and Greco, J. (1964). *Metab. Clin. Exptl.* **13**, 897.
Imoto, T., and Rupley, J. A. (1968). *Fed. Proc.* **27**, 392.
Inagami, T., and Sturtevant, J. M. (1960). *Biochim. Biophys. Acta* **38**, 64.
Ingbar, S. H. (1960). *Ann. N.Y. Acad. Sci.* **86**, 440.
Itano, H. A., and Robinson, E. (1961). *J. Am. Chem. Soc.* **83**, 3339.
Izumi, K. (1962). *Tampakushitsu Kakusan Koso* **7**, 295.
James, J. E., and Trowbridge, C. G. (1965). *Fed. Proc.* Abstract. No. 1896.
Jardetsky, O., and Wade, N. G. (1965). *J. Mol. Pharmacol.* **1**, 214.
Kabat, E. A. (1968). "Structural Concepts in Immunology and Immunochemistry." Holt, Rinehart, & Winston, New York.
Kamen, G. Y., and Yakouleu, (1964). *Antibiotiki* **9**, 151.
Karush, F. (1950). *J. Am. Chem. Soc.* **72**, 2705.
Karush, F. (1951). *J. Am. Chem. Soc.* **73**, 1246.
Kato, I., and Aufinsen, C. B. (1969). *J. Biol. Chem.* **244**, 1004.
Kauzmann, W. (1959). *Advan. Protein Chem.* **14**, 1.
Kauzmann, W., and Simpson, R. B. (1953). *J. Am. Chem. Soc.* **75**, 5154.
Kendrew, J. C., Watson, H. C., Strandberg, B. E., Dickerson, R. E., Phillips, D. C., and Shore, V.C. (1961). *Nature* **190**, 666.
Klotz, I. M. (1953). *In* "The Proteins" (H. Neurath and K. Bailey, eds.), Vol. 1B, Chapter 8. Academic Press, New York.
Klotz. I. M. (1958). *Science* **139**, 1259.
Klotz, I. M. (1960). Brookhaven Symposium of Protein Structure and Function, p. 31. Office of Techn. Ser., Dept. of Commerce, Washington, D.C.
Klotz, I. M., and Urquhart, J. M. (1948). *J. Biol. Chem.* **173**., 21.
Klotz, I. M., and Walker, F. M. (1948). *J. Am. Chem. Soc.* **70**, 943.
Klotz, I. M., and Ayers, J. (1952). *J. Am. Chem. Soc.* **74**, 6178.
Klotz, I. M., and Feiss, H. A. (1960). *Biochim. Biophys. Acta* **38**, 57.
Klotz, I. M., and Luborsky, S. W. (1959). *J. Am. Chem. Soc.* **81**, 5119.
Koshland, D. E., Jr., Nemethy, G., and Filmer, D. (1966). *Biochemistry* **5**, 365.
Krasner, J., and McMenamy, R. H. (1966). *J. Biol. Chem.* **241**, 4186.
Krausz, L. M., and Kauzmann, W. (1965). *Proc. Natl. Acad. Sci. USA* **53**, 1234.
Krespeck, G. C., and Benjamin, L. (1964). *J. Phys. Chem.* **68**, 2476.
Kuniv, C. M. (1966). *Clin. Pharmacol. Therap.* **7**, 166.
Kupke, D. W., and Senter, J. P. (1966). *Fed. Proc.* 792 (Abstract #3417).
Laskowski, M., Jr., and Finkenstadt, W. R. (1965). *J. Biol. Chem.* **240**, 962.
Lauffer, M. A. (1966). *Biochemistry* **5**, 1952.
Lauffer, M. A., Taylor, N. W., and Wunder, C. C. (1952). *Arch. Biochem. Biophys.* **40**, 453.
Lee, J. W., and McInver, R. (1965). *Anal. Biochem.* **13**, 1572.
Lein, L. (1952). *Fed. Proc.* **11**, 91.
Leonard, B. R., Jr., Anderegg, J. W., Kaesberg, P., Shulman, S., and Beeman, W. W. (1951). *J. Chem. Phys.* **19**, 793.

Leonard, J. L., Vijai, K. K., and Foster, J. F. (1963). *J. Biol. Chem.* **238**, 1984.
Lumry, R. (1964). *Abhandl. Deut. Akad. Wiss. Berlin, Kl. Med.* **6**, 125.
Margaria, R., Torelli, G., and Pinni, A. (1963). *Exptl. Med. Surgery* **21**, 127.
Markus, G., Love, R. L., and Wissler, F. C. (1964). *J. Biol. Chem.* **239**, 3687.
Markus, G., Barnard, E. A., Castellani, B. A., and Saunders, D. (1967). *J. Biol. Chem.* **243**, 4070.
McCabe, W. C., and Fisher, H. F. (1965). *Fed. Proc.* **24**, 880.
McMeekin, T. L., Polis, B. D., Della Monica, E. S., and Custer, J. H. (1949). *J. Am. Chem. Soc.* **71**, 3606.
McMeekin, T. L. (1952). *Science* **116**, 142.
McMenamy, R. H., and Lee, Y. (1967). *7th Intern. Cong. Biochem. 7th Tokyo*, IV, 586; (1967) *Arch. Biochem. Biophys.* **122**, 635.
McMenamy, R. H., Madeja, M. I., and Watson, F. (1968). *J. Biol. Chem.* **243**, 2625.
Mellon, E. F., Korn, H. H., Hoover, S. R. (1947). *J. Am. Chem. Soc.* **69**, 827.
Mellon, E. F., Korn, H. H., Hoover, S. R. (1948). *J. Am. Chem. Soc.* **70**, 3040.
Mellon, E. F., Korn, H. H., Hoover, S. R. (1949). *J. Am. Chem. Soc.* **71**, 2761.
Milar, A., Milarova, R., and Andrasina (1962). *Cesk. Farm* **11**, 24.
Miles, J. L., Robinson, D. A., and Canaday, W. J. (1963). *J. Biol. Chem.* **238**, 2932.
Miller, G. L., and Price, W. C. (1946). *Arch. Biochem.* **10**, 467.
Mitsuda, H., Yasumoto, K., and Yamamoto, A. (1967). *Intl. Biochem. Cong., 7th Tokyo* Abst. IV, 764.
Mohammadzadeh-K, A., Feeney, R. E., Samuels, R. B., and Smith, L. M. (1967). *Biochim. Biophys. Acta* **147**, 583.
Mohammadzadeh-K, A., Feeney, R. E., and Smith, L. M. (1969a). Unpublished.
Mohammadzadeh-K, A., Smith, L. M., and Feeney, R. E. (1969b). Unpublished.
Muldoon, T. G., and Westphal, U. (1967). *J. Biol. Chem.* **242**, 5636.
Mullin, J. D. (1962). Thesis, Univ. Microfilms, Inc., Xerox Co., Ann Arbor, Michigan, Order No. 63-4356.
Murayama, M. (1964). *Nature* **202**, 4929.
Nagel, R. L., Gibson, O. H., and Characha, S. (1967). *Biochemistry* **6**, 2395.
Nakagaki, M., Koga, N., and Terada, H. (1964). *Yakugaku Zasshi* **84**, 516.
Neer, E. J., Konigsberg, W., and Guidotti, G. (1968). *J. Biol. Chem.* **243**, 1971.
Nemethy, G., and Scheraga, H. A. (1962). *J. Phys. Chem.* **36**, 3401.
Nemethy, G., and Scheraga, H. A. (1962). *J. Phys. Chem.* **66**, 1773.
Nobbs, C. L. (1965). *J. Mol. Biol.* **13**, 325.
Noelkin, M. E., and Timasheff, S. N. (1967). *J. Biol. Chem.* **242**, 5080.
Noguchi, H. N. (1956), *Biophys. Biochem. Acta* **22**, 459.
Noguchi, H. N. (1960). *Biophys. Biochem. Acta* **64**, 155.
Noguchi, H. N. (1961). *Progr. Theor. Phys. Suppl.* **17**, 41.
Nozaki, Y., and Tanford, C. (1963). *J. Biol. Chem.* **238**, 4074.
Oncley, J. L., Scatchard, G., and Brown, A. (1947). *J. Phys. Colloid Chem.* **51**, 184.
Osario, C. (1963). *Salicylates, Intern. Symp. London* 1962 82.
Ozawa, K., and Laskowsi, M., Jr. (1966). *J. Biol. Chem.* **241**, 3955.
Pauling, L., and Coryell, C. D. (1936). *Proc. Natl. Acad. Sci. U.S.* **22**, 210.
Pearlman, W. H., and Crepy, O. (1967). *J. Biol. Chem.* **242**, 182.
Pehelin, V. A., Izmailove, V. N., and Bullshova, G. P. (1962). *Dokl. Akad. Nauk. SSR* **142**, 950.
Peller, L. (1959). *J. Phys. Chem.* **63**, 1199.
Peterson, H. A., and Foster, J. F. (1965). *J. Biol. Chem.* **240**, 2503.
Peterson, H. A., and Foster, J. F. (1965b). *J. Biol. Chem.* **240**, 3858.
Peterson, H. A., Foster, J. F., Sogami, M. A., and Leonard, W. J., Jr. (1965). *J. Biol. Chem.* **240**, 2495.

Phelps, R. A., and Cann. J. R. (1957). *J. Am. Chem. Soc.* **79**, 4677.

Polet, H., and Steinhardt, J. (1968). *Biochemistry* **7**, 1348.

Raftery, M. A., Dahlquist, F. W., Chan, S. I., and Parsons, S. M. (1968). *J. Biol. Chem.* **243**, 4175.

Rapser, J., and Kauzmann, W. (1962). *J. Am. Chem. Soc.* **84**, 1771.

Ray, A., Reynolds, J. A., Polet, H., and Steinhardt, J. (1966). *Biochemistry* **5**, 2606.

Reynolds, J. A., Herbert, S., Polet, H., and Steinhardt, J. (1967). *Biochemistry* **6**, 937.

Reynolds, J. A., Herbert, S., and Steinhardt, J. (1968). *Biochemistry* **7**, 1357.

Richards, F. M., and Logue, A. D. (1962). *J. Biol. Chem.* **237**, 3693.

Ritland, H. N., Kaesberg, P., and Beeman, W. W. (1950). *J. Chem. Phys.* **18**, 1237.

Rosenthal, H. L., O'Brien, G., and Austin, S. (1962). *Arch. Biochem. Biophys.* **99**, 319.

Rossi-Fanelli, A., Antonini, E., and Caputo, A. (1961). *J. Biol. Chem.* **236**, 397.

Rossi-Fanelli, A., Antonini, E., and Caputo, A. (1964). *Advan. Protein Chem.* **19**, 74.

Roughton, F. J. W., Otis, A.B., and Lyster, R. L. J. (1955). *Proc. Roy. Soc. London,* **B144**, 29.

Rozengart, V. Z., Brestgin, A. P., Godovikov, N. N., Kabachnik, M. I., Mikhailov, S. S., and Mikhelson, M. Y. (1967). *7th Intern. Cong. Biochem. 7th Tokyo* Abst. IV, p. 817.

Ruiz-Torres, A., and Meinig, R. H. (1965). *Arzneimittel Forsch.* **15**, 445.

Rupley, J. A., Butler, L., Gerring, M., Hartdegen, F. J., and Pecoraro, R. (1967). *Proc. Natl. Acad. Sci.* **57**, 1088.

Rupley, J. A., and Gates, V. (1967). *Proc. Natl. Acad. Sci.* **57**, 496.

Sanborn, B. M., and Hein, C. E. (1968). *Biochemistry* **7**, 3616.

Scatchard, G., Scheinberg, I. H., and Armstrong, S. H., Jr. (1950a). *J. Am. Chem. Soc.* **72**, 535.

Scatchard, G., Scheinberg, I. H., and Armstrong, S. H., Jr. (1950b). *J. Am. Chem. Soc.* **72**, 540.

Scatchard, G., Wu, V. Y., and Shen, H. (1959). *J. Am. Chem. Soc.* **81**, 6104.

Schachman, H. K., and Lauffer, M. A. (1949). *J. Am. Chem. Soc.* **71**, 536.

Schellman, J. S., Lumry, R., and Samuels, L. T. (1954). *J. Am. Chem. Soc.* **76**, 2808.

Scheraga, H. A., Nemethy, G., and Steinberg, I. Z. (1962). *J. Biol. Chem.* **237**, 2506.

Schlamowitz, M., Shaw, A., and Jackson, W. T. (1968). *J. Biol. Chem.* **243**, 2821.

Schmid, K. (1959). *J. Biol. Chem.* **234**, 3163.

Schmid, R., and Polis, A. (1960). *J. Biol. Chem.* **235**, 1321.

Schoenborn, B. P. (1965). *Nature* **208**, 760.

Scholtan, W. (1963). *Intern. Cong. Chemotherapy Proc. 3rd, Stuttgart* 261.

Scholtan, W. (1964). *Arzneimittel Forsch.* **14**, 348.

Scholtan, W. (1964). *Arzneimittel Forsch.* **14**, 1139.

Scholtan, W., and Schmid, J. (1963). *Arzneimittel Forsch.* **13**, 288.

Scholtan, W., Schlossman, K., and Rosenkranz, H. (1966). *Arzneimittel-Forsch.* **16**, 109.

Schrier, E. E., Ingwall, R. T., and Scheraga, H. A. (1965). *J. Phys. Chem.* **69**, 298.

Seal, M. S., and Doe, R. P. (1962). *J. Biol. Chem.* **237**, 3136.

Seal, M. S., and Doe, R. P. (1963). *Endocrinology* **73**, 371.

Sears, D. A., and Huser, H. J. (1965). *Proc. Soc. Exptl. Med.* **121**, 111.

Sharp, D. G., Taylor, A. R., McLean, I. W., Beard, D., and Beard, J. W. (1945). *J. Biol. Chem.* **159**, 29.

Sharp, D. G., Taylor, A. R., and Beard, J. W. (1946). *J. Biol. Chem.* **163**, 289.

Shore, J. D., and Gilleland, M. J. (1968). *Meeting, Am. Chem. Soc. Sept.*

Simko, J. P., and Kauzmann, W. (1962). *Biochemistry* **1**, 1005.

Slaunwhite, W. R. (1960). *In* "Hormones in Human Plasma" (H. N. Antoniades, ed.), p. 425. Little, Brown, Boston, Massachusetts.

Sluyterman, L. A. (1964). *Intern. Biochem. Cong., New York 6th* **11**, 177.

So, L. L., and Goldstein, I. J., (1968). *J. Biol. Chem.* **243**, 2003.

Sogami, M., and Foster, J. F. (1968). *Biochemistry* **7**, 2172.

St. George, R. C. C., and Pauling, L. (1951). *Science* **114**, 629.
Steiner, R. A., and Edelhoch, H. (1963). *Biochim. Biophys. Acta.* **66**, 341.
Steiner, R. F., Roth, J., and Robbins, J. (1965). *J. Biol. Chem.* **241**, 560.
Steinhardt, J., and Moezie, F. (1964). *Fed. Proc.* **23**, no. 2, Mar.-Apr.
Steinhardt, J., Fugitt, G. H., and Harris, M. (1943). *J. Res. Natl. Bur. Std.* **30**, 123.
Steinhardt, J., Ona, R., Beychok, S., and Ho, C. (1963). *Biochemistry* **2**, 256.
Steinhardt, J., Polet, H., and Moezie, F. (1966). *J. Biol. Chem.* **241**, 3988.
Strauss, G., and Strauss, M. P. (1958). *J. Phys. Chem.* **62**, 1321.
Sumita, N., Okazaki, T., Sh kuya, R., and Kajiro, K. (1964). *J. Biochem. (Tokyo)* **55**, 188.
Tabachnik, M. (1964). *J. Biol. Chem.* **234**, 1242.
Tabachnik, M., and Giorgio, N. A., Jr. (1964). *Arch. Biochem. Biophys.* **105**, 563.
Takashima, S. (1962). *J. Polymer Sci.* **62**, 233.
Taketa, F., Smuts, M. B., di Bond, F. J., and Lessard, J. L. (1967). *Biochemistry* **6**, 3809.
Tanford, C. (1961). "Physical Chemistry of Macromolecules." Wiley, New York.
Tanford, C. (1962). *J. Am. Chem. Soc.* **84**, 420.
Tanford, C. (1964). *in* Subunit Structure of Proteins, Brookhaven Symposia in Biology, No. 17.
Tanford, C. (1968). *Advan. Protein Chem.* **23**, 121.
Tanford, C., and Roberts, G. H., Jr. (1952). *J. Am. Chem. Soc.* **74**, 2509.
Tanford, C., and Buzzell, J. C. (1956). *J. Phys. Chem.* **60**, 225.
Tanford, C., and De, P. K. (1961). *J. Biol. Chem.* **236**, 1711.
Tanford, C., Bunville, L. G., and Nozaki, Y. (1959). *J. Am. Chem. Soc.* **81**, 4032.
Tang, J. (1963). *Nature* **199**, 1094.
Therrault, D. G., and Taylor, J. F. (1964). *J. Am. Oil Chemists' Soc.* **41**, 481.
Timasheff, S. N., and Inove, H. (1968). *Biochemistry* **7**, 2501.
Tritsch, G. L. (1967). *Intern. Biochem. Cong. Tokyo 7th* **IV**, 592.
von Muralt, A. L. (1930). *J. Am. Chem. Soc.* **52**, 3518.
Wallace, R. A., Kirtz, A. N., and Niemann, C. (1963). *Biochemistry* **2**, 824.
Wang, J. H., Anfinsen C. B., and Polestra, F. M. (1954). *J. Am. Chem. Soc.* **76**, 4755.
Watson, H. C. (1966). *in* "Hemes and Hemoproteins" (B. Chance, R. Estabrook, and T. Yonetani, eds.), p. 63. Academic Press, New York.
Weber, J., and Anderson, S. R. (1965). *Biochemistry* **4**, 1942.
Weintraub, B. D., Hamilton, G. A., Henshaw, C., and Chase, A. M. (1964). *Arch. Biochem. Biophys.* **107**, 224.
Westphal, U. (1964). *J. Am. Oil Chemists' Soc.* **41**, 481.
Westphal, U., and Devenuto, F. (1966). *Biochim. Biophys. Acta* **115**, 187.
Wetlaufer, D. B., and Lovrien, R. E. (1964). *J. Biol. Chem.* **239**, 596.
Wetlaufer, D. B., Malik, S. K., Stolar, L., and Coffin, R. L. (1964). *J. Am. Chem. Soc.* **86**, 508.
Wilson, I. B. (1952). *J. Biol. Chem.* **197**, 215.
Wilson, I. B. (1952). *J. Biol. Chem.* **199**, 113.
Wishnia, A. (1962). *Proc. Natl. Acad. Sci. U.S.* **48**, 2200.
Wishnia, A. (1963). *J. Phys. Chem.* **67**, 2079.
Wishnia, A. (1964). *Fed. Proc.* **23**, 160 (Abst. 357).
Wishnia, A., and Pinder, T. W., Jr. (1964). *Biochemistry* **3**, 1377.
Wishnia, A., and Pinder, T. W., Jr. (1965). *Fed. Proc.* **24**, 288.
Wishnia, A., and Pinder, T. W., Jr. (1966). *Biochemistry* **5**, 1534.
Wittenberg, J. B., Noble, R. W., Wittenberg, B. A., Antonini, E., Brunori, M., and Wyman, J. (1967). *J. Biol. Chem.* **242**, 629.
Woeber, K. A., and Ingbar, S. H. (1963). *Endocrinology* **73**, 118.
Woehler, V. F., and Speckman, R. (1960). *Arzneimittel Forsch.* No. 859.

Wong, K.-P., and Foster, J. F. (1968). Meeting, Am. Chem. Soc. (Sept.).

Wyman, J., Jr. (1948). *Advan. Protein Chem.* **4**, 407.

Wyman, J., Jr. (1964). *Advan. Protein Chem.* **19**, 224.

Wyman, J., Jr. (1965). *J. Mol. Biol.* **11**, 631.

Yoon, J. O., and Shin, H. D. (1967). *Intl. Biochemical Congress, Tokyo, 7th* Abst. IV, 801.

V

Hydrogen-Ion Equilibria

I. Introduction

Experimental methods of determining the equilibria between proteins and their dissociable protons have been discussed in Chapter III, and the theoretical basis for interpretation of results has been summarized in Chapter II. The most recent comprehensive treatments of this subject are given by Edsall and Wyman (1958), Linderström-Lang and Nielsen (1959), Tanford (1962), and Steinhardt and Beychok (1964).

In view of the wealth of older reviews in this field and the relatively small amount of additional information made available since the publication of the last two references above, an extensive survey will not be presented here. Instead the model systems in terms of which hydrogen-ion equilibria of proteins are analyzed will be discussed, the ambiguities and uncertainties which sometimes occur will be illustrated by some representative acid–base titration curves, certain recent investigations in this area will be described, and the contribution of studies of this nature to an understanding of the higher order structure and biological function of proteins in solution will be indicated.

II. Prototropic Groups in Proteins

Table 5-1 presents a list of the amino acid residues found in proteins which ionize in aqueous media, and Table 5-2 the apparent dissociation constants of these and related acids, bases, and model peptides. While all such groups would be expected to be accessible to solvent and ionize with "normal" pKs in linear unstructured macromolecules, these groups do not always

TABLE 5-1

Prototropic Groups in Proteins[a, b]

Group	Uncharged form	Number titrated in denatured protein is proportional to content of:
Side-chain carboxyl	R³COOH	Aspartic and glutamic acids less amide
Side-chain amino	R³NH₂	Lysine
Imidazole	NH	Histidine
Phenylhydroxyl	R—OH	Tyrosine
Sulfhydryl	R³—SH	Cysteine
Guanidyl	—	Arginine
Terminal carboxyl	RCOOH	Separate polypeptide chains; may be fewer in number but not greater
Amide	RCONH₂	Asparagine and glutamine
Peptide	RCONHR¹	Total number of amino acids

[a] R^3 stands for an aliphatic chain containing at least two carbon atoms attached to a peptide group (CONH). R and R^1 may stand for any of the aliphatic groups found in an amino acid.

[b] Taken from Steinhardt and Beychok (1964).

titrate normally in proteins. An important object of studies of hydrogen-ion equilibria of biological macromolecules is to determine which of the prototropic residues are normal in that they have pKs similar to model compounds, and which are in some manner abnormal due to either steric inaccessibility or specific interactions with other charged groups in the macromolecule.

It is evident from Table 5-2 that proton titration curves proceeding from pH 5.5 to pH below 2.0 will involve only α-, β-, and γ-COOH groups, providing no structural changes occur in this pH range. If unfolding occurs as the result of protonation, ionizable residues may be exposed which would normally be protonated at higher pH values but instead will appear to titrate at the pH of unfolding. Assuming no conformational change occurs in this pH range, an analysis of this region in terms of the Linderström-Lang model [see Eq. (2-45) in Chapter II] is straightforward. A recent study of the intrinsic dissociation constants of aspartyl and glutamyl carboxyl groups (Nozaki and Tanford, 1967) in uncharged model peptides shows intrinsic pK values at 25° and zero ionic strength of 4.08 for aspartyl groups and 4.50 for glutamyl groups. Thus, the acidic portion of the protein titration curve should not be treated as a single set of groups, but rather a curve-fitting procedure should be employed which uses an estimated w (Chapter II) plus two values each of n_i and pK_i. If the n_i are not known, this is most easily accomplished by

TABLE 5-2

EXPECTED pK'S OF TRIVALENT AMINO ACIDS

Type of substance	Group	pK
I. Expected Values of Side-Chain pKs in Proteins at 25°		
Aspartic acid[a]	β-COO$^-$	4.08
Glutamic Acid[a]	γ-COO$^-$	4.50
Tyrosine[b]	—OH	9.6
Histidine[b]	R = S—H	6.3
Cysteine[b]	RS—H	8.3
Lysine[b]	ε-NH$_3^+$	10.4
Arginine[b]		>12
II. pKs of Terminal Groups		
—	α-COO$^-$ [b]	3.4
—	α-NH$_3^+$ [b]	7.5
III. pKs of Side-Chain Groups in Peptides		
Glycyltyrosine[a]	Phenolic	10.4
Glycylaspartic acid[a]	γ-COO$^-$	4.45
Aspartylglycine[a]	β-COO$^-$	4.53
Acetylisoasparagine[b]	β-COO$^-$	3.99
Acetylisoglutomine[b]	γ-COO$^-$	4.34
Carbobenzoxyisoasparagine[b]	β-COO$^-$	4.05
Carbobenzoxyisoglutamine[b]	γ-COO$^-$	4.39

[a] Nozaki and Tanford (1967).
[b] Steinhardt and Beychok (1964); Tanford (1962).

computer using an iterative program which varies the five parameters until the best fit is obtained.

Between pH 5 and 8, imidazoles, α-amino groups, and sulfhydryls may be involved, and some independent knowledge, such as amino acid composition, of the numbers of identical groups in at least two of the above three sets is necessary.

From pH 8 to 12 both ε-amino and tyrosines dissociate their protons. Fortunately, the tyrosine ionization curve can be determined independently by spectrophotometric titration (Chapter III, p. 42) and the results subtracted from the potentiometric data to give n for ε-amino groups only.

Arginine residues generally titrate only above pH 12, and their total number, n, in any given protein is computed by the following means.

The total number of protons dissociated between the acid end point and the isoionic point, $\Delta\bar{Z}_{max}$, is by definition equal to the total number of positive charges on the protein at $Z = 0$. Thus, once the number of charged imidazoles, α-aminos, and ε-aminos at $Z = 0$ is known, the arginine count is established by subtracting the sum (His$^+$ + α-amino$^+$ + Lys$^+$) from $\Delta\bar{Z}_{max}$.

The ionizable residues in proteins may also be identified by their heats of ionization, as Wyman (1939) and others have shown. It is clear from Table 5-3

TABLE 5-3

HEATS OF IONIZATION OF AMINO ACIDS[a]

Substance	ΔH (kcal/mole)				
	COO$^-$	Imidazole	Phenolic	NH$_3{}^+$	Gu[b]
Glycine	0	—	—	+10.7	—
Alanine	−0.45	—	—	+11.6	—
Valine	−0.30	—	—	+10.6	—
Histidine	+1.20	+6.90	—	+ 9.4	—
Lysine	+0.30	—	—	+11.6	—
Arginine	+1.0	—	—	+11.2	+12.4
Aspartic acid					
Terminal COO$^-$	+1.6	—	—	+11.2	—
Sidechain COO$^-$	+2.1	—	—	—	—
Glutamic acid					
Terminal COO$^-$	+1.9	—	—	+11.2	—
Sidechain COO$^-$	+1.04	—	—	—	—
Tyrosine	—	—	+6.0	—	—

[a] From Steinhardt and Beychok (1964), and Tanford (1962).
[b] Gu is guanidinium.

that carboxyl groups have $\Delta H_{ionization} \simeq \pm 2$ kcal/mole, while for imidazoles and phenolic groups $\Delta H_{ionization} \simeq 5$–$6$ kcal/mole, and for ammonium and guanidinium $\Delta H_{ionization} \simeq 10$–$12$ kcal/mole. Figure 5-1 shows $\Delta H_{ionization}$ for the dissociation of H$^+$ from serum albumin. Approximately 100 groups have $\Delta H_{ionization}$ values anticipated for COO$^-$, 10 have $\Delta H_{ionization} \simeq 7$ kcal/mole. The fact that tyrosine and lysine titrate in the same pH region but have different $\Delta H_{ionization}$ is noted in Fig. 5-1 where $\Delta H_{ionization}$ varies continuously with r (number of protons dissociated) above $r = 115$.

Since the free energy of unpaired charged groups is considerably less in water than in a medium of low dielectric constant such as is found in the interior of a protein, most ionizable residues in proteins are at the "surface"

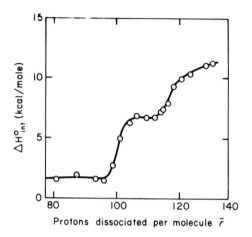

Protons dissociated per molecule $\bar{r}$

Fig. 5-1. ΔH°_{int} for the dissociation of H$^+$ ions from serum albumin, as a function of the average number of protons dissociated per molecule. Where ΔH°_{int} is independent of $\bar{r}$ it is likely that a single type of acidic site is involved. [C. Tanford et al. (1955b). J. Am. Chem. Soc. 77, 6414.]

in contact with the aqueous medium. Thus, most of these groups are "normal," i.e., with pKs similar to model compounds.

The relatively few abnormalities commonly encountered in the titration of native proteins may be enumerated as follows:

(1) abnormal pKs,
(2) abnormal values of n, i.e., lack of agreement with amino acid analysis,
(3) abnormal values of w.

When a conformational change occurs in the pH region under investigation, some previously unavailable groups may be released and appear to be titrated with abnormal pKs. Thus, imidazoles may appear in the carboxyl region as the result of unmasking well below pH 6.0, where they will be protonated quantitatively at the pH of the conformational change. Strong cooperative effects will appear in this case, and no simple multiple equilibrium K will fit the data. However, a forced fit will give the abnormal pK.

The apparent number of ionizable residues within a specific, identical set may be less than that indicated by amino acid analysis. Infrared and other techniques have shown that this anomaly results from burial of part of the set in the hydrophobic interior of the protein.

Experimental values of w are commonly lower than the values for this factor calculated by means of the Debye-Hückel theory. A discussion of the uncertainties in the calculation of this parameter is given in Chapter II. It should be noted here that changes in the experimental value of w from one set of groups in the same protein to another are generally due to alterations in the shape or solvent permeability of the protein rather than to inductive effects from near neighbors.

III. Some Experimental Details

Chapter III contains a complete description of the potentiometric method used to determine the number of equivalents of hydrogen ion bound per mole of protein, and Chapter II provides a discussion of the theoretical basis for treatment of this data. In this section we discuss two important experimental quantities necessary to the interpretation of hydrogen-ion titration curves, and provide an example of a full titration curve of a protein in random-coil conformation, showing the group count of titratable residues within the pH ranges described above.

A. Isoionic Point

Since application of the Linderström-Lang equation to experimental data requires knowledge of $\bar{Z}$, the average net macromolecular charge, it is necessary to establish the pH at which the protein has zero net charge. This pH is called the *isoelectric* point and is determined experimentally by observing the motion of a protein in an electric field as a function of pH. At the isoelectric pH the protein will undergo no net motion toward either pole.

The *isoionic* point is the pH of a protein solution which contains only protein and ions arising from dissociation of the solvent. A solution of protein in deionized water may be made isoionic by passage through an ion-exchange resin or exhaustive dialysis against deionized water. The resulting solution may be very close to isoelectric if the true isoelectric point lies between pH 4 and pH 10 and if the protein combines only with hydrogen and hydroxyl ions. For example, at protein concentrations, $C_p = 10^{-3}$ M and an isoelectric pH of 3.0, the following equations apply:

$$C_p Z + C_{H^+} = C_{OH^-} \tag{5-1}$$

At $Z = 0$, pH 3.0,

$$|C_{H^+} - C_{OH^-}| \leq 10^{-3} M \tag{5-2}$$

Then Eq. (5-1) becomes

$$10^{-3} Z \leq 10^{-3}$$
$$Z \leq 1 \tag{5-3}$$

and the charge on the protein is less than 1 at the isoionic point. Clearly, decreasing the protein concentration will result in the isoionic point being farther removed from the isoelectric point. At somewhat higher pH values, this concentration effect becomes unimportant.

B. DEFINITION OF pH

The problem of defining pH and determining the equivalents of hydrogen ion bound when cells with liquid junctions are used has been discussed in Chapter III. The definition

$$pH = -\log a_{H^+} = -\log[H^+] + \log \gamma_{H^+} \tag{5-4}$$

cannot be used since γ_{H^+} cannot be measured. Instead, it is customary to set

$$pH = -\log[H^+] + \log \gamma_{\pm HCl} \tag{5-5}$$

and to carry out the titration in a fixed concentration of KCl in which $\gamma_{\pm HCl}$ is known (Harned and Owen, 1950). Between pH 3 and 10 this procedure introduces only a small error in determining $[H^+]$ since the free hydrogen- and hydroxyl-ion concentrations are low relative to the bound species. At extremes of the pH scale, however, the error becomes much larger, leading to uncertainties in determining acid and alkaline end points. In addition, the exact calibration of the electrode may fail as liquid-junction potentials become important at low pH.

IV. An Experimental Titration Curve

Figure 5-2 shows the potentiometric acid and base titration of ribonuclease in 6 M GuHCl[1] (Tanford and Nozaki, 1967) at 25°. The ordinate in Fig. 5-2 is the number of protons bound per mole of protein taking the isoionic point of pH 9.54 as $Z = 0$. An almost equally acceptable representation of data is the total average hydrogen ions dissociated, h, in which the ideal acid end point is taken as $h = 0$.

[1] The results in GuHCl (Gu = guanidinium) are given because they are entirely free of complications due to noncovalent structure.

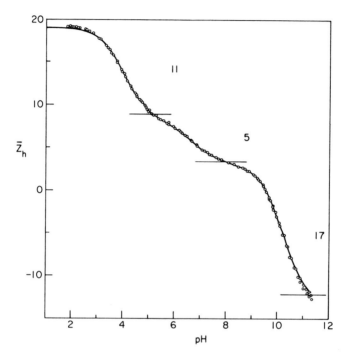

FIG. 5-2. Electrometric titration of ribonuclease in 6 M guanidine hydrochloride, at 25°. [C. Tanford and Y. Nozaki (1967). *J. Am. Chem. Soc.* **89**, 742.]

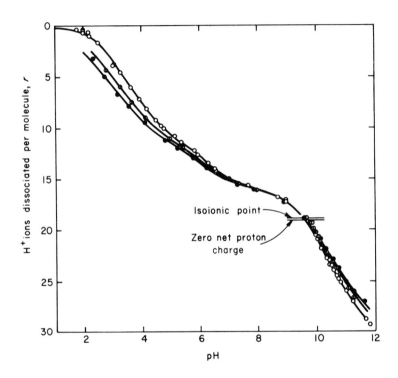

FIG. 5-3. Titration data for ribonuclease at 25°; ionic strengths 0.01 (●), 0.03 (◍), and 0.15 (○). The figure shows the point of zero net charge (corresponding to $r = 19$) and also the isoionic pH at the particular concentration which was used. [C. Tanford and J. D. Hauenstein (1956). *J. Am. Chem. Soc.* **78**, 5287.]

The curve may be divided into three regions: (1) an acid branch representing protonation of 11 carboxyl groups, (2) a neutral branch representing protonation of 5 imidazoles and 1 α-amino, and (3) an alkaline branch representing deprotonation of 17 tyrosyl and ε-amino groups. A complete discussion of the proton binding of ribonuclease in both native and denatured states will be found in Sections V, C and V, E of this chapter. At this point we call attention to the general shape of the curve in Fig. 5-2 and the obvious inflections at pH 5.5 and 8 which mark the onset of protonation of sets of residues with very different pKs. Note that within the sets tyrosine-lysine and α-amino-imidazole, it is not possible to distinguish two separate groups by inspection. Spectrophotometric titration of the ionized phenolic chromophore of tyrosine enables one to separate the former two groups of residues, and amino acid analysis plus a knowledge of approximate pKs from model compounds allows the separate analysis of the latter two groups.

Figure 5-3 shows the potentiometric titration of native ribonuclease at a number of salt concentrations. The intact protein has a broadened titration curve reflecting a larger value of w, the electrostatic interaction factor, as compared with the denatured protein. There are three phenolic groups which do not deprotonate below pH 12 in the native macromolecule. This phenomenon is reflected as a difference in total groups titrated between Figs. 5-2 and 5-4.

V. Anomalies Illustrated by Specific Proteins

Table 5-4 provides a list of a large number of proteins studied to date, together with the number of ionizable groups in each set, their respective pKs, and the electrostatic interaction factor, w, associated with each set. In the discussion of individual proteins and their hydrogen-ion equilibria which is presented in the following sections, the full titration curve of each protein will not be discussed in detail. Instead the emphasis will be on certain anomalous characteristics and their application to protein structure. The set of residues referred to following each subheading is not necessarily the only anomalous set in the particular protein discussed (the others, if any, are shown in Table 5-4) but is the one on which attention will be focused.

A. Bovine Serum Albumin—Abnormal Carboxylate Groups

Early titration data by Tanford *et al.* (1955) at a variety of ionic strengths were analyzed by means of the Linderström-Lang equation with the assumption that all groups present in amino acid analysis were also available for

TABLE 5-4

CHARACTERISTICS OF ACID–BASE TITRATION CURVES OF PARTICULAR PROTEINS

Protein	Reversible range (or limits of titration if reversible throughout) (no pH drifts)	pH of rapid reversible confor-mational change within reversible region	Isoionic point	$pK_{int}{}^a$		
				α-Car-boxyl	Side-chain COOH	Imid-azole
Actin	—	—	—	—	—	—
Alkaline phosphatase	5.0–12.0	—	6.3	—	4.08	7.10
Casein (α, β, γ)	—	—	—	—	—	—
Carbonic anhydrase (human fraction L, denatured)	4.2–11.0	—	—	—	—	—
Chymotrypsinogen	1.5–12.6	—	9.66	—	—	—
In 8 M urea	—	—	9.8	—	—	—
Chymotrypsin	—	—	9.25	—	—	—
In 8 M urea	—	—	—	—	—	—
Clupeine	—	—	—	5.05	—	—
Collagen	—	—	—	—	—	—
	2–12	—	—	—	3.95	7.1
Heat-denatured	2–12	—	—	—	4.1	6.8

^{a} Values of pK_{int} obtained with a number of different salt concentrations have been combined without correction. The effect of ionic strength on pK will not usually exceed 0.1 unit.

TABLE 5-4 (*Continued*)

Phen-oxy	ε-Amino	Guani-dine	w_{obs}/w_{calc}	n_{obs}/n_{anal}	References
			$pK_{int}{}^a$		

Phen-oxy	ε-Amino	Guani-dine	w_{obs}/w_{calc}	n_{obs}/n_{anal}	References
—	—	—	—	0 Phenoxy	Mihashi and Ooi (1965)
10.5	10.7	12	1.0	0.20 Phenoxy 0.75 Imidazole 1.0 All others	Reynolds and Schlesinger (1967)
—	—	—	—	—	Hipp *et al.* (1952)
—	—	—	~1.0	0.6 Imidazole 0.3 Phenoxy 1.0 All others	Riddiford and Scheraga (1962)
—	—	—	—	1.0 All groups	Marini and Wunsch
—	—	—	—	1.0 All groups	(1966)
—	—	—	—	1.0 All groups	Marini and Wunsch
—	—	—	—	1.0 All groups	(1966)
—	~8.3 (α-Amino)	—	—	1.0 Carboxyl 1.0 α-Amino	Linderström-Lang (1935), Rasmussen and Linderström-Lang (1935)
—	—	—	—	>1.0 Carboxyl <1.0 ε-Amino	Bowes and Kenten (1948)
10.5	—	—	—	0.60 Carboxyl 0.85 Imidazole 0.63 Phenolic + ε-Amino	Bakermann and Hartman (1966)
10.6	—	—	—	0.66 Carboxyl 1.0 Imidazole 0.85 Phenolic + ε-Amino	

(*Continued*)

TABLE 5-4 (*Continued*)

| Protein | Reversible range (or limits of titration if reversible throughout) (no pH drifts) | pH of rapid reversible conformational change within reversible region | Isoionic point | pK_{int}[a] | | |
				α-Carboxyl	Side-chain COOH	Imidazole
Conalbumin	4.2–11.2	<4.2	6.8	—	4.42	6.75
α-Corticotropin	2–12	—	8.6	—	4.6	∼7
Cytochrome C	—	—	—	—	—	∼6.6 (1 of 3) ∼3.5 (linked to Fe) (iron link broken at pH 2.1)
	—	—	9.8	—	—	—
8 *M* urea	—	—	—	—	—	—
Enterotoxin B (Staph)	1.5–11.0	—	—	—	—	—
Fibrin	—	—	—	—	—	—
Fibrinogen	Range limited	—	—	—	—	—
Gelatin	—	—	—	—	—	—
Gluten	—	—	7.5	—	4.77	6.43
Glutenin	—	—	—	—	4.76	6.6
Hemoglobin Horse Hb$^+$	4–11	3.4–4.5	∼6.7	—	—	—
	—	—	—	—	—	—
Horse HbCO	2.9–11.5	below 3.5	∼7.4	—	—	—

TABLE 5-4 (*Continued*)

pK_{int}[a]					
Phen-oxy	ε-Amino	Guani-dine	w_{obs}/w_{calc}	n_{obs}/n_{anal}	References
9.41 >13.(7)	9.64	—	Slightly under 1.0 all groups	1.03 Carboxyl 1.00 Imidazole 0.58 Phenoxy 1.00 ε-Amino	Wishnia *et al.* (1961)
9.8	10.1	~12	Low	~1.0 All groups	Leonis and Li (1959)
—	—	—	—	—	Theorell and Akeson (1941), Paleus (1954), Margoliash *et al.* (1962), Bull and Breese (1966)
10.05	—	—	—	0.25 Phenoxy	Stellwagon (1964), Rupley (1964)
10.4, 11.0	—	—	—	1.0 Phenoxy	Stellwagon (1964)
6(10.3) 8(11.65) 7(12.85)	—	—	—	0.3 Phenoxy 1.0 All others	Chu (1968)
—	—	—	—	—	Mihalyi (1954)
—	—	—	—	—	Mihalyi (1954), Chaudhuri (1948), Shulman and Ferry (1954)
—	—	—	—	—	Kenchington and Ward (1954), Rousselot (1944)
10.26	10.78	13.0	—	1.0	Wu and Dimler (1963)
10.42	10.6	>13	—	1.0	Wu and Dimler (1963)
—	—	—	—	0.48 Imidazole	Beychok and Steinhardt (1959)
—	—	—	—	0.68 Imidazole	Nozaki and Tanford (1967)
—	—	—	—	0.68 Imidazole	Geddes and Steinhardt (1968) (see text)

(*Continued*)

TABLE 5-4 (*Continued*)

Protein	Reversible range (or limits of titration if reversible throughout) (no pH drifts)	pH of rapid reversible conformational change within reversible region	Isoionic point	$pK_{int}{}^a$		
				α-Carboxyl	Side-chain COOH	Imidazole
Human Hb+	4.2–11	—	—	—	—	—
Human CoHb	—	—	—	—	—	—
Denatured form	—	—	—	—	—	—
Insulin	—	—	—	—	—	—
Zinc-free	2–11	—	5.6	3.6	4.7	6.4
Zinc insulin	2–11	—	5.6	4.1	5.0	6.6
Iodinated	—	—	—	—	—	—
γ-Globulin (Native)	—	—	—	—	—	—
6 M GuHCl (Denatured)	—	—	—	<3.5	4.26	6.58
Lactoglobulin	1.5–9.7	(7.4)	5.3	—	4.8 (50 groups) 7.3 (2 groups)	7.4
Denatured	—	—	—	—	—	—
Native β-A β-B β-C					Comparison of pH transitions for	
Keratin	—	—	—	—	4.2 (high salt)	—
Lactic dehydrogenase	—	—	—	—	—	—

TABLE 5-4 (*Continued*)

pK_{int}[a]					
Phenoxy	ε-Amino	Guanidine	w_{obs}/w_{calc}	n_{obs}/n_{anal}	References
—	—	—	—	0.32 Imidazole	Hiremath and Steinhardt (1967), Yip and Bucci (1968)
10,43, 10.48	—	—	—	About 0.3–0.66 Phenoxy	
—	—	—	—	1.0 All groups	
—	—	—	—	—	Tanford and Epstein (1954)
9.6	9.6	11.9	~1.0 Except in insoluble region	—	
10.2, 11.6	10.5	—	—	—	Fredericq (1954, 1956)
Reduced pK_{int}	—	—	—	—	Gruen *et al.* (1959)
10.30	10.24	—	—	1.0 Carboxyl	Nozaki and Tanford (1969), Gould *et al.* (1964)
9.9	10.0	—	—	1.0 Lysine	
				1.0 Phenolic	
9.9	9.9	—	Slightly low (all groups)	0.0 Sulfhydryl 0.96 Carboxyl (50/52) 1.5 Imidazole (6/4) 1.0 Phenoxy, amino, guanidine	Cannan *et al.* (1942), Nozaki *et al.* (1959)
—	—	—	Expected low value	1.0 all groups	Tanford *et al.* (1959)
genetic variants between pH 4.5 and 9.5					Timasheff *et al.* (1966)
—	—	—	—	—	Steinhardt *et al.* (1940a,b) Steinhardt (1941)
10.25	—	—	—	0.3 Phenoxy	Di Sabato (1965)

(*Continued*)

TABLE 5-4 (*Continued*)

| Protein | Reversible range (or limits of titration if reversible throughout) (no pH drifts) | pH of rapid reversible confor-mational change within reversible region | Isoionic point | pK_{int}[a] | | |
				α-Car-boxyl	Side-chain COOH	Imid-azole
Lysozyme	2–12	—	11.1	< 1 (3 groups) (more than one pK_{int} for others)	6.8 5.8 (hen egg white) 7.6 (human)	—
Metmyoglobin	4.5–11.5	—	7.0	—	4.40	6.62 (6 groups) < 1 (6 groups)
Denatured	—	—	—	—	—	6.48 (12 groups)
Myosin	—	—	—	—	~4.4 (in 1.2 M KCl); ~3.0 when salt absent	Reduced by salt
Meromyosin	—	—	—	—	Mg^{2+} reduces	—
Nuclease (staph)	—	—	—	—	—	5.6, 5.9, 6.1, 6.6
Ovalbumin	2–12	4.0	4.9	—	4.3 1 (possibly 8 groups)	6.7

TABLE 5-4 (*Continued*)

Phen-oxy	ε-Amino	Guani-dine	w_{obs}/w_{calc}	n_{obs}/n_{anal}	References
	pK_{int}^{a}				
10.4	—	—	~1.0 Except for carboxyl region	~1.0 Except for carboxyl which varies with preparation	Tanford and Wagner (1954), Donovan *et al.* (1960, 1961a,b), Meadows *et al.* (1967)
—	10.6 (7.80 for α-amino)	—	~0.75 Imidazole and carboxyl	0.5 Imidazole	Breslow and Gurd (1962)
—	—	—	~0.4 After de-naturation	—	
—	—	—	Very low (but salt affects curves strongly due to ion binding)	~1.2 Carboxyl 1.0 Imidazole 0.67 Phenoxy up to 6M urea	Mihalyi (1950), Stracker (1960), Dubuisson and Hamoir (1943)
—	—	—	0.2	1.0 Carboxyl 1.0 Imidazole 0.1 Phenoxy up to 5 M urea (L-meromyosin) 1.0 Phenoxy (H-meromyosin)	Nanninga (1954)
—	—	—	—	—	Meadows *et al.* (1967)
13.3 (all)	10.1	—	~0.8 all groups	0 Phenoxy ~1 Other groups	Scatchard (1949), Harrington (1955), Charlwood and Ens (1957)

(*Continued*)

TABLE 5-4 (*Continued*)

Protein	Reversible range (or limits of titration if reversible throughout) (no pH drifts)	pH of rapid reversible conformational change within reversible region	Isoionic point	α-Carboxyl	pK_int^a Side-chain COOH	Imidazole
					$pK_{int}{}^{a}$	
Papain	—	—	—	—	—	—
Paramyosin	—	—	—	—	3.0, 6.0 (insoluble)	—
	—	—	—	—	4.55	6.40
					(0.3 M KCl) (insoluble)	
In guanidine hydrochloride	—	—	—	—	4.37 (soluble)	6.80
Pepsin	5–6	—	—	—	6.5 (for 3 to 6 of 38 groups)	—
Pepsinogen	6–9.5	—	—	—	—	—
Peroxidase (clearly parallel to hemoglobin)	Partial range	—	—	—	—	—
Denatured	—	—	—	—	—	—
Ribonuclease	2–11.5	—	9.6 (9.23 for minus component)	—	4.0, 4.7	6.5
5 M Guanidine hydrochloride	—	—	—	—	4.6	—
Urea	—	—	—	—	4.6	—
Native	—	—	—	—	—	5.6, 6.0, 6.2, 6.4

TABLE 5-4 (*Continued*)

| | $pK_{int}{}^a$ | | | | |
Phen-oxy	ε-Amino	Guani-dine	w_{obs}/w_{calc}	n_{obs}/n_{anal}	References
10.3 (12 of 17) > 12 (4), > 13 (1)	—	—	—	0.7 1.0 After alkaline denaturation	Glazer and Smith (1961)
—	—	11.5	Not spherical $w = 0.0019$ (Imidazole and carboxyl)	0.85 Phenoxy	Johnson and Kahn (1959)
9.62 (44 of 58) 13 (9)	9.65	—	$w = 0.0052$ (Amino, sulfhydryl, arginyl)	~1.0 All groups	
10.22	10.60	12	Lower when in guanidine	—	Riddiford and Scheraga (1962)
—	—	—	—	Possibly 0.0 α-amino and imidazole ~0.9 Carboxyl 6 groups appear at pH 6.7	Edelhoch (1958)
—	—	—	—	—	Perlmann et al. (1967)
> 12.4	—	—	—	~0.76 Carboxyl and imidazole ~0.0 Phenoxy	Morita and Kameda (1958)
10.6	—	—	—	—	Theorell (1943)
9.9 (3 of 6) >13) (3 of 6)	10.2	—	~1.0 Phenoxy 1.0 Carboxyl	0.5 Phenoxy 1.0 Other groups	Tanford et al. (1955b) Schugar (1952) Hermans and Scheraga (1961)
—	—	—	—	—	Cha and Scheraga (1960) Blumenfeld and Levy (1958)
—	—	—	—	—	Meadows et al. (1967)

(*Continued*)

TABLE 5-4 (*Continued*)

| Protein | Reversible range (or limits of titration if reversible throughout) (no pH drifts) | pH of rapid reversible conformational change within reversible region | Isoionic point | $pK_{int}{}^a$ | | |
				α-Carboxyl	Side-chain COOH	Imidazole
Serum albumin	2–12	3.8–4.2	5.4 (expected value 5.9)	—	4.0	6.9
N form	—	—	—	—	(3.7)	—
F form	—	—	—	—	(4.4)	—
Titration curves of BSA in dodecylbenzene-sulfonate solutions	—	—	—	—	—	—
Silk fibroin	2–13	—	—	—	—	—
Taka-Amylase A	—	—	—	—	~4.3 <2.0	—
TMV Protein	2.7–11.0	—	4.3–4.6	—	—	—
Thrombin	5.5–8.9	—	—	—	—	—
Thyroglobulin	2–11.4	Several	—	—	—	—
Trypsinogen	—	—	—	—	—	—
Trypsin	—	—	—	—	~3.5	—

TABLE 5-4 (*Continued*)

| $pK_{int}{}^a$ | | | | | |
Phen-oxy	ε-Amino	Guani-dine	w_{obs}/w_{calc}	n_{obs}/n_{anai}	References
10.35	9.8	—	~0.9 all groups	1.1 Carboxyl	Tanford *et al.* (1955a,c)
—	—	—	—	1.0 All other groups (at least in F conformation)	Aoki and Foster (1957) Vijai and Foster (1967)
—	—	—	—	0.6 Carboxyl	Decker and Foster (1967)
11.9 (0°)	—	—	—	~1.0 Phenoxy	Gleysteen and Harris (1941)
10.5 (native) irreversible	—	—	—	0.5 Phenoxy and carboxyl reported, but data suggest imidazole are also involved 1.0 After de-naturation by acid or base	Takagi and Isemura (1960, 1961)
—	—	—	—	—	Scheele and Lauffer (1967)
—	—	—	—	—	Winzor and Scheraga (1963)
—	—	—	—	1.0 Carboxyl, phenoxy	Edelhoch (1960a,b), Edelhoch and Metzger (1961)
~9.6 (4.8)	—	—	—	0.5 Phenoxy 1.0 Phenoxy after reversible denaturation	Smillie and Kay (1961)
—	—	—	—	>1.0 Carboxyl 1.0 Imidazole	Duke *et al.* (1952)

TABLE 5-5

TITRATION DATA FOR SERUM ALBUMIN[a]

Type of group	Number of groups		pK_{int}, 25°
	Analysis	Titration curve	
α-Carboxyl	1⎱	100	⎰—
Side-chain carboxyl	90⎰		⎱4.0
Imidazole	17⎱	18	⎰6.9
α-Amino	1⎰		⎱—
Thiol	<1⎱	57	⎰—
Side-chain amino	57⎰		⎱9.8
Phenolic	18	19	10.35
Guanidino	22	—	—
$\sum N^+$	97	96	—

[a] The data are for bovine albumin, with an assumed molecular weight of 65,000. Analytical data from Stein and Moore (1949); titration data from Tanford *et al.* (1955).

protonation in the native protein. The results are shown in Table 5-5. Plots of pH $-\log[r/(n-r)]$ vs. $\bar{Z}$ [Eq. (2-49), Chapter II] were not linear outside the range $\bar{Z} = +5$ (pH 4.3) to $\bar{Z} = -55$ (pH 10.5). A large decrease in w occurs outside the above titration range and the apparent pKs (Table 5-4) of carboxyls, phenolics, and ε-amino groups are distinctly anomalous. Subsequently, other investigations have shown that conformational changes occur in bovine serum albumin (BSA) at approximately the pH limits given above (see Foster, 1960, for a summary of these investigations). The largest effect on w in the acid region, however, takes place at a higher pH than that of the major conformational change observed by viscosity and optical measurements. Tanford (1962), reviewing his own results and those of other investigators, pointed out that the anomalous acid branch of the titration curve for BSA could be explained either by invoking buried carboxylate ions in the native form which are exposed at low pH, or, alternatively, assuming the number of available carboxyls to be identical in both states of the protein but with different pKs. Vijai and Foster (1967) have shown by an investigation of the infrared spectra of bovine serum albumin as a function of pH that the former alternative is correct in that the charged form of approximately 40 carboxyls is stabilized in the native molecule and unavailable for protonation at a pH above 4.3. These buried carboxylates may be stabilized by ε-amino groups or arginines in a cleft in the protein, but there is no direct evidence at hand to substantiate this possibility.

In addition to the buried carboxylate residues, approximately 30% of the 21 tyrosines in this protein have been shown by the solvent perturbation technique (Herskovits and Laskowski, 1961) to be unavailable to contact with sucrose or ethylene glycol in aqueous solution. This does not necessarily imply that they are unavailable to protons.

B. β-LACTOGLOBULIN—ABNORMAL CARBOXYL AND THIOL GROUPS

Early studies of the hydrogen-ion equilibria of β-lactoglobulin were carried out by Cannan *et al.* (1942), Tanford *et al.* (1959), and Nozaki *et al.* (1959). The experimental data could be reproduced by a theoretical curve using the *n* values shown in Table 5-6. Note that the latter two investigators

TABLE 5-6

GROUP COUNTING FOR β-LACTOGLOBULIN[a]

Type of group	Amino acid analysis[b]		Titration curve[c]			
	β-Lact A	β-Lact B	Native β-Lact A	Native β-Lact B	Native mixture[d]	Denatured mixture[d]
α-COOH	2	2⎫	52	50	51	53
Side-chain COOH	52	50⎭				
Imidazole	4	4	6	6	6	4
α-NH₂	2	2	2	2	2	2
Thiol	2	2	—	—	(0)[e]	(2)[e]
Phenolic	8	8	—	—⎫	(34)[e]	⎧ (6)[e,f]
Side-chain NH₂	28	28	—	—⎭		⎩ (28)[e]
Guanidyl	6	6	—	—	—	—
$\sum N^+$	40	40	40	40	40	40

[a] Table taken from Tanford (1962).

[b] Gordon *et al.* (1961), Piez *et al.* (1961). The figures have been adjusted to the nearest even integer for a two-chain molecule of molecular weight 35,500.

[c] Titration data of Nozaki *et al.* (1959), Tanford *et al.* (1959), and Tanford and Nozaki (1959).

[d] The mixture contained essentially equimolar amounts of the two genetic isomers, β-lactoglobulins A and B.

[e] Figures in parentheses are subject to considerable uncertainty.

[f] The number of phenolic groups was determined from the total change in extinction at 295 mμ in going from native protein with undissociated phenolic groups to denatured protein with all phenolic groups dissociated. No correction was made for the change in extinction at this wavelength which results from unfolding of the protein as a result of the emergence of the tryptophan residues from the inside of the native structure. There are four tryptophan residues per molecule, so that this change can be expected to be quite large, certainly large enough to account for an error of two groups in the count of phenolic groups.

studied the two genetic variants A and B as well as a mixture. Two anomalous carboxyls and four inaccessible thiol groups were observed in the native protein. The two carboxyls which do not titrate in the normal acid pH range appear with the histidines between pH 6.5 and 9.0 in both genetic species as indicated by the apparent increase by two in the number of imidazoles known to be present from amino acid analysis.

A more recent study by Timasheff *et al.* (1966) shows that all three known genetic variants, β-A, β-B, and β-C, undergo two discrete conformational changes in the region pH 4–9.5 as evidenced by ORD and sedimentation measurements. One transition between 6.5 and 9.5 is essentially identical in all three proteins and involves the two abnormal carboxyl groups referred to above. Since β-lactoglobulin exists as a dimer with two identical polypeptide chains in this pH range, it is assumed that one carboxyl per chain is involved in this transition.

Between pH 4 and 6, β-B and β-C undergo a second transition involving the ionization of one group, while the second transition of β-A appears to involve two groups. There is no clear-cut evidence as to the nature of these ionizable residues, but the authors have suggested that they may be one aspartyl in β-A which is substituted for one glycyl in β-B and β-C plus the one histidine in β-C which is substituted for a glutamine in β-A and β-B.

C. RIBONUCLEASE—ABNORMAL PHENOLIC GROUPS

Figure 5-4 shows the spectrophotometric titration of ribonuclease (Tanford *et al.*, 1955). It is clear that the reversible portion of the curve below pH 12 differs by three groups from the back-titration curve after exposure of the protein to pH 12.7. Analysis of these data by means of the Linderström-Lang equation, assuming three tyrosine residues ionized below pH 12, gives a normal pK of 9.9.

In addition to the above anomaly, the carboxyl portion of the potentiometric titration of this protein presents some ambiguities. The expected number of groups are titrated but w is abnormally large. Tanford and Hauenstein (1956) have pointed out that w is normal for this pH region if two sets of carboxyl groups are assumed, five with a pK of 4.0 and five with a pK of 4.7. Hermans and Scheraga (1961) fit the same data by assuming three sets of carboxyls—one with a pK of 2.5, one with a pK of 3.65, and eight with a pK of 4.6.

It is not possible to decide from the experimental evidence whether there are two or three distinct sets of carboxyl side chains or whether the abnormally large w obtained with the assumption of only one set is the result of inadequacies in the Linderström-Lang approximation. However, the recent work of Nozaki and Tanford which shows different pK's for aspartyl and glutamyl

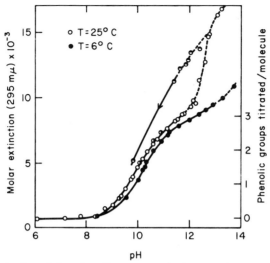

FIG. 5-4. Ionization of the phenolic groups at ionic strength 0.15. The ionization is independent of time where solid lines have been drawn; it increases with time where dashed lines have been drawn. (◑, Solutions at 25° reversed after exposure to pH 11.5; ◒, solutions at 25° reversed after exposure to pH 12.7. [C. Tanford *et al.* (1955). *J. Am. Chem. Soc.* **77,** 6409.]

groups (see p. 178) strongly suggests that the Tanford and Hauenstein proposal is correct.

A recent nuclear magnetic resonance study by Meadows *et al.* (1967) in which the chemical shifts of the C-2 protons on the four histidine residues in ribonuclease were measured as a function of pH (see Fig. 5-5) shows a distinctly different pK for each imidazole group. Two of these residues are known from x-ray data to be in the active site and a third is partially buried. However, the vast difference in individual pKs for a presumed identical set of sites is startling and demonstrates that a fit to the Linderström-Lang equation within plus or minus one group cannot be relied on for discriminating information as to pK_{int}.

D. Hemoglobin—Abnormal Imidazole Groups

Figure 5-6 shows the hydrogen-ion titration of cyanoferrihemoglobin between pH 3 and 8 at 0.3 M KCl obtained by Steinhardt *et al.* (1962). The back-titration of acid-denatured protein differs from the forward titration for native hemoglobin by 22 groups/67,000 molecular weight or 5.5 groups/heme. All of these groups were once tentatively identified as imidazoles, 4 of which are heme-linked. Since there are only 38 imidazoles in horse hemoglobin

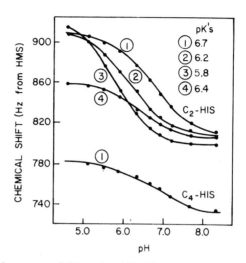

FIG. 5-5. Titration curves of C-2 peaks of histidine residues of RNase A. Approximate pK's are as follows: curve 1, 6.3; curve 2, 5.9; curve 3, 5.6; curve 4, 6.1. [D. H. Meadows *et al.* (1967). *Proc. Natl. Acad. Sci.* **58**, 1307.] (Slightly revised pK's were published in a later paper, Meadows *et al.*, 1968.)

(tetramer), almost two-thirds of these groups would have to be buried in the native protein. Extensive comparable titration data are available for the various hemoglobins (Steinhardt and Zaiser, 1951, 1955; Steinhardt *et al.*, 1958, 1962, 1963; Beychok and Steinhardt, 1959; Nozaki, 1959; and Geddes, and Steinhardt 1968). Hiremath and Steinhardt (1967) reported one more inaccessible histidine per heme in human than in horse hemoglobin.

In addition to the anomaly of masked imidazoles, there are specific ionizable residues affected by ligand binding to the heme group, or more specifically by the oxidation state of the iron in the heme. Thus, four groups (imidazoles) with a pK near 7.9 in reduced hemoglobin are titrated with a pK of 6.7 in oxyhemoglobin, and another four groups with a pK near 5.25 in reduced hemoglobin have a pK near 5.75 in oxyhemoglobin (Wyman and Ingalls, 1951).

Tanford and Nozaki (1966) have carefully analyzed the titration data of Antonini *et al.* (1965) for horse oxy- and deoxyhemoglobin in the pH range 5–9. Their results suggest that 2–3 imidazoles/heme are inaccessible in oxyhemoglobin and 3–3.5 imidazoles/heme in the deoxy protein. This difference between the two forms of hemoglobin reflects the altered pK of the group associated with the acid Bohr effect (see above, pK 5.25 in reduced hemoglobin and pK 5.75 in oxyhemoglobin). Human hemoglobin titration data were also examined by these authors, who find that 4 rather than 3 imidazoles/heme are inaccessible in this protein in the oxygenated form.

Steinhardt *et al.* (1962) determined the maximum number of buried imidazoles in horse ferrihemoglobin (5.5 imidazoles/heme) by difference counting assuming that the entire difference between native and acid denatured protein in this pH range is attributable to histidines. The pK of the carboxyls in denatured hemoglobin is probably slightly different from that in native protein (due to very small changes in w), so that some of the difference curve may be attributable to accessible carboxyls.

A subsequent analysis of the Antonini *et al.* (1965) human hemoglobin data by Bucci *et al.* (1968) points out that equally consistent with the experimental findings are 3.5–4.5 masked histidines/heme in oxyhemoglobin. The principal differences in the approach by these authors and that used by Tanford and Nozaki are as follows:

(1) Bucci *et al.* assume 1.5 ionizable —SH groups per human chain while Tanford and Nozaki assume 0.5/chain.

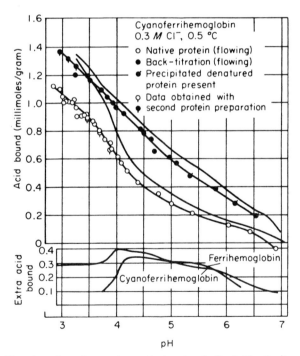

FIG. 5-6. Titration data for native and denatured (back-titration) cyanoferrihemoglobin at 0.5° in the presence of 0.3 M chloride. The difference in acid bound is shown as a function of pH in the inset at the bottom of the figure. Similar data for ferrihemoglobin are included as smooth curves for comparison. [J. Steinhardt *et al.* (1962). *Biochemistry* **1**, 29.]

(2) Bucci *et al.*, assume 1 carboxyl associated with the acid Bohr effect with a pK of 6.26 in oxyhemoglobin. Tanford and Nozaki assume all carboxyls are normal, and then observe that there is a difference of 0.5 groups between the titration of the histidine residues in oxy- and deoxyhemoglobin.

In a recent investigation by Geddes and Steinhardt (1968) horse COHb has been titrated anaerobically in a rapid flow apparatus. Data from this study suggests a maximum of 12 imidazoles/tetramer (3/heme) masked in the native hemoglobin. The additional ionizable residues exposed by acid treatment (12/tetramer; 3/heme) are identified tentatively as both carboxyl groups (possibly on the hemes) and more basic residues such as lysine or tyrosine.

The maximum difference in the titration curves of horse ferrihemoglobin determined by Steinhardt *et al.* (1963) is about 22 groups/tetramer, which corresponds to 5 groups/heme. From independent determination of the equilibrium constant between native and denatured hemoglobin (Beychok and Steinhardt, 1959; Steinhardt *et al.*, 1963; Steinhardt and Zaiser, 1955) $\partial \ln K/\partial \ln a_{H^+} = \Delta \bar{v}_{H^+} = 3$ to 5 [Eq. (2-68)] depending on the range of pH in which it is measured. Where appropriate allowances are made for the effect of the buffers used in determining $\partial \ln K/\partial \ln a_{H^+}$ the slope is -5 at pH values below 4.4 and about -3 at pH values above 4.6. At the same temperature and ionic strength the maximum apparent $\Delta \bar{v}$ (22) is reached at about pH 4.4. Since $\Delta \bar{v}_{H^+}$ should agree point by point with the difference titration curves, the above results suggest that the transition between native and denatured hemoglobin may occur within a single chain. Thus

$$\alpha_1(\text{native})\beta_1(\text{native}) \overset{K}{\rightleftarrows} \alpha_1(\text{denatured})\beta_1(\text{native})$$

not

$$\alpha_1(\text{native})\beta_1(\text{native}) \rightleftarrows \alpha_1(\text{denatured})\beta_1(\text{denatured})$$

which would give $\partial \ln K/\partial \ln a_{H^+} = \Delta \bar{v}_{H^+} = 10$. This aspect of the hemoglobin data seems worthy of further investigation and definition.

E. Insulin and Zinc Insulin

These particular examples are chosen to illustrate the kinds of information relating to the sites of metal–protein binding which can be obtained from hydrogen ion equilibria studies. Table 5-7 gives an analysis of the experimental titration data for insulin and zinc insulin obtained by Tanford and Epstein (1954). The count of imidazole groups is reduced from four to two when zinc is bound to the apoprotein; histidines are thus tentatively identified as zinc binding sites. $Zn(H_2O)_4^{2+}$ normally exists in solution with four acidic waters. Since only two acidic waters are titrated in zinc insulin, the metal has formed two metal–protein bonds.

TABLE 5-7

Titration Data for Insulin at 25° [a,b]

Type of group	Analysis	Number of groups		pK_{int}
		Titration		
		Zinc-free insulin	Zinc insulin	
α-Carboxyl	4 ⎱	12.5	14.5[d]	⎰3.6[e]
Side-chain carboxyl	8.5[c] ⎰			⎱4.7
Imidazole	4	4	2	6.4
α-Amino	4	4	4	7.4
Side-chain amino	2 ⎱	10	10	9.6[f]
Phenolic	8 ⎰			
Guanidyl	2	2	2	11.9
$Zn(H_2O)^{2+}$	—	—	2	—

[a] Table taken from Tanford (1962).

[b] Data of Tanford and Epstein (1954), calculated for an insulin dimer of molecular weight 11,466. The zinc insulin preparation contained one zinc atom dimer molecule. The pK_{int} values are for the zinc-free protein.

[c] The fractional number arises from the probable presence of two forms of insulin which differ in the number of free carboxyl groups.

[d] Two of the groups titrating as carboxyl groups are the imidazole groups to which the Zn^{2+} ion is bound.

[e] This pK was determinable because the titration curve of the carboxyl groups was clearly not compatible with the presence of 12.5 identical groups. Assuming 4 groups with a lower pK, this was the value required.

[f] No attempt was made to distinguish between amino and phenolic groups in the analysis.

F. Paramyosin, a Rodlike Protein

The previous examples have stressed the presence of anomalous titratable residues in a few globular proteins. Paramyosin is a protein which is not spherical in shape, but rodlike. The hydrogen-ion equilibria of a number of such proteins have been reported (e.g., Lowey and Kucera, 1964; Scheele and Lauffer, 1967; Bakerman and Hartman, 1966). However, many such investigations cover only a limited pH range or do not contain a complete analysis of the data. Paramyosin, prepared from the adductor muscle of *Venus mercenaria*, is a long cylindrical protein with length, 1400 Å and radius, 9.3 Å. The hydrogen-ion equilibria of this macromolecule were studied by Riddiford and Scheraga (1962) in 0.3 M KCl as well as in a denaturing solvent containing 5 M guanidine hydrochloride and 1.2 M urea. (This solvent did not completely disorder the native structure of the protein.) All prototropic groups are found to be exposed to solvent in the native protein. Spectrophotometric titration of the phenolic groups in the two solvent systems showed a 15% lower total absorbance change at 2950 Å in 0.3 M KCl than in guanidine. However, the author's conclusion that nine tyrosines were buried in the native conformation is probably erroneous since $\Delta\varepsilon$/ionized-tyrosine varies from solvent to solvent (Wetlaufer, 1962).

Significantly, this investigation established that the experimentally observed electrostatic interaction factor, w, is of the order of 10^{-3} for the native protein. This value is to be compared with the theoretical value of 2.74×10^{-3} calculated from the Hill equation for a rigid cylinder (Chapter II).

VI. Hydrogen-Ion Equilibria of Denatured Proteins

The term "denatured" has customarily been applied to any macromolecular conformation differing from the native state. In the present context it is applied to denatured states in which there are no important noncovalent interactions and in which the protein behaves as a random coil as understood by polymer chemists (Flory, 1953). One simple criterion of random-coil behavior which has been applied by Tanford and co-workers is the theoretical linear relationship between the logarithm of the degree of polymerization (number of amino acid residues per chain) and the logarithm of some hydrodynamic property such as intrinsic viscosity or sedimentation coefficient. A protein in random-coil conformation should have all protonatable residues exposed to solvent with approximately the pKs found in model compounds, provided the ionic strength is high. In addition, the electrostatic interaction [or any other interaction energy as defined in Eq. (2-31)] should ideally be reduced to zero. In actual practice, it is unlikely that zero electrostatic interaction will be observed since no solvent system is likely to be ideal for a molecule in which both hydrophobic and hydrophilic residues are found, but electrostatic interactions are negligible at such high electrolyte concentrations. In this sense, no protein is probably ever truly "random" in solution in the same way that polyisobutylene is a random coil in an ideal solvent such as benzene at 25°.

Figure 5-2, which has been briefly discussed in Section IV of this chapter, shows the hydrogen-ion equilibria of ribonuclease in 6 M guanidine hydrochloride. A complete analysis of these data by means of the Linderström-Lang equation [Eq. (2-50)] gives $w = 0.017$ for the phenolic groups if all six are presumed identical, $w = 0.020$ for carboxyls if both aspartyl and glutamyl residues have the same intrinsic pK, and $w = 0$ for the lysines. If, however, the carboxyl side chains are divided into two classes, glutamyl and aspartyl, in accord with the known amino acid content of the protein and assigned pKs of 3.8 and 4.3, respectively, the acid branch of Fig. 5-2 can be fitted with $w = 0$. In addition, if three of the phenolics are assumed to have a pK of 9.75 and three a pK of 10.15, the alkaline branch of Fig. 5-2 can be fitted also with $w = 0$. The assignment of two different pKs in the acid region rests on the previously discussed work of Nozaki and Tanford (1967) (see Section II). The justification for assuming three somewhat abnormal tyrosines lies in the sequence of ribonuclease in which two of the tyrosyl groups (25 and 73) are adjacent to disulfide bonds and a third (115) occurs in the sequence Pro-Tyr-Val-Pro-Val. The important conclusion to be drawn from this work is that ribonuclease, which appears to be in random-coil conformation in 6 M guanidine hydrochloride as evidenced by hydrodynamic measurements (Tanford *et al.*, 1967), also has a greatly reduced, if not actually zero, electrostatic interaction factor for hydrogen-ion equilibria in this solvent.

VII. Unfolding as a Function of Protonation

Most proteins undergo conformational changes as the net charge on the macromolecule is increased through alterations in proton binding. A few such cases will be discussed in this section to illustrate the following observations:

(1) When a rapid, reversible conformational change takes place as a function of pH of a protein solution, it is not possible to analyze the titration curve by means of the simple model of Linderström-Lang (Chapter II). The number of accessible groups in the native state may be altered by such a transition, w will change with pH, and it may be necessary or appear to be necessary to assume several values of pK for one type of ionizable residue to fit the experimental data.

(2) Stabilization against pH-induced unfolding may occur through the binding of prosthetic groups or other ligand molecules to the protein.

A. Bovine Serum Albumin

It has been pointed out (p. 117, *et seq.*) that conformational transitions occur in bovine serum albumin at pH 4–4.5 (N → F transition), pH 7.0, and above pH 11.0. These alterations in protein structure have been well documented by viscosity and optical measurements (see Foster, 1960, for a concise review of the properties of BSA). At pH below 4.0 this protein undergoes a continuous, rapid, reversible expansion which leads to a Linderström-Lang plot of the type shown in Fig. 5-8. The same situation occurs when the proton binding data is plotted for phenolic and lysine residues shown in Fig. 5-9. It is not possible to tell from the hydrogen-ion titration data, treated by conventional

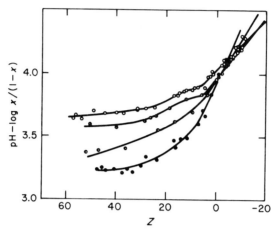

FIG. 5-7. Logarithmic plot for the dissociation of carboxyl groups, at ionic strength 0.01 (●); 0.03 (◐); 0.08 (◑); 0.15 (O). [C. Tanford *et al.* (1955b). *J. Am. Chem. Soc.* **77**, 6414.]

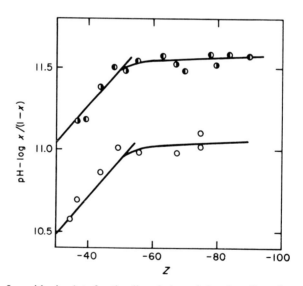

FIG. 5-8. Logarithmic plots for the dissociation of the phenolic and ε-amino groups. The upper curve represents phenolic groups, using the data of Tanford and Roberts (1952), using buffered solutions (◐) and points taken from a smooth curve through unbuffered solutions (◑). The lower curve represents the ε-amino groups. [C. Tanford *et al.* (1955b). *J. Am. Chem. Soc.* **77**, 6414].

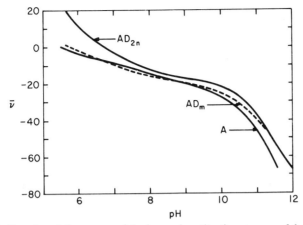

FIG. 5-9. Experimentally measured hydrogen-ion titration curves of bovine plasma albumin, A, and its detergent complexes, AD_m and AD_{2n}. [A. Decker and J. F. Foster (1967). *J. Biol. Chem.* **242**, 1526.]

means, how many groups are accessible in the native state of bovine serum albumin since w certainly changes with increased charge, and the back-titration curve is indistinguishable from the forward titration, since regeneration is extremely rapid.

A recent study by Decker and Foster (1967) reported the hydrogen-ion titration curves for BSA between pH 5.5 and 11.0. These authors also investigated the proton binding behavior of the two complexes of BSA with 11 and 76 dodecylbenzenesulfonate ions. It was shown that serum albumin undergoes cooperative unfolding as the result of tyrosine ionization but that the complex BSA(detergent)$_{11}$ was stabilized against this transition. The complex BSA(detergent)$_{76}$ appeared to have undergone the transition prior to titration of the tyrosine residues. This stabilization is discussed further in Chapter VII.

It was not possible to examine the acid branch of the titration curve for the BSA–detergent complexes due to precipitation of the protein. However, an interesting phenomenon is shown in Fig. 5-9. BSA(detergent)$_{76}$, which is in a partially unfolded state, appears to have a large number of its carboxylate groups "normalized" in contrast to native BSA, for which it was shown in the previous section (p. 198) that approximately 40 carboxylate ions are buried and inaccessible to protons.

A recent investigation by Avruch *et al.* (1969) showed that when all 57 lysine residues in BSA are blocked by methyl acetimidate hydrochloride, a small expansion of the protein occurs, accompanied by a normalization of some carboxylate and tyrosine residues. The pH-induced transitions at pH 4.5 and 7.0 are observed in the modified protein but appear to produce a larger effect on the optical rotatory dispersion than is observed with native BSA.

B. E. Coli Alkaline Phosphatase

Alkaline phosphatase undergoes a pH-induced transition below pH 5.0 and above pH 9.0 (Reynolds and Schlesinger, 1967, 1968). Zn^{2+} is bound to the native protein (4 Zn^{2+}/86,000 molecular weight) and stabilizes against charge disruption as evidenced by the fact that the above transitions occur at pH 5.5 and 8.0 in the apoprotein (Reynolds and Schlesinger, 1969).

In alkaline phosphatase only tyrosine residues and four histidine residues to which Zn^{2+} is bound are masked in the native state.

Finally, it should be noted that even very high degrees of protonation of proteins do not always lead to total disruption of native conformation. In fact, acid-induced denaturation in the majority of cases leads to intermediate states which still contain residual structure. Tanford (1968) gives a recent review of the extent of disorganization by acid.

VIII. Summary

The most common anomalies encountered in the hydrogen-ion titration curves of native proteins are inaccessible histidine and phenolic residues. It is apparent from Table 5-4 that a large number of proteins have part or all of these groups buried in the native state. Much more uncommon are abnormalities of carboxyl and lysine residues. β-lactoglobulin contains 2 abnormal carboxyl groups which titrate at pH 7.3. Serum albumin has 40 buried carboxylate groups which may be paired with lysine or argenine residues. Most proteins which contain prosthetic groups have some abnormal ionizable residues as the result of interactions with the bound moiety. However, as would have been predicted from chemical considerations, and as is borne out by experimental data, most polar residues in proteins are exposed to the aqueous environment and titrate with pK's not far removed from those of model compounds.

Comparison of proton binding for several states of the same macromolecule is a valuable tool for investigating structural differences. Binding sites of metals (Zn insulin, alkaline phosphatase) are identified by this means. In addition, transitions induced by charge changes on the protein are frequently observed in the analysis of hydrogen-ion titration curves.

REFERENCES

Antonini, E., Wyman, J., Brunori, M., Fronticelli, C., Bucci, E., and Rossi-Fanelli, A. (1965). *J. Biol. Chem.* **240**, 1096.
Aoki, K., and Foster, J. F. (1957). *J. Am. Chem. Soc.* **79**, 3393.
Avruch, J., Reynolds, J. A., and Reynolds, J. H. (1969). *Biochemistry* **8**, 1855.
Bakerman, S., and Hartman, B. K. (1966). *Biochemistry* **5**, 3488.

Beychok, S., and Steinhardt, J. (1959). *J. Am. Chem. Soc.* **81**, 5679.

Blumenfeld, O. O., and Levy, M. (1958). *Arch. Biochem. Biophys.* **76**, 97.

Bowes, J. H., and Kenten, R. H. (1948). *Biochem. J.* **43**, 358.

Breslow, E., and Gurd, F. R. N. (1962). *J. Biol. Chem.* **237**, 371.

Bucci, E., Fronticelli, C., and Ragatz, B. (1968). *J. Biol. Chem.* **243**, 241.

Bull, H. B., and Breese, K. (1966). *Biochem. Biophys. Res. Comm.* **24**, 74.

Cannan, R. K., Palmer, A. H., and Kibrick, A. (1942). *J. Biol. Chem.* **142**, 803.

Cha, C. Y., and Scheraga, H. A. (1960). *J. Am. Chem. Soc.* **82**, 54.

Charlwood, P. A., and Ens, A. (1957). *Can. J. Chem.* **35**, 99.

Chaudhri, D. R. (1948). *Hug. Acta. Physiol.* **1**, 238.

Chu, F. S. (1968). *J. Biol. Chem.* **243**, 4342.

Decker, A., and Foster, J. F. (1967). *J. Biol. Chem.* **242**, 1526.

Di Sabato, G. (1965). *Biochemistry* **4**, 2288.

Donovan, J. W., Laskowski, M., Jr., and Scheraga, H. A. (1960). *J. Am. Chem. Soc.* **82**, 2154.

Donovan, J. W., Laskowski, M., Jr., and Scheraga, H. A. (1961a). *J. Am. Chem. Soc.* **83**, 2686.

Donovan, J. W., Laskowski, M., Jr., and Scheraga, H. A. (1961b). *J. Am. Chem. Soc.* **83**, 2686.

Dubuisson, M., and Hamoir, G. (1943). *Arch. Intern. Physiol.* **53**, 308.

Duke, J. A., Bier, M., and Nord, F. F. (1952). *Arch. Biochem. Biophys.* **40**, 4240.

Edelhoch, H. (1958). *J. Am. Chem. Soc.* **80**, 6640.

Edelhoch, H. (1960a). *J. Phys. Chem.* **64**, 1771.

Edelhoch, H. (1960b). *J. Biol. Chem.* **235**, 1326.

Edelhoch, H., and Metzger, H. (1961). *J. Am. Chem. Soc.* **83**, 1428.

Edsall, J. T., and Wyman, J. (1958). "Biophysical Chemistry," Vol. I. Academic Press, New York.

Flory, P. J. (1953). "Principles of Polymer Chemistry." Cornell Univ. Press, Ithaca, New York.

Foster, J. F. (1960). *In* "The Plasma Proteins" (F. W. Putnam, ed.), Vol. I, 0. 179. Academic Press, New York.

Fredericq, E. (1954). *J. Polymer Sci.* **12**, 287.

Fredericq, E. (1956). Thesis, Université de Liège, cited by Tanford (1963).

Geddes, R., and Steinhardt, J. (1968). *J. Biol. Chem.* **243**, 6056.

Glazer, A. N., and Smith, E. L. (1961). *J. Biol. Chem.* **236**, 2948.

Gleysteen, L. F., and Harris, M. (1941). *J. Res. Natl. Bur. St.* **26**, 71.

Gordon, W. G., Basch, J. J., and Kalan, E. (1961). *J. Biol. Chem.* **236**, 2908.

Gould, H. J., Gill, T. J., III, and Doty, P. (1964). *J. Biol. Chem.* **239**, 2842.

Gruen, J. P., Laskowski, M., Jr., and Scheraga, H. A. (1959). *J. Am. Chem. Soc.* **81**, 3891.

Harned, H. S., and Owen, B. B. (1950). "Physical Chemistry of Electrolyte Solutions." Reinhold, New York (3rd ed. 1958).

Harrington, W. F. (1955). *Biochim. Biophys. Acta* **18**, 450.

Hermans, J., and Scheraga, H. (1961). *J. Am. Chem. Soc.* **83**, 3283, 3293.

Herskovits, T. T., and Laskowski, M., Jr. (1962). *J. Biol. Chem.* **237**, 2481.

Hiremath, G. B., and Steinhardt, J. (1967). *J. Biol. Chem.* **242**, 1294.

Hipp, N. J., Grover, M. S., and McMeekin, J. L. (1952). *J. Am. Chem. Soc.* **74**, 4822.

Johnson, W. H., and Kahn, J. S. (1959). *Science* **130**, 1190.

Kenchington, A. W., and Ward, A. G. (1954). *Biochem. J.* **58**, 202.

Leonis, J., and Li, C. H. (1959). *J. Am. Chem. Soc.* **81**, 415.

Linderström-Lang, K. (1935). *Trans. Faraday Soc.* **31**, 324.

Linderström-Lang, K., and Nielsen, S. O. (1959). *In* "Electrophoresis: Theory and Applications" (M. Bier, ed.). Academic Press, New York.

Lowey, S., and Kucera, J. (1964). Biochem. Muscle Contr. 8–15.

Margoliash, E., Kimmel, J. R., Hill, R. L., and Schmidt, W. R. (1962). *J. Biol. Chem.* **237**, 2148.

Marini, M. A., and Wunsch, C. (1966). *Biochemistry* **2**, 1454.

Meadows, D. H., Jardetzky, O., Epand, R. M., Ruterjans, A. H., and Scheraga, H. A. (1968). *Proc. Natl. Acad. Sci.* **60**, 766.

Meadows, D. H., Markley, J. L., Cohen, J. S., and Jardetzky, O. (1967). *Proc. Natl. Acad. Sci.* **58**, 1307.

Mihalyi, E. (1950). *Enzymologia* **14**, 224.

Mihalyi, E. (1954). *J. Biol. Chem.* **209**, 723, 733.

Mihashi, K., and Ooi, J. (1965). *Biochemistry* **4**, 805.

Morita, Y., and Kameda, K. (1958). *Mem. Res. Inst. Food Sci. Kyota Univ.* **14**, 61.

Nanninga, L. B. (1954). Personal communication.

Nozaki, Y., and Tanford, C. (1967). *J. Biol. Chem.* **242**, 4731.

Nozaki, Y., and Tanford, C. (1969). Personal communication.

Nozaki, Y., Bunville, L. G., and Tanford, C. (1959). *J. Am. Chem. Soc.* **81**, 5523.

Paleus, S. (1954). *Acta Chem. Scand.* **8**, 871.

Perlmann, G., Oplatka, A., and Katchalsky, A. (1967). *J. Biol. Chem.* **242**, 5163.

Piez, K. A., Davie, E. W., Folk, J. E., and Gladner, J. A. (1961). *J. Biol. Chem.* **236**, 2912.

Rasmusson, D. K., and Linderström-Lang, K. (1935). *Compt. Rend. Trav. Lab. Carlsberg* **20**, No. 10.

Reynolds, J. A., and Schlesinger, M. J. (1967). *Biochemistry* **6**, 3552.

Reynolds, J. A., and Schlesinger, M. J. (1968). *Biochemistry* **7**, 2080.

Reynolds, J. A., and Schlesinger, M. J. (1969). *Biochemistry* **8**, 588.

Riddiford, L. M., and Scheraga, H. A. (1962). *Biochemistry* **1**, 95.

Rousselot, A. (1944). *Compt. Rend. Trav. Lab. Carlsberg* **218**, 716.

Rupley, J. A. (1964). *Biochemistry* **3**, 1648.

Scatchard, G. (1949). *Ann. N.Y. Acad. Sci.* **51**, 660.

Scheele, R. B., and Lauffer, M. A. (1967). *Biochemistry* **6**, 3076.

Shugar, D. (1952). *Biochem. J.* **52**, 142.

Shulman, S., and Ferry, J. D. (1954). *J. Phys. Colloid Chem.* **54**, 66.

Smillie, L. B., and Kay, C. N. (1961). *J. Biol. Chem.* **236**, 112.

Stein, W. H., and Moore, S. (1949). *J. Biol. Chem.* **178**, 79.

Steinhardt, J. (1941). *Ann. N.Y. Acad. Sci.* **41**, 287.

Steinhardt, J., and Zaiser, E. M. (1951). *J. Biol. Chem.* **190**, 197.

Steinhardt, J., and Zaiser, E. M. (1955). *Advan. in Protein Chem.* **10**, 151.

Steinhardt, J., and Beychok, S. (1964). *In* "The Proteins," Vol. II, 139. Academic Press, New York.

Steinhardt, J., Fuggitt, C. H., and Harris, M. (1940a). *J. Res. Natl. Bur. Std.* **24**, 335.

Steinhardt, J., Fuggitt, C. H., and Harris, M. (1940b). *J. Res. Natl. Bur. Std.* **25**, 1579.

Steinhardt, J., Zaiser, E. M., and Beychok, S. (1958). *J. Am. Chem. Soc.* **80**, 4634.

Steinhardt, J., Ona, R., and Beychok, S. (1962). *Biochemistry* **1**, 29.

Steinhardt, J., Ona, R., Beychok, S., and Ho, C. (1963). *Biochemistry* **2**, 256.

Stellwagon, E. (1964). *Biochemistry* **3**, 919.

Stracker, A. (1960). *J. Biol. Chem.* **235**, 2302.

Takagi, T., and Isemura, T. (1960). *J. Biochem.* (*Tokyo*) **48**, 781.

Takagi, T., and Isemura, T. (1961). *J. Biochem.* (*Tokyo*) **49**, 43.

Tanford, C. (1962). *Advan. Protein Chem.* **17**, 69.

Tanford, C. (1968). *Advan. Protein Chem.* **23**, 121.

Tanford, C., and Roberts, G. L., Jr. (1952). *J. Am. Chem. Soc.* **74**, 2509.

Tanford, C., and Epstein, J. (1954). *J. Am. Chem. Soc.* **76**, 2163, 2170.

Tanford, C., and Wagner, M. L. (1954). *J. Am. Chem. Soc.* **76**, 3331.

Tanford, C., and Hauenstein, J. D. (1956). *J. Am. Chem. Soc.* **78**, 5287.

Tanford, C., and Nozaki, Y. (1966). *J. Biol. Chem.* **241**, 2832.

Tanford, C., and Nozaki, Y. (1967). *J. Am. Chem. Soc.* **89**, 742.

Tanford, C., Swanson, S. A., and Shore, W. S. (1955). *J. Am. Chem. Soc.* **77**, 6414.

Tanford, C., Buzzell, J. G., Rands, D. G., and Swanson, S. A. (1955a). *J. Am. Chem. Soc.* **77**, 6421.

Tanford, C., Hauenstein, J. D., and Rands, D. G. (1955b). *J. Am. Chem. Soc.* **77**, 6409.

Tanford, C., Swanson, S. A., and Shore, W. S. (1955c). *J. Am. Chem. Soc.* **77**, 6414.

Tanford, C., Bunville, L. G., and Nozaki, Y. (1959). *J. Am. Chem. Soc.* **81**, 4032.

Tanford, C., Kawahara, K., Lapanje, S. (1967). *J. Am. Chem. Soc.* **89**, 729.

Theorell, H. (1943). *Arkiv. Kemi.* **16A**, No. 14.

Theorell, H., and Akison, A. (1941). *J. Am. Chem. Soc.* **63**, 1818.

Timasheff, S. N., Mescanti, L., Basch, J. J., and Townsend, R. (1966). *J. Biol. Chem.* **241**, 2496.

Vijai, K. K., and Foster, J. F. (1967). *Biochemistry* **6**, 1152.

Wetlaufer, D. B. (1962). *Advan. Protein Chem.* **17**.

Winzor, D. J., and Scheraga, H. A. (1964). *Arch. Biochem. Biophys.* **104**, 202.

Wishnia, A., Weber, J., and Warner, R. C. (1961). *J. Am. Chem. Soc.* **83**, 2071.

Wu, Y. V., and Dimler, R. J. (1963). *Arch. Biochem. Biophys.* **102**, 230; **103**, 310.

Wyman, J., Jr. (1939). *J. Biol. Chem.* **127**, 1.

Wyman, J., Jr. (1948). *Advan. Protein Chem.* **4**, 407.

Wyman, J., and Ingalls, E. N. (1951). *J. Biol. Chem.* **139**, 877.

Yip, Y. K., and Bucci, E. (1968). *J. Biol. Chem.* **243**, 5948.

VI

Metal-Ion Binding

The interaction of metallic cations with proteins is a subject which quite naturally follows the previous chapter dealing with hydrogen-ion equilibria since some protein binding sites are the same for metal ions and protons. In this chapter two general classes of proteins will be considered:

(1) Systems in which the metal ion occupies a small number of very high energy sites and is essential for the biological function of the macromolecule (e.g., alkaline phosphatase, carboxypeptidase).

(2) Systems in which metal binds reversibly to specific amino acid residues in the polypeptide chain but is not required for biological activity and indeed may even impair protein function or disrupt protein structure.

Proteins in which metal is found as a complex with a prosthetic group such as heme are properly considered within the first class but will not be dealt with at length here since one case, hemoglobin, is discussed more fully in other chapters (IV, V).

The reader is referred to earlier reviews on metalloproteins (Vallee *et al.*, 1955) and complex formation with metallic cations (Gurd and Wilcox, 1956) for additional discussions of the above two systems.

I. Metal Ions and Their Complexes in Solution

In other sections of this book substances which bind to proteins are referred to as ligands. In a discussion of metallic ions we will reverse this nomenclature in order to conform with that used customarily in inorganic chemistry and refer to the groups which occupy the coordination sites of the metal ions as ligands.

214

Metal ions, like protons, share electron pairs from the donor atoms of a ligand molecule and thus form partially covalent bonds with characteristic heats of formation. This type of binding is distinguished from binding to proteins of neutral molecules or large organic ions such as detergents, where the large binding forces are primarily entropic in origin.

A complete discussion of metal-ion complexes and their physical and chemical properties may be found in Gurd and Wilcox (1956). We will summarize a few of the most important facts necessary to an understanding of metal–protein interactions:

(1) All metal ions have sets of characteristic coordination numbers which represent the number of hybrid bonds available for ligands (Table 6-1).

TABLE 6-1

METAL–LIGAND BONDS[a]

System	No. ligand bonds
$Ag^{1+} + 2NH_3$	2
$Hg^{2+} + 4NH_3$	2
$Zn^{2+} + 4NH_3$	4
$Cd^{2+} + 6NH_3$	4
$Cu^{2+} + 5NH_3$	4
$Ni^{2+} + 6NH_3$	6

[a] Taken from Gurd and Wilcox (1956).

(2) The coordination positions may be filled by sharing the nonbonded electron pair on the oxygen of a water molecule so that in aqueous solution all metal ions exist as complex ions. These metal–H_2O complexes are acidic in that a proton can be lost by the liganded water at an appropriate pH, leading to the formation of a metal hydroxide.

(3) Chelate complexes are formed when two or more donor atoms from the same ligand molecule are linked to the same metal ion. The binding energy for chelates is generally much higher than for simple 1 : 1 complexes.

Table 6-2 gives some overall association constants for metal–amino acid complexes. The order of constants for different metals is without exception

$$Cu > Ni > Zn > Co > Cd > Fe^{2+} > Mn > Mg$$

All natural amino acids have the skeletal structure

TABLE 6-2

LOGARITHMS OF ASSOCIATION CONSTANTS OF COMPLEXES OF AMINO ACIDS (AND ONE DIPEPTIDE) WITH METALS[a]

Amino acid	pK	Cu^{2+}	Ni^{2+}	Zn^{2+}	Co^{2+}	Cd^{2+}	Fe^{2+}	Mn^{2+}	Mg^{2+}	Fe^{3+}
Glycine	9.86	15.4	11.0	9.3	8.9	8.1	7.8	5.5	4	0
L-Proline	10.68	16.8	11.3	10.2	9.3	8.7	8.3	5.5	4	0
DL-Tryptophan	9.55	15.9	10.2	9.3	8.5	8.1	7.6	5.0	4	0
L-Asparagine	8.55	14.9	10.6	8.7	8.4	6.8	6.5	4.5	4	0
DL-Alanine	9.97	15.1	—	—	8.4	7.3	—	—	—	—
DL-Valine	9.72	15.1	—	—	8.6	—	6.8	—	—	—
DL-Phenylalanine	9.31	14.9	—	—	7.9	—	6.3	—	—	—
DL-Serine	9.24	14.6	—	—	8.0	—	7.0	—	—	—
DL-Methionine	9.34	14.7	—	—	7.9	—	6.7	—	—	—
β-Alanine	10.36	12.9	—	—	7.0	—	4.0	—	—	—
L-Tyrosine	—	15.0	10.1	9.1	8.1	—	7.1	2.4	2	—
L-Lysine	—	13.7	8.8	7.5	6.8	—	7.1[b]	2.0	—	—
L-Glutamic Acid	—	—	10.3	8.5	8.1	—	4.6[b]	3.0	—	—
Glycylglycine	—	11.7	7.9	6.6	5.9	—	—	2.2	1.1	—

[a] Data from Greenstein and Winitz (1961).
[b] Value of log K_1.

It is apparent that chelation of a metal ion with such a structure is possible through the formation of a five-membered ring:

$$
\begin{array}{c}
R \\
| \\
C \\
H_2N \diagup \overset{|}{H} \diagdown C=O \\
\backslash \quad \diagup \\
M-O^-
\end{array}
$$

In addition, the side chain, R, may contain nonbonded electrons which will also act as donors to a metal–ligand bond.

When the amino acids are joined in a polypeptide chain, the number of cyclic chelates possible is greatly reduced. Thus, *N*-terminal histidine or cysteine could form cyclic structures such as those shown below

or two or more amino acid residues on a protein molecule could enter a sterically favored chelated structure with a metal ion. More probable binding sites on a protein molecule for metallic ions, however, are single amino acid residues.

II. Experimental Methods and Data Treatment

The binding of metal ions to proteins can be measured by equilibrium dialysis such as has been described in Chapter III with the precautions that the pH of the solutions must be carefully controlled and the number of binding sites and association constants measured as a function of pH. Since metal ions and protons compete for the same sites on a protein molecule, Eq. (2-32) is applicable provided the effects of electrostatic interaction are included.

By analogy with Eq. (2-46)

$$k_{\text{metal}} = K \exp(-2wz_{\text{metal}} Z) \tag{6-1}$$

where k_{metal} is the apparent association constant for metal; K is the intrinsic association constant; z_{metal}, the charge on each metal ion; Z, the net charge on the protein; and

$$k_{\text{hydrogen}} = K' \exp(-2wZ) = 1/K_H \exp(-2wZ) \tag{6-2}$$

where k_{hydrogen} is the apparent association constant for hydrogen-ion; K' is the intrinsic association constant for protons; and K_H, the intrinsic dissociation constant for protons. Substituting Eqs. (6-1) and (6-2) into the equation for competitive binding given in Chapter II [Eq. (2.32)]

$$\frac{\bar{v}_{metal}}{n - \bar{v}_{metal}} = \frac{K \exp(-2wz_{metal}Z)C_{metal}}{1 + a_{H^+}/(k_H)\exp(2wZ)} \tag{6-3}$$

The values of $\bar{v}$ and C_{metal} are determined from equilibrium dialysis measurements and a_{H^+}, Z, w, and k_H are obtained from the hydrogen-ion titration curve of the protein in the absence of metal. It is then possible to calculate K, the intrinsic association constant of metal for the protein.

The treatment above assumes simple competition between one metal ion and one proton for a single site. If the metal–protein complex is a chelate such that each metal ion competes with more than one hydrogen ion, the following treatment is applicable. (For simplicity, we deal with the case of two protein sites for each metal ion. The mathematics is easily extended to higher chelate complexes.)

The following distribution of sites occurs in this example:

(1) A fraction of proton binding sites $\bar{v}/n$ contains a metal ion.
(2) A fraction $[1 - (\bar{v}/n)](1 - \alpha)^2$ contains no metal and two protons, where α is the fraction of sites containing no protons

$$\alpha = \frac{k_H \exp(2wZ)/a_{H^+}}{1 + k_H \exp(2wZ)/a_{H^+}}$$

(3) A fraction $[1 - (\bar{v}/n)](\alpha)(1 - \alpha)$ contains no metal and one proton.
(4) A fraction $[1 - (\bar{v}/n)]\alpha^2$ contains no metal and no protons.

Substituting in Eq. (6-1):

$$\left(\frac{\bar{v}}{n}\right) \bigg/ \left(1 - \frac{\bar{v}}{n}\right)\alpha^2 = K \exp(-2wz_{metal}\, Z)C_{metal}$$

or   (6-4)

$$\frac{\bar{v}}{n - \bar{v}} = K\alpha^2 \exp(-2wz_{metal}\, Z)C_{metal}$$

III. Proteins Containing Metal Ions Necessary for Biological Activity

Table 6-3 contains a list of a number of biologically important proteins which require metal ions for their function. This list is by no means complete or exhaustive but serves to illustrate the wide variety of macromolecules which specifically bind a few metal ions at very high energy sites. A large number of these proteins have only one metal binding site and are thus not examples of *multiple* equilibria.

TABLE 6-3

PROTEINS REQUIRING METAL IONS FOR BIOLOGICAL ACTIVITY

Protein	Metal	No. bound metal/subunit	References
Conalbumin	Fe	2	Aasa *et al.* (1963), Warner and Weber (1953)
Insulin	Zn	$\frac{1}{2}$	Tanford and Epstein (1954)
Alkaline phosphatase	Zn	2, 4	Reynolds and Schlesinger (1968, 1969)
Transferrin	Fe, Zn, Cu	2	Aasa *et al.* (1963) Komatsun and Feeney (1967) Banaszak (1963)
Hemoglobin	Fe	1	Zinoffsky (1886)
Carboxypeptidase	Zn	1	Vallee and Neurath (1954)
Carbonic anhydrase	Zn	1	Rickli and Edsall (1962)
Myoglobin	Fe	1	Theorell (1932)
Actomyosin	Ca	4 μmole/gm	Weber and Herz (1963)
Liver alcohol dehydrogenase	Zn	2	Theorell *et al.* (1955)
Pyruvate kinase	Mn, Mg	—	Suelter and Melander (1963)
D-Lactate cytochrome reductase	Zn	—	Gregolin and Singer (1962)
Yeast enolase	Mg, Zn, Mn	—	Westhead (1964)
Catalase	Fe	1	Agner (1938)
Cytochrome C	Fe	1	Theorell and Akeson (1939)
Ferritin	Fe	1	Laufberger (1937)
Hemerythrin	Fe	1	Klapper and Klotz (1968)

A recent review by Vallee (1969) covers the field of metalloproteins extensively. Most of these complexes have such high binding energies that association constants have not been measured. Indeed, quantitative studies of metal binding in these systems are almost nonexistent, and the assumption is frequently made that added metals are bound stoichiometrically to the protein until the site or sites are filled on each macromolecule. This assumption is theoretically only an approximation, but in practical application may appear correct. For example, a single tightly bound metal ion may not be removed by exhaustive dialysis against distilled water simply because the level of metal contamination is normally $\sim 10^{-7}$ M, and the association constant of metal for protein may be $\geq 10^9$ M.

In this section we discuss in detail the binding of Zn^{2+} to alkaline phosphatase as a particular example of a system in which metal is necessary for biological function and is bound at several high-energy sites.

E. coli alkaline phosphatase is a phosphomonoesterase which has an absolute requirement for metal. It has been isolated as a dimer, molecular weight 86,000, containing two identical subunits and four Zn^{2+}/dimer. Dialysis against 10^{-7} M Zn^{2+} at pH 6.0–8.0 gives $\bar{v} = 4$/dimer. The metal is unnecessary for association of the two subunits to form a dimer, but does stabilize the protein against disruption by high net charge. The metal ions form a chelate complex to the protein in which each metal ion has two ligand positions filled by protein residues (Reynolds and Schlesinger, 1968). One of the binding sites has been shown to be a histidine (Reynolds and Schlesinger, 1968; Tait and Vallee, 1966). Zn^{2+} binding to the apoprotein produces a red shift in the tyrosine absorption. Other metals such as Co^{2+} (Simpson and Vallee, 1968) can be substituted for Zn^{2+} with a resultant lower specific enzymatic activity. The number of binding sites for Co^{2+} is also 4/dimer, and the binding of Co^{2+} and Zn^{2+} is competitive.

At $C[Zn^{2+}] \geq 10^{-4}$ M, pH 8.0, $\bar{v}$ increases to 8/dimer and an enzymatically active tetramer is formed (Reynolds and Schlesinger, 1969).

Another metalloprotein which has been studied in great detail is carbonic anhydrase, which catalyzes the hydration of CO_2, certain aldehydes, and several esters. Rickli and Edsall (1962) showed that the major fraction of human erythrocyte carbonic anhydrase contains one Zn^{2+}/mole protein and that one sulfhydryl group is masked in the native enzyme and exposed in the apoprotein. Coleman (1967) demonstrated that Mn^{2+}, Co^{2+}, Ni^{2+}, Cu^{2+}, Zn^{2+}, Cd^{2+}, and Hg^{2+} all formed $1:1$ complexes with the apoprotein of carbonic anhydrase and compete for the same binding site. Only Zn^{2+} and Co^{2+} however, catalyzed the hydration of CO_2 and p-nitrophenyl acetate. This enzyme like alkaline phosphatase dimer shows no dependence of Zn^{2+} binding over a wide range of pH (4–10) (Coleman, 1965).

Glutamine phosphoribosylpyrophosphate amidotransferase has recently been isolated in a highly purified form from pigeon liver by Rowe and Wyngaarden (1968). This protein like alkaline phosphatase exists in several enzymatically active forms—a tetramer ($M = 200,000$), dimer ($M = 100,000$), and monomer (obtained only by reducing agents) ($M = 50,000$). Three Fe^{3+} are removed only after treatment with reducing agents, suggesting a Fe—S covalent bond. Binding of AMP and Mg^{2+} or GMP and Mg^{2+} to the enzyme prevents loss of the enzymatically active Fe^{3+}.

IV. Protein–Metal Complex Formation

A. Bovine Serum Albumin

Table 6-4 shows the variety of divalent metal ions whose interactions with BSA have been studied in detail. It must be kept in mind that the extent of binding is pH-dependent, and therefore, the number of sites and association

TABLE 6-4

BOVINE SERUM ALBUMIN

M	Site[a]	References
Hg^{2+}	S—H	Hughes (1947)
		Saroff and Mark (1953)
Cu^{2+}	α-NH_2	Peters and Blumenstock (1967)
		Breslow (1964)
		Peters (1960)
		Klotz and Curme (1948)
		Klotz and Fiess (1951)
Zn^{2+}	Im	Gurd and Goodman (1952)
		Tanford (1951)
Ca^{2+}	COO^--ε-NH_2	
	or Im	Saroff and Lewis (1963)
	chelate	
Pb^{2+}	COO^-	Gurd and Murray (1954)
Cd^{2+}	Im	Tanford (1952)
		Rao and Lal (1958)
Mn^{2+}	Im + α-NH_2	Mildvan and Cohn (1963)

[a] Im, imidazole.

constants may vary with protein charge. When a single amino acid–metal bond exists (as opposed to chelation phenomena) the intrinsic association constant is usually quite close to that for the free amino acid–metal system. The average log K_i for Zn^{2+}—BSA between pH 5.74 and 5.98 is 2.82 (Gurd and Goodman, 1952), which is to be compared with the value 2.58 for the first association constant of Zn^{2+} to imidazole.

A recent study (Shearer *et al.*, 1967) of the *N*-terminal peptide of BSA (1–24) containing three histidyl residues at positions 3, 9, and 18 has found two Cu^{2+} binding sites of appreciable strength. The first Cu^{2+} binds to a site presumed to be composed of the α-amino group and histidine 3. The second site has not been identified. At pH greater than 8.5, a third binding site for Cu^{2+} has been observed. However, it must be kept in mind that serum albumin itself undergoes a transition at pH 7.5, and the exposure of additional or different binding sites as a result of a transition would not be unexpected.

B. SPERM WHALE MYOGLOBIN

A major contribution to the understanding of metal–protein interactions was made by Gurd and co-workers in their studies of copper and zinc binding to sperm whale metmyoglobin. Cu^{2+} and Zn^{2+} are found (Breslow and Gurd, 1963) to compete for what is considered to be the same binding site on metmyoglobin in the pH range 5–8. Six to seven metal ions are bound per molecule of protein, but one or two sites of higher energy than the rest are observed. The following experimental evidence supports the view of the metal–protein interaction as chelate formation rather than a single ligand–metal bond:

(1) The association constants for Zn^{2+} and Cu^{2+} binding to metmyglobin were found to be 10^5–10^6, considerably larger than those observed with single amino acid–metal complexes (Table 6-2).

(2) At least one hydrogen ion is displaced at pH 5 or above for each Cu^{2+} bound (the solution becomes more acid). This eliminates the possibility of simple binding to a set of independent imidazole groups which would not all be deprotonated below about pH 8.0.

A subsequent x-ray study of crystalline metmyglobin in the presence of bound Cu^{2+} and Zn^{2+} by Banaszak et al. (1965) clearly established two overlapping binding sites occupied by these metals (see Fig. 6-1). The Zn^{2+} and Cu^{2+} sites are about 7 Å apart and are formed of three potential protein ligand groups. Two of these are common to both sites, lysine A 14 and asparagine GH4.

In addition to their studies of the nature of the metal–protein binding sites Breslow and Gurd (1963) presented spectral and solubility evidence for a binding-induced conformational change in metmyoglobin when $\bar{v} \geq 2$. A more complete study of this transition was published by Hartzell et al. (1967) in which both native metmyoglobin and a carboxamidotmethyl derivative were investigated. The maximum binding of Cu^{2+} in the unmodified protein was reduced in the derivative by an amount proportional to the formation of dicarboxamidomethylhistidine. The Soret bands of both native and modified metmyoglobin decreased by a large factor when metal binding became complete; this change was coupled with a loss of the extrinsic Cotton effect in ORD associated with Soret absorption (Fig. 6-2). These structural alterations are presumed to result from disruption of heme–protein interaction. It has been shown by Polet and Steinhardt (1969) that the loss of this interaction in ferrihemoglobin is accompanied by disruption of tertiary structure of the apoprotein and dimerization of the heme which is responsible for loss of the Soret band.

Further evidence of the effect of Cu^{2+} and Zn^{2+} binding on heme–protein interaction was presented by Gurd et al. (1967) in a study of the electron paramagnetic resonance of metmyoglobin. The binding of 1 mole of metal per mole of protein did not affect the Fe resonance. However, the EPR signal due to Fe decreased linearly with the addition of 2–7 moles of metal per mole of protein until it reached a zero value. The fact that Zn^{2+}, which is not paramagnetic, induced the same effect as Cu^{2+} strongly suggested that the

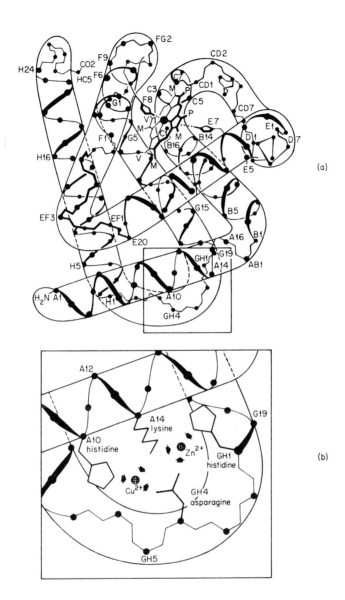

(a)

(b)

FIG. 6-1. (a) Diagrammatic representation of the myoglobin molecule, after Dickerson (1964). (b) Enlarged sketch of the part of the myoglobin molecule showing the relationship between the Cu^{2+} and Zn^{2+} ions and potential binding groups. [L. Banasjak *et al.* (1965), *J. Mol. Biol.* **12**, 130.]

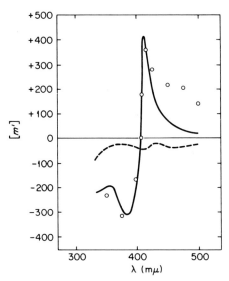

Fig. 6-2. Optical rotatory dispersion spectra in the Soret region of metmyoglobin Fraction IV in the presence and absence of cupric ion. Identical results were obtained with whole metmyoglobin and with all three carboxamidomethyl metmyoglobin Preparations A, B, and C. The temperature was 23°. ——, Without added cupric ion; – – –, in the presence of 0.4 mmole CuCl₂; O, after the addition of 0.44 mmole of EDTA to the copper-containing solutions of Fraction IV and Preparation A. [C. R. Hartzell *et al.* (1967). *J. Biol. Chem.* **242**, 47.]

loss in intensity of the Fe resonance signal was not the result of dipolar coupling.

Hartzell *et al.* (1968) have compared sperm whale, porpoise, and harbor seal myoglobin and found that the latter two proteins bind one more copper ion per molecule of protein than the protein of sperm whale. In addition, the rates of denaturation due to Cu^{2+} binding differed in the three proteins in that sperm whale myoglobin unfolded much more slowly than the other two species (Fig. 6-3).

C. RIBONUCLEASE

The interaction of ribonuclease with Cu^{2+} and Zn^{2+} (which inhibit enzymatic activity) has been studied by Breslow and Girotti (1966). Table 6-5 shows the number of protons displaced at various pH values as a function of added Cu^{2+} in the presence and absence of the enzyme inhibitors 2′- and 3′-CMP. At pH 11 a chelate complex is formed between each Cu^{2+} and four ligand groups in the protein. The metal binding site apparently varies with pH, as evidenced by the difference in protons displaced as a function of pH.

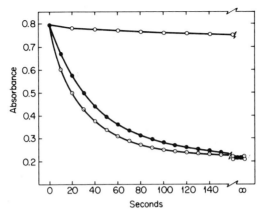

FIG. 6-3. Plot of absorbance of myoglobin solutions at 409 mμ with respect to time in seconds after mixing 5 μmole protein solutions with 0.4 mmole copper(II) chloride at 15° in 2-(N-morpholino)ethanesulfonic acid buffer, pH 6.2, ionic strength 0.05. O, Whale; ●, seal; ◉, porpoise myoglobin. [C. R. Hartzell *et al.* (1968). *J. Biol. Chem.* **243**, 690.]

TABLE 6-5

pH-STAT TITRATION OF PROTONS DISPLACED FROM RNASE BY
CuCl$_2$ UNDER DIFFERENT CONDITIONS[a,b]

				Number of protons displaced[c]		
					At pH 5.5	
Molar addition of CuCl$_2$	At pH 5.3	At pH 7.0	At pH 11	No CMP	With 2′-CMP	With 3′-CMP
1st	0.53	1.7	4.34	0.79	0.60	1.45
2nd	0.55	1.6	4.03	0.80	0.46	1.28
3rd	0.43	1.7	3.8	0.77	0.38	0.60
4th	0.36	1.7	3.7	0.55	0.35	0.33
5th	0.27	(Precipitation)	3.7	0.43	0.31	0.24
6th	0.27	—	3.7	0.32	—	0.19
7th	—	—	3.7	—	—	—
8th	—	—	3.7	—	—	—

[a] At all pH values, studies were done at an initial protein concentration of 1 %. At pH 7, studies were also done with an initial protein concentration of 3.6 %; no effects of concentration on the data at this pH were noted, although Cu(OH)$_2$ precipitation attended the addition of the fifth Cu(II) only at the higher protein concentration.

[b] Breslow and Girotti (1966).

[c] This number has the same significance as the term $-\Delta \bar{h} / \Delta Cu^{2+}$ calculated from continuous titration data.

The addition of 2'-CMP does not alter the titration curve in the presence of Cu^{2+}, but 3'-CMP increases the number of protons displaced by each bound Cu^{2+}.

The results of studies of the visible absorption spectra of ribonuclease–Cu^{2+} complexes by these authors are shown in Fig. 6-4. The pronounced

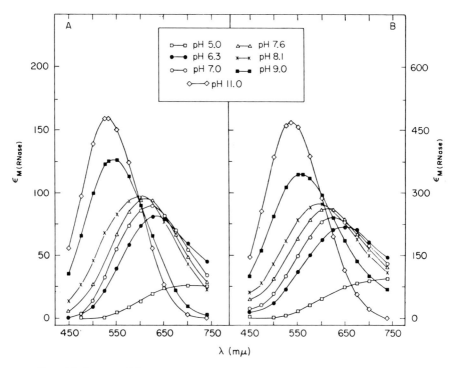

FIG. 6-4. Spectra of RNase in the presence of CuCl$_2$. The conditions were: protein concentration of 3% to 4%; ionic strength, 0.16. A, molar ratio of CuCl$_2$ to RNase of 1; B, molar ratio of CuCl$_2$ to RNase of 3. All data are corrected for a small amount of scattering estimated from the optical density at 450 mμ. Results are reported as the extinction per mole of RNase. The ordinate in B is 3 times the ordinate in A. [E. Breslow and A. W. Girotti (1966). *J. Biol. Chem.* **241**, 5651.]

shift in $\lambda_{\max}$ above pH 8.0 suggests, as do the data in Table 6-5, a different binding site at pH 8.0–11.0 than at pH 7.0. 2'-CMP does not alter the spectra at pH 7.0. 3'-CMP shifts the $\lambda_{\max}$ to longer wavelengths and lowers the intensity of the transition. Comparison of the spectral data with model systems of Cu^{2+} small molecule complexes (Table 6-6) led Breslow and Girotti to suggest that at pH 6.3, Cu^{2+} is bound to a site containing two nitrogen bonds, at pH 8.0 to a site containing three nitrogen bonds, and above pH 8.0 to a site containing four nitrogen bonds.

TABLE 6-6

EFFECT OF LIGANDS ON VISIBLE ABSORPTION SPECTRA
OF Cu(II) COMPLEXES[a]

Ligands to Cu(II)[b]	λ_{max}
1 imidazole	735
2 imidazoles	690
4 imidazoles	600
2 NH_3	675
4 NH_3	600
2 $-NH_2$	660
1 imidazole, 1 peptide nitrogen	660–685
1 imidazole, 2 peptide nitrogens	590
1 imidazole, 3 peptide nitrogens	545
1 $-NH_2$, 1 peptide nitrogen	635–660
1 $-NH_2$, 2 peptide nitrogens	555
1 $-NH_2$, 3 peptide nitrogens	510–520
1 $-NH_2$, 1 peptide nitrogen, 1 OH^-	650
1 $-NH_2$, 1 C$=$O, 1 COO^-, 1 Cl^-	730
1 $-NH_2$, 2 COO^-, 2 C$=$O[c]	620
2 proline-NHR, 2 COO^-	610

[a] From Breslow and Gerotti (1966).
[b] The ligands cited represent the groups other than H_2O which are bound to Cu(II). Except where specifically stated, these can be assumed to be among the four closest ligands to Cu(II) in their respective complexes and hence the main contributors to the Cu(II) ligand field and visible absorption spectrum.
[c] These data are taken from the structure of the Cu(II)—glutamate complex. The 2 C$=$O are not among the four closest ligands to Cu(II).

More recent thermodynamic studies of Cu^{2+} binding to ribonuclease by Breslow and Girotti (1968) using gel filtration techniques show five sites between pH 5.5 and 7.0. At pH 5.5 the data were fitted with the assumption of one site, $K = 1.5 \times 10^3$ and four sites, $K = 1.2 \times 10^2$. It was concluded that at this pH ribonuclease binds Cu acetate with the same affinity as Cu^{2+}. At pH 7.0 the data were fitted with the assumption of one site, $K(Cu^{2+}) = 5 \times 10^5$, and four sites $K(Cu^{2+}$ and Cu acetate$) = 1.9 \times 10^4$. It is by no means established that this is the only distribution of binding sites which will fit the data. The small difference in association constants for the two sets of sites makes analysis difficult since there is overlapping between the two isotherms. It is significant that the protein binds copper acetate to the same extent as the free metal ion at low pH and emphasizes the need for care in using buffers for studies of this nature.[1] Preliminary reports by the above authors state that 2'-CMP competes for one or more of the metal binding sites, while 3'-CMP increases the affinity of ribonuclease for two Cu^{2+} ions.

Shearer *et al.* (1966) studied a tryptic peptide (residues 38–61) of oxidized bovine pancreatic ribonuclease A. The peptide sequence is shown below and the arrows indicate peptide bonds that may interact with Cu as chelating sites which contain (1) NH_2 terminus, (2) histidine residue, (3) COOH terminus. This peptide forms an α-helix in 2-chloroethanol and trifluoro-ethanol. Three moles of Cu^{2+} are bound per mole of peptide in 50:50 H_2O–trifluoroethanol. The characteristic α-helix Cotton effect trough at 2330 Å is reduced from -5000 deg ml/gm decimeter when no Cu^{2+} is bound to -2300 deg ml/gm decimeter at three Cu^{2+} bound. Metal–peptide interaction is also accompanied by the formation of a positive Cotton effect at 2750 Å and a decrease in the intensity of the visible absorption band between 4000 and 7000 Å. The disruption of helical structure in this peptide by metal binding is interpreted as the incompatibility of chelates with the rigid conformation of an α-helix.

$$
\begin{array}{c}
\quad SO_3H \qquad\quad NH_2 \\
\downarrow\quad \downarrow\;|\;\downarrow \qquad\quad |\quad\;\;\downarrow\quad\;\downarrow\quad\;\downarrow \\
\text{Asp-Arg-Cys-Lys-Pro-Val-Asp-Thr-Phe-Val-His-Glu-} \\
\;38\quad 39\quad 40\quad 41\quad 42\;\,43\quad 44\;\;45\quad 46\;\;47\;\;48\;\;49
\end{array}
$$

$$
\begin{array}{c}
\qquad\qquad\qquad\qquad\qquad NH_2 \qquad\quad SO_3H\;\;NH_2 \\
\qquad\qquad\qquad\qquad\qquad |\qquad\;\; |\;\downarrow\quad\;\downarrow|\downarrow \\
\text{Ser-Leu-Ala-Asp-Val-Glu-Ala-Val-Cys-Ser-Glu-Lys} \\
\qquad 50\;\;\;51\;\;\;52\;\;\;53\;\;\;54\;\;\;55\;\;\;56\;\;\;57\;\;\;58\;\;\;59\;\;\;60\;\;\;61
\end{array}
$$

D. Vasopressin and Oxytocin

Lysine vasopressin forms a one-to-one complex with Cu^{2+} with an apparent association constant of $2 \times 10^5 M$ (Campbell *et al.*, 1960, 1963). The wavelength of maximum absorbance of this complex is 5250 Å and corresponds to such a model system as Cu^{2+}–tetraglycine where the metal ion is bound to four nitrogen atoms. A total of four protons are dissociated between pH 4 and 8 from lysine vasopressin when one Cu^{2+} is bound. One of these protons is shown to correspond to an α-amino group. The other three are assumed to be the results of ionization of peptide nitrogens.

---

[1] Some anions which form particularly strong bonds with transition metals may either remove the metal from the protein by competition or bind to the protein by forming a complex with the metal ligand positions which are not occupied by the protein. The removal of Zn^{+2} from alkaline phosphatase by citrate is an example of the former (Reynolds, unpublished data). The binding of acetate to Cu^{+2}–ribonuclease (Breslow and Girotti, 1966) and phosphate to Zn^{+2}–alkaline phosphatase tetramer (Reynolds and Schlesinger, 1969) are typical examples of the latter.

Breslow (1961) studied the interaction of Cu^{2+} with oxytocin and also proposed a binding site consisting of the α-amino group and three peptide nitrogens.

E. INSULIN

The binding of Zn^{2+} to insulin has been briefly discussed in Chapter V. Tanford and Epstein (1954) determined the value of $\bar{v}_{Zn}$ and $C_{eq}(Zn^{2+})$ at a variety of pHs using polarography. The polarographic potential is a measure of the reduction potential of Zn^{2+}. In the system the current was assumed to a first approximation to represent only free Zn^{2+} since the contribution of bound Zn^{2+} to the current is extremely small. Using Eq. (6-4) and knowing the value of Z at various pHs from the hydrogen-ion titration curve, $K_{Zn}{}^{2+}$ was found to be 10^6 (association constant) with two of the imidazole groups chelated to Zn^{2+}. The dependence of the polarographic data on pH could not be reproduced with an assumed 1:1 ratio of metal to protein with $K_{Zn}{}^{2+} = 10^3$ (a value anticipated from metal–amino acid model systems). It will be recalled that the hydrogen-ion titration of insulin and Zn insulin showed two groups which were protonated in insulin with pK 6.5–7.0, but appeared in Zn insulin at pH 4.0. These groups were assumed to be two imidazoles to which the one Zn^{2+} ion is bound.

F. MEMBRANES

Abrams and Baron (1968) have prepared intact membrane ghosts from *Streptococcus fecalis* and studied the binding of ATPase to these membranes in the presence and absence of Mg^{2+}. It was found that the enzyme binds to membranes even in the absence of metal but the association constant increases when Mg^{2+} is bound to the membrane. There is no change in the apparent number of enzyme binding sites, however, in the presence of Mg^{2+}. A ternary complex—membrane, ATPase, Mg^{2+} is proposed as the in vivo mechanism of attachment of the enzyme to intact membranes. An example of a membrane protein that binds Ca^{2+} is cited by Pardee (1968).

G. RIBOSOMES

While no quantitative measure has been made of the number of sites or of association constants of Mg^{2+} to ribosomes, a number of interesting semi-quantitative observations have appeared in the literature. There is no doubt that Mg^{2+} forms a ternary complex between ribosomal proteins and ribosomal RNA. The metal stabilizes the quarternary structure and preserves the biological function. In growing cells of *Aerobacter aerogenes* (Marchesi and Kennell, 1967) Mg^{2+} starvation for a period of 8 hours led to almost total loss of prelabeled protein from ribosomes. Ribosomal extracts reversibly associate and dissociate as the Mg^{2+} content is raised and lowered (Tissieres *et al.*, 1959). The optimal Mg^{2+} concentration in vitro is 0.01 M, and at 0.001 M Mg^{2+} only 7% of the ribosomal activity remains.

H. S-100, A PROTEIN OF THE NERVOUS SYSTEM

A very complete study of the interaction of Ca^{2+} with a protein extracted and purified from nerve tissue from beef brain has been carried out by Calissano *et al.* (1969). The protein appears to be hydrodynamically and electrophoretically homogeneous and has a molecular weight of approximately 24,000. However, the addition of calcium ions leads to the formation of five separate bands in acrylamide gel with no concomitant change in the sedimentation or chromatography pattern. It is not yet clear what produces these five separate species, but Calissano *et al.* (1969) do not favor an association–dissociation explanation due to the identity of sedimentation behavior for all five proteins.

Figure 6-5 shows equilibrium dialysis data for the binding of Ca^{2+} to S-100. The scatter of the low $\bar{v}$ data is too great to allow an accurate analysis in terms of two possible sets of sites of different energy. The intercept at $1/c = 0$ corresponds to 8–10 sites with an apparent $K = 10^3$ (pH 8.3). Fluores-

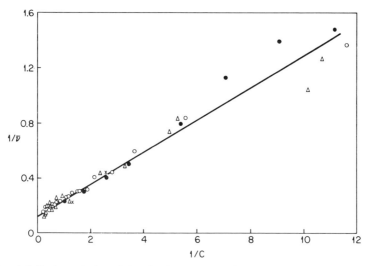

FIG. 6-5. Reciprocal plot of data for binding of Ca^{2+} by S-100. The concentration of Ca^{2+} is c and the average number of Ca^{2+} ions bound per molecule of S-100 (M.W. = 24,000) is $\bar{v}$. The symbols O, ●, and △ refer to three experiments at 1 mg/ml S-100 and × refers to one experiment at 0.5 mg/ml. [P. Calissano *et al.* (1969). *Biochemistry* **8**, (to be published).]

cence titration with Ca^{2+} at the same pH is shown in Fig. 6-6. It is apparent that either 2 or 3 sites with $K \cong 2 \times 10^3$ provides a good fit to the data. Additional Ca^{2+} binding did not affect the protein fluorescence, indicating that there are two sets of sites, one of 2–3 and another 5–6. Hydrodynamic measurements indicate no major alteration in protein structure on Ca^{2+} binding. However, difference spectra and spectrophotometric titration of the tyrosine residues in the presence and absence of Ca^{2+} suggest that Ca^{2+}–protein interaction leads to an exposure to solvent of the single tryptophan residue and some of the tyrosine and phenylalanine residues which had been previously masked. Two of the three cysteine residues become unreactive toward DTNB when Ca^{2+} is bound.

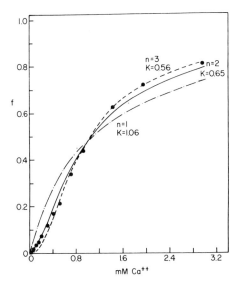

FIG. 6-6. Fluorescence titration of S-100 with Ca^{+2}. The three lines are calculated for different numbers of Ca^{+2} binding sites ($n = 1, 2, 3$). The filled circles represent experimental data.

REFERENCES

Aasa, R., Malmstrom, B. G., Saltman, P., and Vanngard, J. (1963). *Biochim. Biophys. Acta* **75**, 203.

Abrams, A., and Baron, C. (1968). *Biochemistry* **7**, 501.

Agner, K. (1938). *Biochem. J.* **32**, 1702.

Banaszak, L. J., Andrews, P. A., Burgner, J. W., Eylar, E. H., Gurd, F. R. N. (1963). *J. Biol. Chem.* **238**, 3307.

Banaszak, L. J., Watson, H. C., and Kendrew, J. C. (1965). *J. Mol. Biol.* **12**, 130.

Breslow, E. (1961). *Biochem. Biophys. Acta* **53**, 606.

Breslow, E. (1964). *J. Biol. Chem.* **239**, 486.

Breslow, E., and Gurd, F. R. N. (1963). *J. Biol. Chem.* **238**, 1332.

Breslow, E., and Girotti, A. W. (1966). *J. Biol. Chem.* **241**, 5651.

Breslow, E., and Girotti, A. W. (1968). *J. Biol. Chem.* **243**, 216.

Calissano, P., Moore, B. W., and Friesen, A. (1969). *Biochemistry* **8** (to be published).

Campbell, B. J., Schlueter, R. J., Weber, G. F., and White, W. F. (1960). Abst. 138th Meeting ACS 18C.

Campbell, B. J., Chu, F. S., and Hubbard, S. (1963). *Biochemistry*, **2**, 764.

Coleman, J. S. (1965). *Biochemistry* **4**, 2644.

Coleman, J. E. (1967). *Nature* **214**, 193.

Dickerson, R. E. (1964). *In* "The Proteins" (H. Neurath and K. Bailey, eds.), Vol. II, Chapter 11. Academic Press, New York.

Greenstein, J. P., and Winitz, M. (1961). "Chemistry of the Amino Acids," vol. I. Wiley, New York.

Gregolin, C., and Singer, T. P. (1962). *Biochim. Biophys. Acta* **57**, 410.

Gurd, F. R. N., and Goodman, D. S. (1952). *J. Am. Chem. Soc.* **74**, 670.

Gurd, F. R. N., and Murray, G. R. (1954). *J. Am. Chem. Soc.* **76**, 187.

Gurd, F. R. N., and Wilcox, P. E. (1956). *Advan. Protein Chem.* **11**, 312.

Gurd, F. R. N., Falk, K. E., Malmstrom, B. G., and Vanngard, J. (1967). *J. Biol. Chem.* **242**, 5731.

Hartzell, C. R., Hardman, K. D., Gillespie, J. M., and Gurd, F. R. N. (1967). *J. Biol. Chem.* **242**, 47.

Hartzell, C. R., Bradshaw, R. A., Haysner, K. D., and Gurd, F. R. N. (1968). *J. Biol. Chem.* **243**, 690.

Hughes, W. S., Jr. (1947). *J. Am. Chem. Soc.* **69**, 1836.

Klapper, M. H., and Klotz, I. M. (1968). *Biochemistry* **7**, 223.

Klotz, I. M., and Curme, H. G. (1948). *J. Am. Chem. Soc.* **70**, 939.

Klotz, I. M., and Fiess, H. A. *J. Phys. Colloid Chem.* **55**, 101.

Komatsun, S. K., and Feeney, R. E. (1967). *Biochemistry* **6**, 1136.

Laufberger, M. (1937). *Bull. Soc. Chim. Biol.* **19**, 1575.

Marchesi, S. L., and Kennell, D. (1967). *J. Bacteriol.* **93**, 357.

Mildvan, A. S., and Cohn, M. (1963). *Biochemistry* **2**, 910.

Pardee, A. B. (1968). *Science* **162**, 632.

Peters, J., Jr. (1960). *Biochim. Biophys. Acta* **39**, 546.

Peters, J., Jr., and Blumenstock, F. A. (1967). *J. Biol. Chem.* **242**, 1574.

Polet, H., and Steinhardt, J. (1969). *Biochemistry* **8**, 857.

Rao, M. S. N., and Lal, H. (1958). *J. Am. Chem. Soc.* **80**, 3222, 3226.

Reynolds, J. A., and Schlesinger, M. J. (1967). *Biochemistry* **6**, 3552.

Reynolds, J. A., and Schlesinger, M. J. (1968). *Biochemistry* **7**, 2080.

Reynolds, J. A., and Schlesinger, M. J. (1969). *Biochemistry* **8**, 588.

Reynolds, J. A., and Schlesinger, M. J. (1969). *Biochemistry* **8**, in press.

Rickli, E. E., and Edsall, J. T. (1962). *J. Biol. Chem.* **237**, 258.

Rowe, P. B., and Wyngaarden, J. B. (1968). *J. Biol. Chem.* **243**, 6373.

Saroff, H. A., and Mark, H. J. (1953). *J. Am. Chem. Soc.* **75**, 1420.

Saroff, H. A., and Lewis, M. F. (1963). *J. Phys. Chem.* **67**, 1211.

Schearer, W. J., Brown, R. K., Bryce, G. F., and Gurd, F. R. N. (1966). *J. Biol. Chem.* **241**, 2665.

Schearer, W. J., Bradshaw, R. A., Gurd, F. R. N., and Peters, J. (1967). *J. Biol. Chem.* **242**, 5451.

Simpson, R., and Vallee, B. L. (1968). *Biochemistry* **7**, 7, 4343.

Suelter, C. H., and Melander, W. (1963). *J. Biol. Chem.* **238**, PC 4108.

Tait, G. H., and Vallee, B. L. (1966). *Proc. Natl. Acad. Sci. U.S.* **56**, 1247.

Tanford, C. (1952). *J. Am. Chem. Soc.* **74**, 211.

Tanford, C. (1951). *J. Am. Chem. Soc.* **73**, 2066.

Tanford, C., and Epstein, J. (1954). *J. Am. Chem. Soc.* **76**, 2163, 2170.

Theorell, H. (1932). *Biochem. Z.* **252**, 1.

Theorell, H., and Akeson, A. (1939). *Science* **90**, 67.

Theorell, H., Nygaard, A. P., and Bonnischen, R. (1955). *Acta Chem. Scand.* **9**, 1148.

Tissieres, A., Watson, J. D., Schlesinger, D., and Hollingsworth, B. R. (1959). *J. Mol. Biol.* **1**, 221.

Warner, R. E., and Weber, I. (1953). *J. Am. Chem. Soc.* **75**, 5094.

Weber, A., and Herz, R. (1963). *J. Biol. Chem.* **238**, 599.

Westhead, E. W. (1964). *Biochemistry* **3**, 1062.

Vallee, B. L. (1955). *Advan. Protein Chem.* **10**, 318.

Vallee, B. L. (1970). *In* "The Proteins" (H. Neurath, ed.), Vol. 5, 2nd ed. Academic Press, New York (to be published).

Vallee, B. L., and Neurath, H. (1954). *J. Am. Chem. Soc.* **76**, 5006.

Zinoffsky, O. (1886). *Z. Physiol. Chem.* **10**, 16.

VII

Binding of Organic Ions by Proteins

I. Introduction

The tendency of proteins to form tightly bound complexes with a variety of ions was noted early in this century. Sorenson's observations of the "protein error" when pH indicators were used in protein solutions may be the earliest explicit recognition of such combinations (1909). Other inferences of the binding of common *anions* arose from studies of the transport function of blood proteins (Bauer and Burschkies, 1933; Dalton *et al.*, 1930). Observations of the acid-dyeing of wool, cytological staining, and precipitation of proteins with certain dyes and with metaphosphoric acid did not lead to explicit ion binding interpretations, but to the conclusion that coprecipitation was responsible for the apparent interaction. A serious attempt to relate dye binding to proton binding was made by Chapman *et al.* (1927). The earlier work, including the interaction of metals with proteins, has been described by Greenberg (1951).

An early systematic study of the ability of a large number of small ions to interact with two proteins was made by Steinhardt and his collaborators (Steinhardt *et al.*, 1941, 1942; Steinhardt, 1941), who titrated wool keratin with 30 different strong acids and found that every acid anion combined with the protein with affinities that varied widely. More important, all of the strong acids tested with dissolved crystalline ovalbumin *in solution* also combined and to very different extents. These investigators calculated "association constants" and demonstrated that they increased with increasing molecular weight of the anion. In a later paper it was shown that high molecular weight *cations* showed the same tendency to combine with wool (Steinhardt and Zaiser, 1950). Steinhardt's semiempirical analysis of the data has since been modified by the more exact treatment of Scatchard (1949) but the qualitative conclusions as to the differences in affinity and the order of affinities are unchanged. In 1946, Klotz and co-workers (Klotz *et al.*, 1946) published the first of a long series of papers dealing with experimental methods and theoretical analysis of the interaction of organic anions with dissolved proteins. Somewhat later Scatchard and Black (1949) examined the binding of small monovalent anions to serum albumin, and Scatchard (1949) used the Linderström-Lang model (developed for the analysis of hydrogen-ion titration curves—see Chapter II) to explain electrostatic effects on the binding of small ions to proteins. This field of investigation has continued during the ensuing years and a number of exhaustive review articles dealing with experimental methods and theoretical analysis have appeared (Klotz, 1950, 1953; Gurd and Wilcox, 1956; Vallee, 1955; Rosenberg and Klotz, 1960; Scatchard *et al.*, 1954)

It is logical to couple a discussion of ion binding with acid–base equilibria, since (1) the theory of multiple equilibria is applicable to both; (2) in many instances prototropic sites are involved in the binding of other small ions; and (3) binding may be affected by and affect the total protein charge.

However, there is no simple covalent binding of ions to the constituent amino acids and peptides such as is observed with protons and most metal ions (excluding the alkali metals) (Chapter VI).

Many proteins bind anions, but only a few complex with univalent cations. It is not uncommon for proteins to combine with anions even at pH values at which they bear a net negative charge. Although a number of mechanisms for this binding have been proposed, there is no general agreement as to the exact mechanism of the differences between proteins in ability to bind simple singly charged anions such as Cl^-, I^-, SCN^-, and CCl_3COO^-. The reasons for the differences in affinity of the same protein for different anions are also still matters for speculation.

Although proteins differ with respect to whether or not they show measurable tendencies to bind small anions, all proteins which have been examined bind large organic anions (the longer-chain fatty acids, ionic detergents, and such aromatic compounds as dyes) to some extent. In general, within an homologous ligand series the binding affinity increases with the size of the ion. Under some conditions the binding of these large ions results in precipitation of the complex formed. However, binding and precipitation do not go together in any simple way—for example, with detergents some of the precipitates redissolve in still higher concentrations of the precipitating ion in a manner reminiscent of the dissolving of antigen–antibody complexes in an excess of antibody. With other non-surface-active, precipitating anions, such as picrate (which is useful in removing proteins from mixtures), redissolving does not occur.

The binding of anions by those proteins which have been investigated in detail cannot be expressed as the result of simple multiple equilibria which involve sets of identical binding groups (i.e., having a single intrinsic binding constant), modified only by the electrostatic effects resulting from changes in charge as the protein interacts with different numbers of ions. As in the case of hydrogen-ion equilibria recourse must be had to more than a single intrinsic constant. In the case of hydrogen ion these intrinsic constants are associated with different prototropic groups, i.e., carboxyl, amino, phenoxy, sulfhydryl, etc., and this attribution has been justified by demonstrating a close stoichiometric correspondence between the numbers of dissociations in each set and the content of the corresponding side chains in the protein. With anion binding, it has so far proved impossible to associate the affinity constants for specific, identical sets of binding sites with particular amino acid residues or clusters of such residues. There is not even an unambiguous indication that the binding sites are stereotyped, identifiable structures or subconformations which are identical in different proteins. Indeed there are signs that in some cases not all of the sites exist in the native protein, but some result from conformational changes induced by the initial binding on a few preformed sites. There is the additional complication that the binding constant in the case of ions other than hydrogen ion depends not only on the site but on the ion as well. The nature of the binding may be quite different with different ions, whereas with hydrogen ion the formation of a covalent bond is always involved.

These difficulties may be partly due to the fact that detailed ion binding measurements on soluble proteins have been made on a very small number of proteins. They may also result from the fact that the most detailed and exact data, obtained primarily with bovine and human serum albumin, have principally involved small anions which are bound about as weakly as the amide or peptide groups bind hydrogen ion. The understanding of protein prototropic equilibria would have been much more difficult to achieve if proteins had not contained many much more strongly basic groups than peptide or amide.

Larger anions, such as dyes (e.g., methyl orange) and detergents (e.g., dodecylsulfate) have binding constants comparable with those of hydrogen ion to carboxylate (10^4) or imidazole (10^6).

Titration curves (entirely analogous to hydrogen-ion titration curves) may be constructed by varying the free concentrations of anions at constant pH and ionic strength if noncompetitive buffers or neutral salts are available. There are indications that dihydrogen and monohydrogen phosphate ions have very little affinity for serum albumin; other ions reported to have low affinity are Tris buffer and zwitterions generally (Klotz, private communication). Titration curves may then be plotted in the usual way, equivalents bound per gram or mole, against pA ($-\log[A]$). If there are several sets of *preformed* groups of identical intrinsic association constants of moderate magnitude ($K \geq 10^2$), and the affinities of these sets are *sufficiently distinct from one another*, their existence will be apparent on inspection by the existence of discrete sets of equilibria with separate points of inflection at $-\log C$ equal to $\log K$ for each set. Such work as has already been done with some of the more tightly bound ions such as dodecylsulfate and dodecylbenzenesulfonate, indicates that unmasking of previously unavailable anion binding sites can be brought about by anion binding at constant pH, just as unmasking of certain proton binding sites is often brought about as the result of certain levels of proton binding, i.e., there are "cooperative" effects with anions as well as with hydrogen ions.

An additional precaution will be necessary in such investigations. Many of the ions which bind most tightly are detergents and tend to form micellar aggregates in solution when the concentration exceeds certain very low levels (CMC, critical micelle concentration). Above this concentration the activity of the monomer ion is constant as the affinities of monomer for other monomers or micelles compete with their affinities for protein sites. It is perhaps significant that the micelle-formers are among the ions most tightly bound to protein. A good deal is known about the nature of the forces stabilizing micelles. Experimentally, nevertheless, it is probably desirable to limit investigations initially to concentration ranges at which the equilibrium concentration of free anion is well below the CMC. With the larger anions this can be a severe constraint. When the CMC is below 10^{-3} moles/liter and the binding constant is very large, the equilibrium concentrations become vanishingly small, and their measurement (as by isotopic labeling) is difficult. In addition, indirect methods (Chapter III) which permit equilibrium concentrations to be calculated rather than measured are subject to errors which become very large when the difference between amounts added and amounts not bound approach one another. Consequently, the recourse to reversible electrode methods (when available) for direct measurement of pA, or the utilization of potentials across permselective membranes, becomes compellingly attractive.

In many respects analysis of ion binding is similar to the analysis of the binding of uncharged molecules, as set forth in Chapter IV:

(1) The principal difference might appear to be the need to allow for the effects of electrical interaction with free ions which increases as the protein charge is increased by ion binding. It will be shown, however, that although this interaction *must* be taken into account in dealing with hydrogen-ion association, its effect is small, or even negligible, in the case of the adsorption of other ions (Ray *et al.*, 1966; Reynolds *et al.*, 1967; Cassel and Steinhardt, 1969). Were it required, it would be necessary to know the net charge of the

protein–ion complex or the distribution of charges on the protein surface. The net charge cannot be assumed to be equal to the difference between the number of hydrogen ions bound (if acid to the isoionic point) and the number of anions bound, since counterions may partly neutralize the charge.[1] In analyses of hydrogen-ion titration curves association with counterions is indistinguishable from anion or cation binding and may be allowed for whenever ion-association constants are available (Chapter V). When anion or cation titration curves are under investigation at constant pH, the counterions (if any) are most unlikely to be hydrogen or hydroxyl ions (unless extremes of pH are involved, or the solutions are buffered) and there is usually no direct method for determining to what extent the counterions diminish the charge. In addition, calculation of binding constants requires determination of free ion concentrations. These will be much smaller fractions of the total ligand concentrations, since greater affinities are found for ions than for homologous uncharged molecules.

(2) There is the same need as with hydrogen-ion binding to distinguish between "statistical" and "cooperative" binding: the latter (which implies unmasking of new sites) is much more likely to be encountered at the high mole ratios attainable with ions than in the low ranges to which measurements are usually limited with most neutral molecules.

(3) Finally, disturbance of the charge distribution of the protein, whether isoionic or at pH values remote from the isoionic point, may be sufficiently great to disrupt the tertiary structure as the result of internal electrostatic repulsion, or to precipitate the protein from solution by reduction of its polarization interactions with water. Redistribution of internal hydrophobic clustering by the formation of new hydrophobic bonds with ligands can occur of course with certain types of ions as well as with homologous neutral molecules.

One of the complications due to charge which has serious effects in the binding of hydrogen ions (Chapter V) will be almost disregarded here: the effect of charge accumulation on the central (protein) ion as successive ligand ions are bound. The reasons why this simplification is justified follow:

(1) Empirically it is found that when the charge of the protein ion is changed, as by combination with various amounts of hydrogen ion, there is often little effect on the association constants of anions (Ray et al., 1966; Reynolds et al., 1967). The fact that anion binding to proteins bearing a negative charge occurs with large negative ΔF° shows that coulombic interactions can be, at most, a small fraction of the binding energy. Hydrogen ion

---

[1] "Counterions" are ions of opposite charge, which are closely associated and not described by the electrical interaction with a Debye-Hückel ion atmosphere (Tanford, 1961).

does not bind to neutral molecules (except ammonia derivatives and water) or to cationic molecules except in the most strongly protic solvents. There are no analogs to such solvents for anion binding, but binding of anions by negative protein ions nevertheless occurs.

(2) Even the interactions with local (rather than net) charges are small. The $\Delta F°$ of binding of neutral molecules and their ionic homologues differs by less than 2 kcal/mole, sometimes much less: there is little difference in $\Delta F°$ for long-chain alcohols and the corresponding fatty acid anions (see p. 273).

(3) Efforts to apply electrostatic corrections, such as the *wz* term in the Linderström-Lang equation ([Eq. (2-49)] lead to anomalous deviations from simple stoichiometric law of mass action behavior, while the use of *uncorrected* data does not lead to these anomalies.

It will be shown elsewhere that although the charge on a ligand usually has a small or moderate enhancing effect on $\Delta F°$, the extent to which the charge is *delocalized* has a very strong bearing on $\Delta F°$. Because of the exponential relation of the association constant K to $\Delta F°$, the effects of charge delocalization on the binding of long-chain ions can loom very large. The ratio of the K's of *n*-dodecanol and *n*-dodecylsulfate is about 0.10, although the same ratio for dodecanol to dodecanoate is about 0.65 (Reynolds *et al.*, 1968).

II. Large Organic Ions—Ionic Detergents

In the pages that follow the binding of large organic ions is considered first because such binding is common to a very large number of proteins. Since the largest body of work to date has been done with the *n*-dodecylsulfate ion, its C_6 to C_{14} homologues, and the corresponding sulfonates, these ions are considered first. The discussion is then extended to other large organic ions, including fatty acids, quarternary alkyl amines, and acid dyes. We then proceed to the binding of smaller, sometimes monoatomic, ions, in which proteins differ most from one another. In distinction to the procedure in Chapter IV (uncharged molecules) the material is organized primarily by classes of ligands, rather than by individual proteins—this arrangement is practical since so much of the work has been done on a very small number of proteins, by far the greatest part with one, serum albumin.

A. Early Work on Detergent Anions (long chain aliphatic sulfate half-esters, homologous sulfonates, alkylaryl sulfonates, and fatty-acid anions)

Detergent anions include long-chain aliphatic sulfate half-esters, homologous sulfonates, and alkyl aryl sulfonates. A review by Putnam (1948) covers the early studies of the interactions of these substances and fatty acid anions with proteins.

1. *Destabilization by Detergents, Crude Isotherms*

The pronounced destabilizing effects of mixed alkyl sulfates (e.g., Duponol) were observed (Anson, 1939) a few years prior to the first measurements of the high affinities of a series of purified sulfate half-esters (among other ions) and of dodecylsulfonate for the insoluble protein, wool keratin (Steinhardt *et al.*, 1941). Destructive effects on proteins and viruses by even low concentrations of detergents were also reported by Sreenivasaya and Pirie (1938), Bawden and Pirie (1940), Pfankuch and Kansche (1940), Kerlin and Hartree (1940), Kuhn *et al.* (1940), and by Smith and Pickels (1941). This destructive action could be detected by changes in viscosity (Putnam and Neurath, 1943).

2. *Electrophoretic Data*

Early electrophoretic experiments with sodium dodecylsulfate (SDS) and ovalbumin (Lundgren *et al.*, 1943) were interpreted as showing that the dodecylsulfate ion was bound by individual molecules of this protein in an "all or none" fashion, forming a complex containing a full complement of detergent, equivalent to the number of cationic groups in the protein. After denaturation this property disappeared. Putnam and Neurath (1944) showed that SDS could be used to precipitate various purified proteins completely in the pH region acid to their isoelectric points, i.e., where the proteins bore a net positive charge. They reported a fairly wide region of detergent concentration at the isoelectric point within which precipitation was complete; the concentrations required depended linearly on the protein concentration. Below this pH region there was a fairly abrupt transition to no protein precipitated at any concentration; above it, as at the isoelectric point itself, the precipitate could be redispersed in excess detergent. The addition of detergent causes the pH to rise, a consequence, as Scatchard and Black (1949) later showed, of the binding of anions in excess of the binding of cations. The addition of NaCl up to 0.2 M enhances precipitation under conditions where it is otherwise incomplete. The precipitation effectiveness increases with temperature, which suggests that unfolded, rather than native, protein participates in the insoluble complex. It was estimated that 145 moles of SDS were combined for every mole of horse serum albumin in the precipitate. More recently a figure in excess of 160 moles per mole was reported for bovine serum albumin on the basis of conductivity measurements *in solution* (Strauss and Strauss, 1958). Other data show the figure may go much higher (Reynolds *et al.*, 1967) at equilibrium concentrations that do not exceed the critical micelle concentrations for pure detergent in water.

Electrophoretic measurements (Putnam and Neurath, 1945) with horse serum albumin at concentrations between about 0.6% and 2%, at SDS concentrations of 0.0052 M and 0.0104 M,[2] at both 1° and 20°, showed that (1) at all concentrations and ratios investigated, the amount of protein migrating with a boundary mobility corresponding to the original protein, or unchanged protein combined with a small number of anions (slightly enhanced mobility at pH 6.8), was greatly diminished; and that (2) part or all of the protein, depending on the ratio of protein to detergent, migrated with a second boundary of higher mobility. At the lowest ratios of protein to detergent, a still faster additional boundary appeared, although some protein still migrated with the mobility of the first complex to be formed. Putnam and Neurath calculated, on the basis of a number of assumptions, that the molal ratio in the first large complex was 55, and in the second large complex 110. Numerous later investigations have tended to confirm the doubling of the limited molal ratios in going from the first complex of definite composition to the second.

All subsequent work at these concentrations has indicated that the average amounts of detergent bound per mole which characterize the three boundaries are close to the values just cited. It has also confirmed the disappearance of the "normal" albumin boundary as a result of mass-law combination with fairly small numbers (<12) of dodecylsulfate ions. Whether or not the changed ("unfolded") protein forms two discontinuous complexes of fixed stoichiometry has been the subject of other investigations to be described below. With egg albumin the apparent tendency to form complexes of fixed molal ratio disappeared after heat denaturation.

3. *Protection by Detergents against Denaturation*

Of particular interest is the fact that low concentrations of dodecylsulfate which produce only the slower moving boundary (combination with fewer than 12 ions) protect serum albumin from heat coagulation, or denaturation by urea or guanidine hydrochloride (Boyer *et al.*, 1946), in a manner entirely similar to the protection afforded by fatty acid anions, or by other organic anions with large nonpolar groups (the effect of these other anions is considered more fully below; see Putnam in "The Proteins," 1954). However, the work of Anson and others, already cited, had shown that somewhat larger concentrations caused denaturation: the viscosity increases and unmasking of disulfides produced at these higher concentrations are the same as when brought about by guanidine hydrochloride (Anson, 1941; Mirsky, 1941; Neurath and Putnam, 1945). The hydrodynamic properties (size and shape) of the protein–detergent complex were affected by the presence of neutral salt (Friend *et al.*, 1951).

[2] The CMC is 8×10^{-3} g/l in the absence of other components.

It was concluded from measurements of the concentration of dodecyl-sulfate at which the relative viscosity in solutions containing urea or guanidine reached a minimum that serum albumin forms a stable complex with detergent which contains eight dodecylsulfate ions (Duggan and Luck, 1948). Maximum protection is given with the fatty acid caprylate anion at a concentration at which approximately the same number of ions (nine) are bound. Independent evidence will be cited below that indicates the existence in *native* serum albumin of about four to five sites of high binding energy for this anion. *β*-Lactoglobulin is also stabilized against heat and alkali by combination with dodecylsulfate ions; a crystalline complex containing two ions per mole of protein has been isolated (McMeekin *et al.*, 1949; Groves *et al.*, 1951). Reduction and *S*-carboxymethylation does not impair the ability to complex but methylene-blue-sensitized photooxidation destroys it. Bound dodecylsylfate does not protect the protein from photooxidation (Seibles, 1968). Other reports of stabilizations by organic anions, particularly alkylsulfates, will be cited elsewhere in this chapter. The most recent, by Markus *et al.* (1964), protection of human serum albumin by SDS against unfolding by numerous denaturing agents, is described more fully on p. 289–290.

4. *Early Equilibrium Dialysis Data*

The first effort to determine the equilibrium isotherm between BSA and purified alkyl half-esters was made by Karush and Sonnenberg (1949). Equilibrium dialysis was employed with the 8-, 10-, and 12-carbon compounds in the presence of 0.025 M phosphate at pH 6.1 at two temperatures and at protein concentrations between 0.05% and 0.5%. Under these conditions corrections for Donnan inequalities are negligible. The amounts bound were calculated by determining the concentrations of ligand found in the outside solution at equilibrium when the ligand was initially all within the inner solution containing the protein. The detergent concentration was determined by extracting the complex formed between rosaniline hydrochloride and the ligand into a mixture of chloroform and ethyl acetate and assaying colorimetrically.

Volumes and concentrations of both protein and ligand were chosen such that the outside (protein-free) solution never had an equilibrium concentration less than one-quarter that of the inner solution, which contained the protein-bound ligand. While this precaution avoids the errors attendant on attempting to estimate accurately a very small difference between two large numbers, it has the undesirable effect of limiting the measurements to molal ratios greater than 5. The investigators failed to find in these experiments the dependence of binding on protein concentration reported by Klotz—they therefore felt free to determine different portions of the isotherm with different protein concentrations, so as always to preserve a ratio of equilibrium concentration (inside/outside) greater than 4. It will be shown later that the binding of these substances is indeed practically independent of protein concentration (Cassel *et al.*, 1969) contrary to earlier reports. Few values of $\bar{v}$ below 6 were determined.

Representative results are shown in Figs. 7-1 and 7-2. Unlike the data of Klotz on dye binding, to be referred to later, or the numerous cases of binding neutral molecules (Chapter IV), reciprocal plots were not linear and did not extrapolate to an unambiguous value of $1/n$. For the same reason no

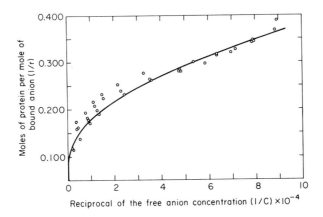

FIG. 7-1. Binding data for octylsulfate: O, low temperature; ●, room temperature. [F. Karush and M. Sonenberg (1949). *J. Am. Chem. Soc.* **71**, 1369.]

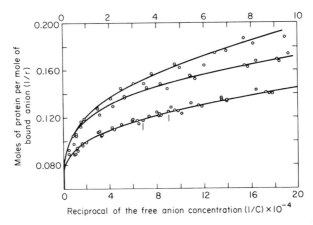

FIG. 7-2. Binding data for decyl- and dodecylsulfates; upper two curves and top scale refer to decylsulfate and lower curve and bottom scale to dodecylsulfate; reversibility points (see text) indicated by arrows; O, low temperature; ●, room temperature. [F. Karush and M. Sonenberg (1949). *J. Am. Chem. Soc.* **71**, 1369.]

unambiguous value of K, the association constant, could be obtained. Karush and Sonenberg had recourse to two expedients to resolve this difficulty. They first applied a correction for the electrostatic effect on the apparent K of the progressively increasing charge of the protein–anion complex, as given by Scatchard (1949). These corrections were applied by substituting $\exp(-2w\bar{v})/C$ for $1/C$; w, the electrostatic interaction parameter was calculated to be 0.0451 at the ionic strength employed. Since the curves were not rectified by this process, the authors concluded, on the basis of Klotz's successful experience with *uncorrected* linear reciprocal plots for the same protein with methyl orange (Klotz *et al.*, 1948) that the application of such corrections is of dubious validity.[3] After considering a number of other alternatives, the deviation from linearity was explained by abandoning the notion of binding sites of identical intrinsic association constants, and adopting a Gaussian distribution of the constants with the dispersion necessary to give the observed results. The results given in Table 7-1 for K_0, the average binding constant; σ,

TABLE 7-1

CONSTANTS AND THERMODYNAMIC DATA FOR BINDING OF ALKYL SULFATES
BY BOVINE SERUM ALBUMIN[a,b]

Compound	Temperature	σ	K_0 $\times 10^{-4}$	$-\Delta F°$ (kcal/mole)	$\Delta S°$ (eu)
Octylsulfate	Room and low	4.5	0.4	5.01[c]	16.7
Decylsulfate[d]	Room	5	2.5	6.03[c]	13.3
Decylsulfate[c]	Low	6	3.4	5.70[e]	13.3
Dodecylsulfate	Room and low	5	18.2	7.22[c]	24.0

    [a] Taken from Karush and Sonenberg (1949).
    [b] The data refer to the binding of 1 mole of alkyl sulfate.
    [c] Calculated for 27°.
    [d] $\Delta H° = -2$ kcal/mole.
    [e] Calculated for 2°.

the standard deviation of the population of K values; and $-\Delta F°$ and $\Delta S°$ were calculated by Karush and Sonenberg (1949) on the basis of a choice of 14 for n.

It is obvious that $\Delta F°$ increases with chain length, and that with all three anions, the reaction is largely entropy-driven. Only with decylsulfate is there

---

[3] It will be shown later that the application of such corrections for anion or cation binding (other than hydrogen ion) is probably not valid, not only because counterions reduce the calculated net charge, but also because the mathematical models for H^+ binding and for anion binding differ.

a favorable enthalpy change as well. For comparison with the values of *unitary* ΔS, defined previously in this book, 8 eu should be added to the values in the table.

Unfortunately, the values given cannot be accepted as more than very crude approximations. It is very unlikely that the *ad hoc* assumption of a Gaussian distribution of intrinsic association constants is valid. If *n* were a considerably smaller number than 14 (for example, 5 for octylsulfate, 8 for dodecylsulfate, as shown by later studies described below), the range of available experimental values of $\bar{v}$ would not suffice for extrapolation to $1/n$ by either Klotz or Scatchard plots. Since only one *table* of values, that for decylsulfate, is given in the paper, and the maximum value of $\bar{v}$ given is 10.8, there is no possibility of testing the data for the existence of a second pre-formed set of more weakly binding sites. Furthermore, as will be seen later, there is a strong presumption that the range of values of $\bar{v}$ covered in Karush's work on dodecylsulfate encompassed both a lower region in which native protein binds anions, and an upper region in which binding occurred, pos-sibly on sites that first became exposed as the dodecylsulfate was bound on the original sites, i.e., the molecule is being altered over the entire range of the measurements. Thus the data represent a much more complicated equilibrium process than that involved in simple binding. In such a case unfolding of the molecules occurs progressively beyond some small molal ratio—almost certainly not a progressive unfolding of each molecule, but a progressive shift in the ratio of unfolded to folded individuals (see Chapter II, p. 29).

B. Isotherms of Anionic Detergents

1. *Alkylbenzenesulfonates*

(a) *Material Containing Impurities. Unfolding by Detergents.* Yang and Foster (1953) investigated the binding of a related substance with a longer chain, sodium dodecylbenzenesulfonate (neither completely aliphatic nor containing an ester linkage) with both BSA and ovalbumin. Although the ligand preparation available to them contained impurities which were demonstrated to affect the results obtained, the paper is historically important because *both* electrophoretic mobility and binding were studied as a function of equilibrium concentration of ligand (at 1°–3° and pH 7.7 at a protein concentration of 0.4%). Inclusion of the benzene group in the ligand per-mitted use of a simple spectrophotometric method for the measurement of equilibrium concentrations. It was shown that equilibrium could be attained rapidly, in under 2 days, if the detergent was initially mixed with the protein and allowed to dialyze outward into an equal volume of buffer. All the protein solutions thus initially contained concentrations of detergent above the equilibrium concentration; it is therefore necessary to assume that all the effects of high detergent concentration on the protein are fully reversible. Karush's failure to fit his data with a single equilibrium constant was confirmed, but the inclusion of points for very low molal ratios made it clear that about 12 binding sites, those having the highest affinity for the ligand, could be fit by a single constant, approximately 160,000. Binding above this level was described as "cooperative" or "all or none," i.e., the amount bound increased rapidly with small changes in *free* ligand concentration, and the fraction of total ligand bound leveled off or even rose slightly, instead of decreasing monotonically as it does in ordinary mass-law binding. In the solutions which showed this "cooperative" binding, a second electrophoretic boundary appeared having a substantially higher mobility. Yang and Foster proposed that the binding of approximately 12 ions per mole of protein triggered a transformation of the protein to a new species which contained many more binding sites. Such a transformation was already known, brought about when approximately 8–10 hydrogen ions are bound (pH ~4.3). It was calculated from the electrophoretic data (Fig. 7-3; Table 7-2), on the basis of assumptions about refractive index, that the new component formed contained 48 bound ions, only 12 of which had been bound in the native form. At still higher concentrations, at which the transformation of the protein into the modified form was complete (see Table 7-2), the new form added additional ions (its mobility therefore increased). Within the

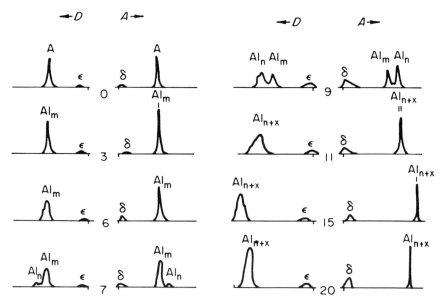

FIG. 7-3. Electrophoretic data for sodium dodecylbenzenesulfonate (SDBS). [J. T. Yang and J. F. Foster (1953). *J. Am. Chem. Soc.* **75**, 5560.]

COMBINATION OF BSA(A) WITH SODIUM DODECYLBENZENESULFONATE SDBS(I) AT 1–3° IN PHOSPHATE–NaCl BUFFER[a,b]

Total SDBS concn. $\times 10^5$ M	Free SDBS concn. $\times 10^5$ M	Av. moles SDBS bound per mole protein r	Mobilities, $\mu^{c,d}$ (cm^2 V^{-1} sec^{-1} $\times 10^5$)				Relative area (%)				Molar ratio I/A in AI$_n$, n
			A	AI$_m$	AI$_n$	AI$_{n+x}$	A	AI$_m$	AI$_n$	AI$_{n+x}$	
0	0	0	6.6	—	—	—	100	—	—	—	—
16.7	0.2	2.8	—	6.7	—	—	—	100	—	—	—
30.3	0.4	5.0	—	7.0	—	—	—	100	—	—	—
41.8	1.0	6.8	—	7.1	—	—	—	100	—	—	—
55.8	3.0	8.5	—	7.3	—	—	—	100	—	—	—
83.6	5.2	12	—	7.2	—	—	—	100	—	—	—
104.4	7.9	15	—	7.3	9.1	—	—	87.9	12.1	—	48
125.4	10.5	18	—	7.3	9.1	—	—	71.6	28.4	—	43
209	17.1	30	—	7.4	9.3	—	—	44.7	55.3	—	48
293	26.1	41	—	7.9	9.9	—	—	15.8	84.2	—	48
418	34.6	60	—	—	—	9.8	—	—	—	100	—
502	45.3	70	—	—	—	11.0	—	—	—	100	—
649	58.0	91	—	—	—	11.5	—	—	—	100	—
735	68.3	100	—	—	—	11.6	—	—	—	100	—
882	83.7	120	—	—	—	12.4	—	—	—	100	—
1044	95.5	150	—	—	—	12.3	—	—	—	100	—
1223	109	170	—	—	—	12.5	—	—	—	100	—
1457	127	200	—	—	—	13.0	—	—	—	100	—
1871	159	260	—	—	—	13.3	—	—	—	100	—
2050	176	290	—	—	—	13.6	—	—	—	100	—

[a] Taken from Yang and Foster (1953).
[b] pH 7.7; m/2 = 0.20; concentration of BSA, 5.9 $\times 10^{-5}$ M.
[c] The values represent the average of the descending and ascending boundaries.
[d] m varies from 1 to about 10, n is about 1 to about 48 assuming the maximum m is 12, and x is a variable. The average n was calculated from the last column.
[e] Relative areas were calculated from the descending patterns.

range of the experiments up to 290 ions per molecule were bound and no estimate of a limiting value was made.

Examination of Table 7-2 shows that the unfolded form (Yang and Foster's 48-ion complex) increased in mobility even within the equilibrium concentration range in which the transition of native to unfolded form was incomplete (from 9.1 to 9.9 mobility units in the equilibrium range, 7.9 to 26.1×10^{-5} M). Within this range, one should expect the relationship between amounts bound and equilibrium ligand concentration to be more complex than a simple mass-law relationship. It is not necessary to assume that only a complex of definite composition is formed since the complex can bind more anions. Yang and Foster, however, suggested that the increase in mobility was due to combination with lower molecular weight impurities. At higher concentrations, where all the protein is unfolded, the binding data seem to obey, not the law of mass action, but a Nernst partition equilibrium (implying infinite binding) with a partition coefficient of $K_2 = 160,000$. Values of $n_1 = 8$ will fit the low-binding data about as well as $n_1 = 12$ if a higher value of K (about 370,000) is used. It should be noted that the value of K_1 given by Yang and Foster for $n_1 = 12$ is the same as K_2 for the partition equilibrium affecting the rest of the binding, but that n_1 is finite and small, while n_2 is infinite. There is no question, however, but that a transformation occurs at $\bar{v}$ values close to, or slightly in excess of, n_1 (depending on whether n_1 is equal to 12 or 8). In addition to the data presented by Yang and Foster, and by Pallansch and Briggs (described below) it had been observed earlier that dodecylsulfate increases the viscosity of BSA solutions only at concentration above those at which $\bar{v}$ exceeds 8 (Duggan and Luck, 1948). Many other indications of a critical change in properties at $\bar{v} = 8$–12 have been reported in more recent years and will be cited later. The questions of interest are (1) whether the n_2 set (or the protein "solvent" phase for the high binding) exists at all in the native form, or is instead formed by the transformation; (2) whether a definite complex of any larger number than 8–12 exists; and (3) whether the observed transformation can be explained solely as a direct consequence of the differences of the free energies of ion binding of the folded and unfolded forms.

The data of Yang and Foster (1953) on *ovalbumin* cannot be understood in terms of the situation described at length above. No part of the binding isotherm for this protein fits the law of mass action. However, it may be significant that, here, small amounts of detergent caused precipitation of part of the protein during dialysis, although larger amounts avoided it. It is likely that in the case of ovalbumin the stoichiometric protein–detergent complex (*n* less than 8) is insoluble, and that it is kept in solution with excess detergent by a process of solubilization similar to the micelle formation. At acid pH BSA–detergent complexes also become insoluble until high concentrations of detergent are present. Micelle formation appears to occur at lower concentrations than the normal CMC when the protein forms part of the micelle. With some other proteins, e.g., human carbonylhemoglobin, insolubility occurs at $\bar{v}$ about 4 (Verpoorte and Steinhardt, unpublished).

(b) *Isotherms and Unfolding with Pure Dodecylbenzenesulfonate.* Decker and Foster (1966) have more recently reported new measurements of the binding by acid-defatted bovine plasma albumin (BPA $\equiv$ BSA) of highly purified *p*-octyl and *p*-dodecylbenzenesulfonate (DBS) at a number of pH values in the presence of various uni–univalent salts at ionic strengths of 0.15 or higher; and have accompanied these measurements with extensive accurate determinations of electrophoretic mobility. A number of important conclusions emerge from this work.

(i) In the region of low binding ($\bar{v} < 12$) the new results with dodecylbenzenesulfonate in 0.1 M KCl agree qualitatively with those reported earlier with the less pure detergent, yielding a value of $n = 12$. At neutral pH, K for the smaller ligand was about 1.8×10^5; but the value for the larger detergent is much larger, about 10^6 (it falls to about 158,000 at pH 9.5, but n remains at about 12). An analysis based on the electrophoretic data, referred to below, results in an estimate of $K = 5 \times 10^6$ at neutral pH. The effect of using purer ligands has been to raise K from the value in the earlier investigation by more than 20-fold. The large and small ligands have K values at the same pH which also differ by a factor of about 20.

(ii) In the region of higher binding limited data at neutrality for the smaller ligand shows much smaller binding (about 0.1 as much) than is found for the large one.

(iii) Analysis of the areas under each of the peaks in the electrophoresis schlieren pictures (Table 7-3) shows that the proportion of native material commences to diminish at $\bar{v}$ over 12, that a complex which contains 38 ions (as determined from the mobility) appears at the same time and increases until it represents 82% of the protein at $\bar{v} = 38$ at which point only 10% of the protein represents unchanged material. At the same value of $\bar{v}$ a small amount of distinguishably faster moving complex (Protein–ligand $= AD_{76}$) appears, and when $\bar{v}$ reaches 86, the new component contains all of the protein. However, Table 7-3 and Fig. 7-4 show that the native material at pH 6.55 varies in mobility (descending arm) between 0.87 and 1.09 cm^2 V^{-1} sec^{-1} $\times 10^4$, the Protein–ligand$_{38}$ ($= AD_{38}$) complex varies in mobility between 1.61 and 1.69, and the AD_{76} complex is characterized by mobilities between 1.94 and 2.16 cm^2 V^{-1} sec^{-1}; thus the first complex may combine with additional ions, rather than going by one step from 38 to 76 combined ions.

(iv) A change in the Moffitt parameter b_0 accompanied the transition from

TABLE 7-3

Electrophoresis Data for BPA–DBS$^{-a,b}$

| Area[c] | Relative (%) | | | Descending mobility, $-\mu$ (cm^2 V^{-1} sec^{-1} $\times$ 10^4) | | |
$\bar{v}$	1	2	3	1	2	3
0	100	—	—	0.87	—	—
2.8	100	—	—	0.96	—	—
5.6	100	—	—	0.95	—	—
8.3	100	—	—	0.97	—	—
12.5	95	5	—	1.01	1.34[d]	—
22.2	52	48	—	1.07	1.61	—
31.9	20	80	—	1.05	1.56	—
38.4	10	82	8	1.09	1.60	1.94
46.2	—	83	17	—	1.69	1.72[d,e]
58.0	—	46	54	—	1.69	1.98
66.9	—	21	79	—	1.69	2.00
75.5	—	5	95	—	1.63	1.97
86.1	—	—	100	—	—	2.12
89.2	—	—	100	—	—	2.14
94.0	—	—	100	—	—	2.16

[a] Taken from Decker and Foster (1966).
[b] System in 0.1 M LiCl at pH 6.55 $\pm$ 0.05 and 22.0°.
[c] Obtained from ascending patterns; component 1 is the slowest; 3 is the fastest.
[d] Subject to some uncertainty because the component appeared as only a shoulder on the main peak.
[e] Only ascending value was available.

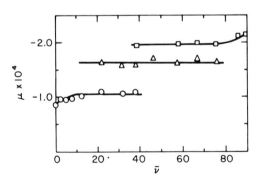

Fig. 7-4. Mobility (μ, cm^2 V^{-1} sec^{-1}) of the BPA–DBS$^-$ complexes vs. $\bar{v}$: pH 6.55 $\pm$ 0.05: 0.1 M LiCl; temperature, 22.0 $\pm$ 0.1°; field strength, 1.4 V/cm. [R. V. Decker and J. F. Foster (1966). *Biochemistry* **5**, 1242.]

the 12-ligand complex to the 38- and 76-ligand complexes (Fig. 7-5). It was estimated that 25% of the helix content present in the native protein is lost in this transition.

An analysis utilizing the mobilities of the three components at pH 6.55, and the overall isotherm is shown in Fig. 7-6. The analysis leads to $n_1 = 11 \pm 1$,

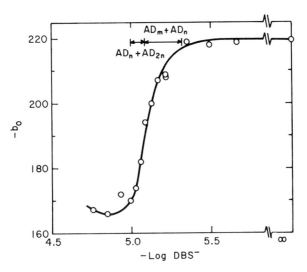

FIG. 7-5. Dependence of the b_0 parameter of the Moffitt equation on the negative logarithm of the free DBS^- concentration, $p[DBS^-]$, for the $BPA–DBS^-$ system; 0.1 M LiCl; pH 6.6; temperature, $24° \pm 2°$. The regions of coexistence of two forms in the electrophoresis studies are designated by arrows at the top of the figure. [R. V. Decker and J. F. Foster (1966). *Biochemistry* **5**, 1242.]

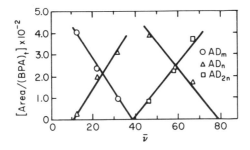

FIG. 7-6. Composition of $BPA–DBS^-$ solutions at various values of $\bar{v}$ at pH 6.55 ± 0.05. Data are plotted as areas of individual peaks (resolved as Gaussian peaks from electrophoresis patterns) divided by the total BPA concentration; temperature, $22.0° \pm 0.1°$; solvent, 0.1 M LiCl; field strength, 1.4 v/cm. [R. V. Decker and J. F. Foster (1966). *Biochemistry* **5**, 1242.]

$n_2 = 38 \pm 1$, and $n_3 = 76 \pm 2$. At higher pH values a disproportionation occurs between PA_{38} and PA_{11} and PA_{76} which can be observed in the electrophoretic patterns.

The assumption was made in the analysis that only three components were present; estimation of the amount of each from the patterns required interpretation of each area in terms of the refractive index contribution of each component, which can be done simply if each component consists only of a single complex containing n_i bound ions. Decker and Foster point out that the exposure of new sets of sites by unfolding at $\bar{v} > 11$ or 12 would not result in saturation of the new sites unless the affinity of the new sites was great enough to combine ligands practically quantitatively at the equilibrium concentrations involved in unfolding, as earlier suggested by Yang and Foster (1966). An alternative is to assume that the two unfolded complexes represent mixed protein–detergent micelles of self-limiting composition. Equations of somewhat similar form are given for the two alternatives. In the first case:

$$\bar{v}_1 = \frac{nK_n[D]}{1 + K_n[D]} \qquad \bar{v}_2 = \frac{mK_m[D]}{1 + K_m[D]} \qquad \bar{v}_3 = \frac{2mK_m^2[D]}{1 + K_m[D]^2} \qquad (7\text{-}1)$$

m represents the number of sites in native protein, K_m the association constant for these sites; n and K_n represent the number of sites in unfolded protein, and the association constant for the latter; $\bar{v}_1$ is the molar ratio of ions bound to native protein; and $\bar{v}_2$ and $\bar{v}_3$ are the molal ratios of ions bound to unfolded protein. Decker and Foster assumed that K_n and K_n^2 referred to "cooperative binding," the first for n detergent ions to unfolded protein, and the second for $2n$ equivalents, with the same standard free energy change per mole. To avoid confusion, the anion is designated as D rather than A, which in this work represents native protein.

The total binding is not the sum of all three values of $\bar{v}$ since at this point no attempt has yet been made to specify how much protein is present as A, B, or C.

In the micellar model:

$$\bar{v}_1 = \frac{mK_n[D]}{1 + K_n[D]} \qquad \bar{v}_2 = \frac{nK_n[D]^m}{1 + K_n[D]^m} \qquad \bar{v}_3 = \frac{2nK_n^2[D]^{2m}}{1 + K_n[D]^{2m}} \qquad (7\text{-}2)$$

m represents the number of sites in native protein, K_n the association constant for these sites; m is the number of ions which form a stable micelle with a single molecule of protein, and K_n is a constant which characterizes the cooperative binding of these ions to the protein. Again $\bar{v} \neq \sum \bar{v}_i$ since each $\bar{v}_i$ refers to a different species of protein.

Decker and Foster postulate that in the first (nonmicellar) case the three forms of the protein are in an equilibrium, which may be written

$$A \underset{}{\overset{K_{AB}}{\rightleftharpoons}} B \underset{}{\overset{K_{BC}}{\rightleftharpoons}} C \qquad (7\text{-}3)$$

where A is uncombined native protein, B is uncombined unfolded protein, and C is another form of uncombined unfolded protein. They then write the equilibrium between $\sum A$ and $\sum B$ (all degrees of ligand binding) in terms of *apparent* equilibrium constants K'_{AB} as

$$K'_{AB} = \frac{[B] + \cdots [BD_n]}{[A] + [AD] \cdots [AD_m]} = K_{AB} \frac{(1 + K_n[D])^n}{(1 + K_m[D])^m} \qquad (7\text{-}4)$$

and derive similar expressions for the second stage K'_{BC} (all exponents doubled) and for the alternative micellar case. The important result is obtained that the relative amounts of native and unfolded protein depend on [D], the equilibrium ligand concentration, when K_{AB}, K_m, K_n, m, and n are given.[4] This signifies

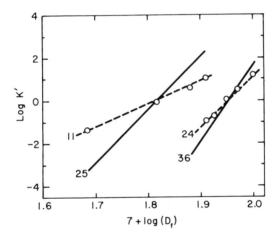

FIG. 7-7. Experimental and theoretical dependence of log $K_{AB'}$ and log $K_{BC'}$ on log D_f. The solid lines were calculated for the statistical binding mechanism; circles and dashed lines are experimental values. [R. V. Decker and J. F. Foster (1966). *Biochemistry* **5**, 1242.]

that unfolding is the result of the fact that there are particular relationships between K_m, K_n, m, and n, i.e., the protein unfolds because there are more binding sites in the unfolded form having a value of K_n near enough to K_m to combine with ligand, thus shifting the equilibrium toward the unfolded form. These relationships were made more explicit by Reynolds *et al.* (1967), as was described in Chapter II (p. 29) although the latter did not describe *two* unfolded species, B and C.

Figure 7-7 shows how log K'_{AB} and log K'_{BC} (so defined) depend on log[D],

[4] The result does not depend on how K_{AB} is defined. If, for example, $K_{AB} = [AD]/[BD]$ it has a different numerical value, but the result is not affected.

the equilibrium concentration at 24° (using the first set of equations), and how, in fact, the experimental ratios run. Decker and Foster suggest that the discrepancy in the first isomerization constant depends on the heterogeneity of the protein, demonstrated in other experiments. Figure 7-8 shows how

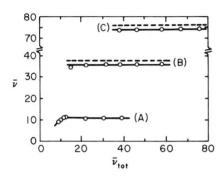

FIG. 7-8. Values for $\bar{v}_A$, $\bar{v}_C$, calculated for the statistical binding model presented as a function of total binding $\bar{v}_{total}$. Dashed lines are for the cooperative model. [R. V. Decker and J. F. Foster (1966). *Biochemistry* **5**, 1242.]

$\bar{v}_1$, $\bar{v}_2$, and v_3 depend on $\bar{v}_{total}$. The best fit of the binding data, using values of the fractions present as A, B, and C from the electrophoretic data, are

$$K_n = 5.0 \times 10^6 \text{ liter mole}^{-1} \qquad \log K_{AB} = -27.0$$
$$K_m = 2.0 \times 10^6 \text{ liter mole}^{-1} \qquad \log K_{BC} = -48.5 \tag{7-5}$$

Note that the affinity of the unfolded protein for the detergent is only slightly lower than that of the native protein. It is difficult to distinguish between the goodness of fit of the data by the model of Eq. (7-5) and the corresponding completely cooperative micellar model of Decker and Foster (Fig. 7-9) because the products of the form $K[D]$ are all much greater than 1. It is therefore unnecessary to invoke protein–ligand micelle formation to explain the cooperative features of the phenomena. Decker and Foster tentatively identify K_{AB} as a pH-dependent parameter responsible for the $N \rightleftarrows F$ transformation near pH 4 (Leonard and Foster, 1961). They point out that the fact that the $N \rightleftarrows F$ equilibrium at a given pH is shifted toward N by the presence of small amounts of detergent indicates stabilization of the protein by small $\bar{v}$. Foster and Aoki (1958) described a model essentially the same as the one given more explicitly by Decker and Foster (see also Foster, 1960). The present model, essentially the same as the one formulated earlier by Foster and Aoki (1958), predicts such stabilization *only if* m *strong sites are replaced by a larger number of sites* (which may be slightly weaker) *on unfolding*, and if K_{AB} is a function of pH.

Figure 7-9 shows how $\bar{v}_1$, and $\bar{v}_2$ then depend on $\log[D]$ and $\bar{v}_{total}$. Two sets of curves are presented in order to show how the calculated results depend on the choice of K_{AB}.

The ideas set forth by Decker and Foster and earlier by Foster and Aoki have the great merit that they can be made to relate binding and unfolding explicitly. Without postulating a mechanism for opening up the protein, it becomes a thermodynamic necessity for the protein to unfold when enough detergent is present if the unfolded protein makes available many more binding sites for a given ligand than does the native protein, provided the new binding sites are not very much weaker than the preexisting ones. The model predicts the observed stabilization of the protein when only small amounts of ligand ($\bar{v} < n$) are bound. The model has the further virtue that it presents one possibility of isolation of the intrinsic isomerization constant K_{AB} from the other parameters involved in unfolding (ligand concentration, binding strengths, numbers of sites on folded and unfolded protein) and, therefore, may permit calculation of the free energy of stabilization of the native conformation. The fact that the model may have all these virtues is strongly in its favor. Nevertheless, the validity and utility of the model for some of these purposes depends critically on the constancy of m, n, and K_{AB} for the same protein in going from one unfolding ligand to another. If these criteria fail, no success in fitting isotherms by free choice of K_{AB} will be enough to carry conviction that the model is valid.

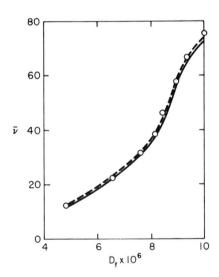

FIG. 7-9. Theoretical binding isotherms as calculated for the mechanisms presented. Experimental values are given by the circles; broken curve, fully cooperative mechanism with constant composition for the three complexes; solid curve, statistical binding to equivalent and noninteracting sites on the three isomeric forms of BPA. [R. V. Decker and J. F. Foster (1966). *Biochemistry* 5, 1242.]

2. Pure Octylbenzenesulfonate

Hill and Briggs measured the binding of *n*-octylbenzene-*p*-sulfonate to β-lactoglobulin (1956).[5] This detergent is more soluble than dodecylbenzene-

[5] Presumably a mixture of A and B genetic variants.

sulfonate, and thus permits work at higher values of $\bar{v}$.[6] Solutions of 0.5%
protein plus buffer were equilibrated with equal volumes of buffer plus
detergent. Few data are given in tabular form, but the graphs given for
representative experiments are quite clear (Figs. 7-10 and 7-11). The data show

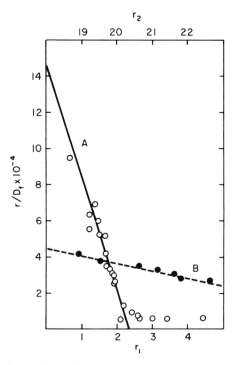

FIG. 7-10. Interaction isotherm plotted according to Scatchard; r_1/D_t vs. r_1 is shown
by curve A and the open points; r_2/D_t vs. r_2 is shown by curve B and solid points. [R. M.
Hill and D. R. Briggs (1956). *J. Am. Chem. Soc.* **78**, 1590.]

that $n = 2$ and $K = 90,000$ (Hill and Briggs give $n = 2.35$ and $K_n = 63,000$).
The existence of two moderately high energy sites ($\Delta F° \simeq 6.2$ kcal) fits in well
with the observation of McMeekin (1949) that two dodecylsulfate ions
crystallize with β-lactoglobulin. Values for m and K_m were calculated by an
indirect method; i.e., determining amounts of folded and unfolded fractions
from electrophoretic patterns, calculating the amount bound by the native
(folded) form from the constants just given, subtracting this from the total
bound, and attributing the residue to the amount of unfolded protein. Thus

---

[6] This substance was also stated to have a higher CMC, but the values given in the
paper are lower than the accepted CMC for, e.g., dodecylsulfate.

$\bar{v}_m$ is subject to the sources of error inherent in this series of estimations. The values of m and K_m, so determined, are 32 and 14,100; a value of K_m about twice as great gives a better fit to the data in the last column of Table 1 of Hill and Briggs (1956).

The electrophoretic patterns show that the amount of fast component (unfolded protein) increases from 2.6% of the total protein to over 65% in the region of $\bar{v}_2$ between 18 and 23 used in the calculation of m and K_m. It will be noted that no observations were made in which $\bar{v}_2$ was appreciably below 19 [although $\bar{v}$ (average) is here only slightly over 3]. No unfolding appears, by

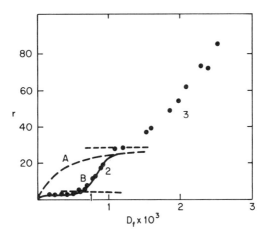

FIG. 7-11. Complete interaction isotherm showing regions 1, 2, and 3. Curve A represents the theoretical bindings isotherm for the fast component using the constants obtained from Fig. 7-10, curve B. Curve B is the theoretical isotherm calculated according to Eq. 7-6. [R. M. Hill and D. R. Briggs (1956). *J. Am. Chem. Soc.* **78,** 1590.]

the electrophoretic criteria, at $\bar{v}$ (average) = 2 to 3. However, only slightly above 2 (i.e., at $\bar{v} = 3.2$) about 5% is unfolded. Transformation is almost complete at $\bar{v}$ values in excess of 16 ($\bar{v}_2$ is here about 30). Since data are given to $\bar{v} = 95$, one may also attempt to calculate n_3 and K_3 for the fully unfolded protein by disregarding $\bar{v}$ values below 30. The best fit results in a partition constant ($K_3 = \bar{v}/C_D$) of 28,000 (n_3 infinite).

These results differ from those of Pallansch and Briggs for dodecylsulfate binding by BSA (p. 261) principally in that there is ample opportunity to study the relation between binding throughout and beyond the transition region. Like the others reported here, it shows only one set of sites in the native protein.

Efforts to apply a binding-controlled model of protein unfolding to the experiments with β-lactoglobulin must also be concerned with the binding of the third set of sites, which may qualify as still another example of the formation of mixed protein–detergent micelles. Before attempting this analysis, it may be well to recall that Wishnia and Pinder (1966) found that each monomer unit of β-lactoglobulin had two hydrocarbon binding sites regardless of whether the monomeric, dimeric, or octameric forms of either the A or B isomorph was under study.

Hill and Briggs calculated theoretical isotherms for the total binding by means of equations used by Pallansch and Briggs (see p. 261), taking from the electrophoresis patterns the amounts of protein present in the two components (electrophoretic boundaries). Thus they use the equation

$$\bar{v}_{1,2} = \bar{v}_1 + \bar{v}_2 = \frac{A_1}{A_t}\left(\frac{2.35\,C}{1.59 \times 10^{-5} + C}\right) + \frac{A_2}{A_t}\left(\frac{32\,C}{7.1 \times 10^{-4} + C}\right) \quad (7\text{-}6)$$

to fit the data up to $\bar{v} = 34$. A_t represents the total area under both peaks; A_1 is the area enclosed under the slow peak; A_2 is the area enclosed under the fast peak; and C is the equilibrium concentration of uncombined ligand. This includes the entire transition region (we note elsewhere that K_2 in the denominator of the second term is rather arbitrarily chosen). Binding at $\bar{v}$ values above 32 is accounted for by an additional binding isotherm, attributed to the formation of multilayers (i.e., mixed-micelle formation). Hill and Briggs therefore proceed to attempt to interpret the entire binding phenomenon for the unfolded protein in terms of a modified Brunauer, Emmett, and Teller gas absorption (1938).

The entire binding isotherm is

$$\bar{v}_1 + \bar{v}_2 + \bar{v}_3 = \frac{A_1(2.35\,C)}{A_t(1.59 \times 10^{-5} + C)} + \frac{A_2(22 \times 14.2\,C)}{A_t\{(D_C - C)[1 + 13.2(C/D_C)]\}} \quad (7\text{-}7)$$

where the critical micelle concentration, D_C is given as 3.3×10^{-3}, as the result of curve fitting. Figure 7-12, reproduced from the paper of Hill and Briggs, appears to indicate that Eq. (7-7) gives a good description of the data if electrophoretic patterns are used for the determination of A_1 and A_2. Thus the binding parameters do not predict the unfolding, which is another explicit input derived from the electrophoretic patterns. In order to reconcile Eq. (7-6) which contains $n_2 = 32$ with the value of $n = 22$ in Eq. (7-7), Hill and Briggs reformulate $\bar{v}_2$ on the basis of a modified Brunauer, Emmett, and Teller (1938) isotherm

$$\bar{v}_2 = \frac{22\,C}{2.32 \times 10^{-4} + C} \quad (7\text{-}8)$$

and obtain, as an expression for $\bar{v}_3$, $22.4\,C/(3.3 \times 10^{-3} - D_C)$ (which can be justified as the completion of a monolayer). Thus, they can rewrite (7-7) as

$$\bar{v}_2 + \bar{v}_3 = \frac{22\,C}{2.32 \times 10^{-4} + C} + \frac{22.4\,C}{3.3 \times 10^{-3} - C} \tag{7-9}$$

An alternative to this treatment would be to consider that 2 or 3 sites exist in the native protein, and that all $\bar{v}$ above 2 or 3 refer to mixed micellar binding on the unfolded protein. This possibility must be rejected because throughout the entire transition region the experimental, $\bar{v}_{\mathrm{obs}} - \bar{v}_2$ (calculated from $K_3 = 28,000$) determined from the largest $\bar{v}$ values reported (see p. 257) exceeds 3.

A number of tentative conclusions may be drawn if the values for K_m, K_n, and n and m of Hill and Briggs are accepted. Since n is very small, relative to m, and the two association constants are not far different, it cannot be expected that stabilization by detergents against denaturation of this protein would occur. It is also rather striking that when unfolded protein appears it does so with 18–19 bound anions out of its *maximum* capacity of 32. Thus unfolded protein is present in rather small amounts as $\bar{v}$ begins to exceed 3 (electrophoretic patterns).[7] The free energy of combination of these 18 anions, about 117 kcal/mole protein, must equal the energy of unfolding plus the rather small free energy of acquiring the same charge by combination with ions which do not unfold (about 8–9 kcal if the Linderström-Lang model is used, less otherwise). The energy of unfolding the native molecule bearing a

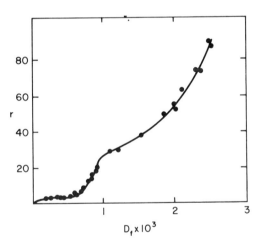

Fig. 7-12. Theoretical interaction isotherm [according to Eq. 7-7] for β-lactoglobulin and octylbenzene-*p*-sulfonate compared with experimental points. [R. M. Hill and D. R. Briggs (1956). *J. Am. Chem. Soc.* **78**, 1590.]

[7] It will be recalled (Chapter IV) that at alkaline pH β-lactoglobulin is stabilized by hydrocarbons (Wetlaufer and Lovrien, 1964).

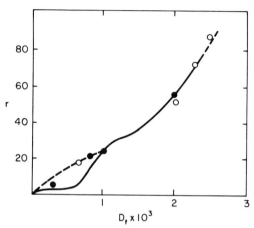

FIG. 7-13. Reversal of detergent–protein interaction (β-lactoglobulin); solid line is initial binding isotherm. Open and closed points obtained after partial removal of detergent by dialysis from initial free detergent concentrations of 32×10^{-4} M and 20×10^{-4} M, respectively. [R. M. Hill and D. R. Briggs (1956). *J. Am. Chem. Soc.* **78**, 1590.]

net charge of minus 18, including two charges on the native sites, is thus of the order of 125 kcal/mole under the conditions of these experiments. This estimate does not depend on assumptions as to any particular mechanism of unfolding. The figure given may be misleading if it actually applies to the energy of unfolding *stabilized* protein binding two detergent molecules on native sites; in such a case, the energy of unfolding the *uncombined* molecule will be smaller.

The experiments of Hill and Briggs are noteworthy as a thorough study of the reversibility of binding and unfolding. Figure 7-13 shows that after the unfolding of β-lactoglobulin which occurs at high $\bar{v}$, subsequent dialysis against buffer to reduce C also reduces $\bar{v}$ so that it follows the same isotherm as in the original dialysis of initially native protein against buffer–detergent mixtures. However, this good agreement is limited to the region of $\bar{v}$ in which the protein is almost entirely in the unfolded form ($\bar{v} > 24$). At lower values of C much *higher* values of $\bar{v}$ are found than when initially native protein is equilibrated with detergent; in fact the data follow the isotherm postulated for the unfolded protein, and vividly confirm the calculated K_m and m.[8] Electro-

---

[8] It would be noteworthy, if true, that in this case, unlike that of BSA, *more* detergent is bound by unfolded than by native protein at concentrations below 10^{-3}. It is obvious, therefore, that in this protein unfolding cannot be induced as in the Reynolds model merely by the existence of a larger number of suitable binding sites in the unfolded than in the native protein, since refolding *reduces* the amount bound in the low $\bar{v}$ region. An energy barrier to unfolding of this kind may exist, which can be overcome, for example, by electrostatic repulsion.

phoresis showed that more "unfolded" protein was present than in the forward equilibration, and the anomalously high $\bar{v}$ found was consistent with the proportions observed of the two electrophoretic components. The refolding reaction is evidently very slow. When more exhaustive dialysis for longer periods was carried out and the detergent-free protein was then reequilibrated with detergent, the final $\bar{v}$ values and mobilities observed were identical with those observed at the same C in the initial equilibration of native protein. Only a single component with one molecular weight appeared on ultracentrifugation. However, the "reversed" native protein could not be crystallized, and its solutions had a *lower* isoionic point than did the original protein.

Mullen has measured the binding isotherm p-octylbenzenesulfonate to BSA (1963). He obtained $n = 10$ and $K_n = 1.25 \times 10^5$, which is only slightly lower than the value deduced from the more recent data of Decker and Foster (1966) for the dodecylbenzene compound. Unfolding appears to occur at concentrations only slightly higher than with the latter. Both are much lower than the amount required for dodecylsulfate (pp. 26, 267).

3. *Isotherms of Alkyl Sulfates and Sulfonates. Microheterogeneity.*

Shortly after publication of the work of Yang and Foster (1953) very similar results were obtained by Pallansch and Briggs (1954) in experiments with 1% BSA and purified dodecylsulfate at 22° and pH 6.8, at somewhat higher ionic strengths. Much lower binding constants, only 12% as great as those of Yang and Foster (and very much lower, less than 1% of those of Decker and Foster on dodecylbenzene-sulfonate) were obtained. On the basis of their results Pallansch and Briggs concluded that there were two sets of groups, one set of 10, each of which had an association constant of 20,000, and another set of 80, having binding constants of 5000. Recalculation shows that the first set could be assigned values for m between 8 and 12, with corresponding small changes in K. In the electrophoretic experiments, a single boundary was found, as in the later work of Decker and Foster, with mobility dependent on $\bar{v}$, up to $\bar{v}$ values of about 8. At higher $\bar{v}$ values, increasing proportions of the total protein appeared in a faster moving boundary, which at its first appearance at $\bar{v} = 10$ had a mobility which would correspond to $\bar{v} > 40$. Since the experiments were not carried to $\bar{v}$ values beyond 43, no data were obtained for solutions in which *all* the protein had been converted to the higher binding (unfolded) form.

By estimating from the electrophoretic patterns the fractions of the total protein present in either form, at each equilibrium ligand concentration, Pallansch and Briggs fitted *the binding data* by Eq. (7-10), which is the sum of two simple law of mass action expressions (for sets of identical binding constants), each weighted by the fraction of protein *calculated from electrophoretic patterns* to be present in each of the two forms. The equation is

$$\bar{v} = \left(\frac{m[A^-]}{K_1 + [A^-]}\right)\frac{P_1}{P_0} + \left(\frac{n[A^-]}{K_2 + [A^-]}\right)\frac{P_2}{P_0} \qquad (7\text{-}10)$$

where $[A^-]$ is the equilibrium dodecylsulfate concentration and P_1 and P_2 are the fractions of the total protein P_0 indicated by the electrophoretic patterns to be present at each value of $[A^-]$. Thus only m sites were present in the native protein.

Pallansch and Briggs determined P_1 and P_2 experimentally. Since there was a considerable range of $[A^-]$ in which both P_1 and P_2 were greater than zero, they suggested that the BSA molecules, suspected from other evidence to be heterogeneous, differed in the threshold values of $[A^-]$ at which they were transformed. It should be clear, however, from their own mathematical model and from those of Foster and Aoki (1958), and of Reynolds *et al.*, (1967) that such an assumption may not be *necessary* at all, since the equilibrium between native and denatured protein is affected by the binding isotherms of the two forms. Unfortunately, the experiments of Pallansch and Briggs did not extend to dodecylsulfate concentrations at which the transformation to denatured protein was complete. It is therefore impossible to determine K_2, which is necessary for application of the equations. However, it should be noted that, since Pallansch and Briggs succeeded in fitting their binding data to Eq. (7-10), it is very likely that the "second" set of binding sites (those in the unfolded protein) does not exist in the native protein.

Certain other features of the data of Pallansch and Briggs deserve particular mention:

(1) The value of K_1 reported is far smaller than any others reported for this compound by other investigators. Thus, Ray *et al.* (1966), who used highly purified material, reported $K_1 = \sim 2 \times 10^6$ with $n = 8$, not far from the value 5×10^6 reported for dodecylbenzenesulfonate by Decker and Foster (1966). It has not proved possible to confirm from the *binding data* tabulated by Pallansch and Briggs their reported value for either n or K_1. The data for large binding shows that a nearly constant fraction of the total ligand is bound, i.e., a close approach to a Nernst partition equilibrium. Almost identical values of K_m and K_n may then be used, when m is much larger than n.

(2) These investigators believed that all BSA preparations are demonstrably heterogeneous in their susceptibility to unfolding (as is known to be the case in the $N \rightarrow F$ transformation); however, they also observed great differences between individual BSA preparations. Some preparations gave no second (unfolded) component (when tested electrophoretically) at equilibrium concentrations which would give $\bar{v} = 80$ with the preparation used in the

experiments described in the paper. Unfortunately no binding data are given for these preparations.

Anderson (1966) in Briggs' laboratory has reported the results of a very thorough study of the heterogeneity with respect to induction of unfolding by detergent (*n*-octylbenzene-*p*-sulfonate) with a number of proteins, including BSA (Fig. 7-14). Different commercial lots of crystallized BSA differ slightly in the equilibrium concentrations near $\bar{v} = 10$–12 which initiate unfolding. Some preparations required almost 50% more free detergent than others. However, the difference in log[A⁻], the quantity usually plotted, is at most only about 0.18 unit. As the amount of unfolded protein produced increases, the difference in free detergent required gradually diminishes to zero. Fractionation of a single preparation by salting out at pH 4 with sodium sulfate resulted in fractions that were slightly more resistant to unfolding, but which

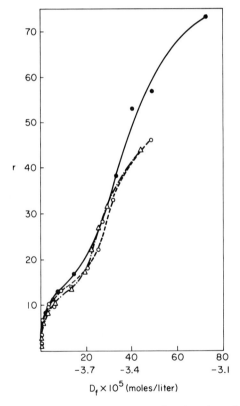

FIG. 7-14. Comparison of adsorption isotherms of various lots of armour and pentex bovine serum albumin at 0.1 ionic strength and pH 5.1. [P. G. Anderson (1966). Thesis. Univ. Microfilms, Xerox Co., Ann Arbor, Michigan, Ord. No. 67-3.]

retain their differences up to the highest $\bar{v}$ values investigated ($\sim$40). The results obtained by fractionating different batches of crystals differed appreciably. Somewhat similar results were obtained with ovalbumin and β-lacto-globulins A and B; however, although all of these showed unfolding at comparable concentrations of free detergent (2 to $6 \times 10^{-3}\ M$), none paralleled the high-affinity region (1–$3 \times 10^{-5}\ M$) of BSA, where about 10 equivalents are bound. The very extensive work of Foster and his collaborators on the microheterogeneity of BSA has already been referred to in Chapters IV and V.

(3) The unfolding brought about at high dodecylsulfate concentrations was reversible when judged by electrophoresis after prolonged dialyses against buffer; however, reversal of unfolding falls slightly short of completion. A shift of the isoelectric point from pH 5.2 to 4.78 appears to indicate that a permanent change in the protein persists. Somewhat similar results were found by Anderson (1966) with octylbenzenesulfonate bound to BSA and two other proteins.

(4) Octyl- and decylsulfates did not appear to cause unfolding at any concentration tried, although, as Reynolds et al. (1967) showed later, high values of $\bar{v}$ may be attained. This observation offers further opportunities to test the suggested model for a link between the energetics of binding and of unfolding.

(5) Tetradecylsulfate produced an unfolded component (as judged by the appearance of a second faster moving boundary) at equilibrium concentrations lower than those required when dodecylsulfate was used.

Another determination of the binding of dodecylsulfate has been made with BSA treated by the Goodman acid extraction procedure (Chapter IV) to reduce contamination by fatty acid. High concentrations of detergent were used in the absence of buffer or any other salts (Strauss and Strauss, 1958). No membrane was involved. The binding was calculated from measurements of the electrical transference of detergent and protein produced by the passage of definite quantities of electricity (Hutzinger et al., 1950). The protein ($3 \times 10^{-5}\ M$) was exposed to total detergent concentrations between 2 and $14 \times 10^{-3}\ M$. The final results are shown in Fig. 7-15, which also includes the data of Pallansch and Briggs in the presence of buffer. The maximum value of $\bar{v}$ shown, 160, must not be interpreted as indicating that no more "sites" or capacity exist; it merely shows that 160 equivalents are bound at the concentration of detergent (CMC) at which pure detergent micelles rather than mixed micelles containing protein must be formed. Too much significance must not be attached to the semblance of agreement with the earlier work of Pallansch and Briggs, since "at these low values of r even a 50 percent discrepancy in r would result in only a slight displacement in the curves" (Strauss

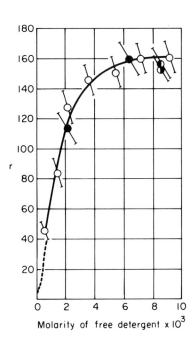

FIG. 7-15. Effect of free detergent concentration on the average number of detergent anions (r) bound per serum albumin molecule; results from transference: O, $3 \times 10^{-5} M$ protein; ●, $6 \times 10^{-5} M$ protein. Results from conductance at CMC: ◖, $3 \times 10^{-5} M$ protein; ◗, $6 \times 10^{-5} M$ protein. The points represent average values, the length of the sloping lines the extent of experimental uncertainty; $----$, data of Pallansch and Briggs (1954) from equilibrium dialysis. [G. Strauss and U. P. Strauss (1958). *J. Phys. Chem.* **62**, 1321.]

Molarity of free detergent x 10^3

and Strauss, 1958). It was also calculated that the sodium ions present were almost wholly dissociated at $\bar{v}$ values up to at least 100, rather than being firmly immobilized as counterions; the dissociation was over 80% at $\bar{v}$ below 50. Dilution experiments showed that the binding was reversible. Reversibility has been well established by the experiments in Foster's and Brigg's laboratories. The dissociation process has been shown to occur quite slowly with β-lactoglobulin and ovalbumin; with BSA the dossociation or refolding rate is too rapid to observe in equilibrium dialysis experiments.

Ray *et al.* (1966) have published values of n and K_n for octylsulfate and octylsulfonate as well as dodecylsulfate; and Reynolds *et al.* (1967) give values for numerous other highly purified normal alkyl sulfates and sulfonates (1967). The purpose of these two investigators was to attempt to resolve the components of the binding energy, by comparing the anions with one another, and with their uncharged homologues.[9] BSA, 0.1%, was used in obtaining normal "statistical" isotherms with values of K_n of the order of 10^6 for all

[9] Both investigators agreed in finding pronounced effects of protein concentration on the isotherms with all but compounds containing chains of fewer than 12 carbon atoms. The apparent effect has since been shown to be the result of the longer equilibration times required with the more concentrated solutions, i.e., with the latter, equilibrium was not obtained (Cassel *et al.*, 1969). However, the data of these investigators obtained at 0.1% protein are not subject to this error.

the compounds containing eight or more carbon atoms; the weaker sites in the unfolded protein were also very similar (K_m about 8000), but the values of m and n varied widely, increasing with the length of the hydrocarbon chain to maximum n of 8 or 9, and a maximum m of about 80. Binding far beyond 80 anions occurred and gave signs of micelle formation. It is noteworthy that uncharged homologues (i.e., n-alcohols) tended to behave similarly, but were characterized by free energies of binding lower (15–22%) than those of the corresponding sulfate anions except for the eight-carbon chain (40%). The difference in free energy between the uncharged alcohols and the sulfonates is even smaller (dodecyl 5.5%, decyl 18.5%, octyl 30%). It is noteworthy that the free energies of binding the corresponding carboxylate anions are almost identical with those of binding the uncharged homologous alcohols, again except for the eight carbon compounds which differ by about 25%. The coulombic contribution when long chains are bound is thus small, but it is important to point out that in these experiments both protein and anion bore the same (negative) net charge. The variation of binding energy with chain length is consistent with the hypothesis that the binding energy is entropic in origin, and also suggests that multiple contacts between protein and ligand are required for high affinity, i.e., the ligands may be thought of as potentially polyfunctional.

4. Models for Unfolding

Reynolds et al. (1967), who measured the binding isotherms of BSA with many unbranched aliphatic sulfates and sulfonates, encountered only two—dodecylsulfate and tetradecylsulfate—which unfolded the protein when amounts larger than about 10 equivalents were bound. This work, and related work from the same laboratory, are discussed more fully on later pages. Here it suffices to indicate the success of these investigations in more closely defining the conditions for unfolding due to binding, and relating them explicitly to numbers of binding sites in native and unfolded protein and to the binding constants of the two states.

The treatment given in Chapter II (pp. 29) employs a model equivalent to that of Foster and Aoki but explicitly predicts both stabilization and disorganization of protein structure by ligand association. In addition, it provides an explicit means of determining the equilibrium constant between two different protein states when the number of binding sites and association constants are known for each state and for a particular ligand. It may be considered a general model for the denaturation of proteins which contain masked binding sites, for any ligand including hydrogen ion.

The model described in Chapter II [Eq. (2-63)] has been applied to the 2° binding isotherms for octyl-, decyl-, and dodecylsulfate to bovine serum albumin (see p. 29). Only the regions below $\log[A] = -2.5$ were used, and state 1 was defined as that protein conformation which corresponded to the lowest specific viscosity plateau (see p. 26). State 2 differed for all three ligand–protein complexes and corresponded to that conformation existing at the first step in the three viscosity curves shown on p. 26. In all three calculations the function, $F[A]$, went through a minimum at low anion concentration. The computer values for U are not identical in these cases and indeed should not be since the final states are different. Figure 7-16 is an example of

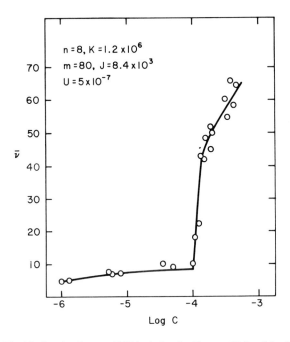

FIG. 7-16. The binding isotherm of BSA–dodecylsulfate at 2° fitted by Eqs. 2-63 and 2-64, with the parameters given on the figure. [J. Reynolds *et al.* (1967). *Biochemistry* **6**, 945.]

the computer fit to the binding of dodecylsulfate to BSA, and Fig. 7-17 is a plot of $\log F[A]$ vs. $\log[A]$ for the same system. An obvious experimental test of this model would be a determination of U for a protein–ligand system in which several ligands produced the same final protein state. In this case U should be independent of the ligand used. There are indications in the work of Decker and Foster (1966) and those of Reynolds *et al.*, (1967) that dodecylsulfate and dodecylbenzenesulfonate represent such a pair since both bound on 76–80 sites in the unfolded state.

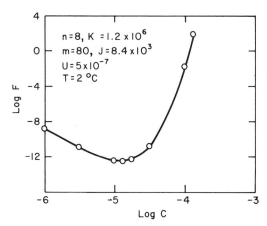

FIG. 7-17. Predicted stabilization by dodecylsulfate. Variation in the ratio of the logarithm of the ratio of denatured to native protein as a function of equilibrium concentration of ligand. [J. Reynolds *et al.* (1967). *Biochemistry* **6**, 945.]

It will be noted that the treatment just described omits Foster's intermediate unfolded state which is combined with 38 anions. This is a serious shortcoming since the existence of the intermediate state in the case of the aromatic anion rests on solid electrophoretic evidence. The ORD data of Reynolds *et al.* serve as partial confirmation of the finding of Decker and Foster that massive loss of helical structure sets in at $\bar{v} \simeq 38$ (Figs. 2-2 and 2-3). However, with dodecyl- and tetradecylsulfates, the disorganization seems to set in at $\bar{v} > 50$. This large effect is not shared by any of the other anionic detergents investigated by Reynolds *et al.* However, all of the detergents decrease the depth of the Cotton effect trough at 233 mμ by about 6–7%, as a result of the initial binding by the native protein: this corresponds to an increase in $[\alpha]_{546}$ from $-74°$ to $-72°$. The initial binding is also accompanied by shifts in the uv spectrum which are described in later pages. These changes are probably not accompanied by any change in helix content.[10] Further work is required to assess the significance of the apparently lower $\bar{v}$ required for unfolding with the aromatic detergent anion, and for the apparent absence of a well-marked 38-anion intermediate unfolded form in the case of the aliphatic detergent anions. It is noteworthy that the region of the binding isotherm in which unfolding occurs with dodecylbenzenesulfonate at pH 6.58 lies at equilibrium concentrations only 0.01 as great as those required to unfold with dodecylsulfate at approximately the same pH.[11] In

[10] The change in the 233-mμ trough is not paralleled by any change in the maximum at lower wavelengths.

[11] Decker and Foster's experiments were carried out in the presence of 0.1 *M* LiCl, those of Reynold in 0.033 ionic strength phosphate buffers.

terms of the model just described, and in view of the fact that the association constants of the two ligands to BSA are approximately the same, *the aromatic anion must be bound much more strongly to the denatured protein than is the long-chain aliphatic ion.* Such large differences between the two unfolding ligands may be related to the possible presence of a 38-anion complex in one of them and not in the other. However the equations of Decker and Foster lead to overall isotherms which are not greatly different from those of Reynolds *et al.*

5. *Relations to Hydrogen-Ion Binding*

Decker and Foster (1967) have titrated BSA with acid and base in the presence of dodecylbenzenesulfate (the AD_m and AD_{2m} complexes were used). Between pH 6 and 9 titration curves of the uncombined protein and AD_n are practically indistinguishable (Fig. 5-7). Below pH 6 AD_m binds slightly more H^+, and above pH 9 the amount of base bound by AD_m gradually becomes smaller than the amount bound by protein alone, until it becomes equal to the amount bound by AD_{2m}. Acid bound by the latter rises sharply at pH below about 9.5, and the curve for base bound lies at about 0.25 pH units higher than for uncomplexed protein. The sharp increase in H^+ bound by AD_{2m} at acid pH appears to be due to the fact revealed by studies of the infrared absorption as a function of pH (Fig. 7-18) that only 60 out of 100

FIG. 7-18. Tracings of representative infrared difference spectra over the range 1600–1900 cm^{-1}. Reading from top to bottom the curves correspond to solutions of "indicated pH" of 5.58, 4.77, 4.16, 3.58, 3.32, 2.97, and 2.34. In all cases the reference solution was at an indicated pH of 8.50. [K. Vijai and J. F. Foster (1967). *Biochemistry* **6**, 1152.]

carboxylic acid side chains are available for titration in the native protein in the normal range (Vijai and Foster, 1967), or in AD_m. All of them can be titrated in AD_{2m}. The latter behaves in titration in all respects as an unfolded protein; i.e., the electrostatic interaction factor is small compared with its value in the native protein; the tyrosine titration, determined spectrophotometrically, does not distinguish between exposed and buried tyrosine, possibly because all are buried in the native protein and in AD_m (see Chapter V) and released in the range pH 10–12 where they quantitatively combine with base. Spectral and fluorescent effects incident to unfolding also manifest themselves at $\bar{v} > m$ (Polet and Steinhardt, 1968; Lenz and Steinhardt, 1969).

6. Relations to Unfolding by Acid, and to Precipitation

Before leaving the foregoing discussion of the "unfolding" interaction of two proteins with a number of detergents it will be well to recall the relation of the unfolding or stabilization produced by some detergents to similar effects produced by acid and base (see Chapter V). This relationship has been well studied in the case of serum albumin (Aoki, 1958), with recent emphasis directed to the relation of the phenomenon to microheterogeneity of the protein (Peterson and Foster, 1965,a,b), and to the relation of the latter to tightly bound fatty acid (Sogami and Foster, 1968; Wang and Foster, 1968). Since similar disorganizing effects of acid and base can be demonstrated with most other proteins it may be presumed that the relation of the phenomena to detergent binding found with serum albumin is not unique.

By the time of Aoki's work electrophoretic patterns had demonstrated in both horse and bovine serum albumin the existence of at least two components in BSA at pH values between 3.5 and 4.5 [see Chapter V and Vijai and Foster (1967) for a discussion of the titration curve in this region]. Below this pH region the isomerized protein "expands" (Tanford, 1955; Scatchard, 1952), as shown by changes in viscosity (Yang and Foster, 1954; Tanford et al., 1955) and sedimentation behavior (Kronman and Foster, 1957; Charlwood and Ens, 1955). Changes in electrophoretic patterns also occur at pH values above pH 7.5, and again above pH 9, where changes in optical rotation also occur (Jirgenson, 1956). The addition of sodium decylsulfate to solutions at pH 3.5 to 4.5 which contained both N and F forms converted all the protein to N (stabilized) by electrophoretic criteria. A cationic detergent, dodecylpyridinium bromide, of somewhat lower affinity, converted all the protein to F.[12] Sodium decylsulfate reduced the charge on the protein ion; dodecylpyridinium bromide increased it. It is possible that the unfolding or refolding is entirely controlled by accumulation of a threshold net electrostatic charge.[13]

[12] The interaction of this detergent with serum albumin has been studied by Foster and Yang (1954).

[13] Such a simple mechanism is not compatible with the results of Reynolds et al. (1967).

C. The Binding of Fatty Acids Compared to other Ligands. Nature of the Binding Site

BSA and human serum albumin (HSA) bind other anionic detergents such as dissociated long-chain fatty acids (Goodman, 1958; Reynolds *et al.*, 1968; Zakrzanski and Goch, 1968). Table 7-4 summarizes all of the data for BSA that have been obtained with all the anionic detergents, including the carboxylic acids, and includes the homologous alcohols, when data are available, for comparison.

The values for the longest-chain compounds listed, the fatty acids with 15 carbon atoms, are Goodman's, obtained by partition equilibrium with heptane, and represent more vigorously defatted protein than the material used with the other ligands.[14] Where data are available for comparison with Goodman's (dodecanoate) the principal difference is in the appearance in Goodman's experiments of two sites having about 1.2 kcal/mole higher free energy of binding than the other five sites; there is good agreement in the association constants reported for the latter by Goodman and the value for six to seven sites reported by Reynolds *et al.* (1968). There is some doubt as to how much Goodman's defatting treatment may have affected his results. Protein defatted by Chen's milder but more exhaustive charcoal method has been investigated by Gallagher and Steinhardt (1969) and is discussed on later pages.

It is noteworthy that the affinities of anions possessing the same length of hydrophobic tail to native BSA *increase* as the polar end group goes from OH to COO^- to SO_3^- to SO_4^-, and that the span of this increase is very large. The

[14] Goodman used human serum albumin exhaustively defatted by treatment with acetic acid and extraction with organic solvents. The six long-chain fatty acid anions investigated at pH 7.45 at 23° (ionic strength 0.16) were equilibrated with the protein by partition between two phases, one aqueous, the other *n*-heptane (the latter has been shown by Alfsen to produce a conformation change in bovine serum albumin). With oleate and linoleate at least, the appearance of the isotherm suggests the existence of cooperative binding at amounts bound slightly in excess of that represented by the first two sets (7 sites). Since Goodman's experiments were conducted at pH 7.45 (0.16 M phosphate buffers) the apparent association constants given in Table 7-4 are probably sensitive to pH. The intrinsic constants, corrected for competition by phosphate ions, would be only slightly higher than those in the table except in the case of the two highest-energy sites, which might have substantial larger intrinsic binding constants.

The way in which K_1 depends on chain length indicates that the two high-energy sites were constructed to have a high degree of specificity for 16- and 18-carbon chains, especially those containing a double bond; on the basis of unpublished data, it was also suggested that these two sites did not bind other anions of high affinity to serum albumin, such as methyl orange. The second set is characterized by a lower structural specificity, i.e., the binding constants differ by much smaller amounts (the free energies of binding are roughly proportional to chain length), and may be available also for the binding of the large number of other ions and molecules that combine with this protein. Other evidence bearing on these ideas will be introduced later.

TABLE 7-4

BINDING BY DEIONIZED NATIVE BSA OF DERIVATIVES OF NORMAL HYDROCARBONS

Ligand	pH	n	K_{int}	$-\Delta F°$ (kcal/mole)	$-\log C$ at 23°, pH 5.6, at which $\bar{v} = 50$ (a measure of unfolding power or affinity to denatured protein)	References
Dodecylbenzenesulfonate and octylbenzenesulfonate	(6.3–9.52)	11 ± 1	5×10^{6a}	9.17	6.0	Decker and Foster (1966)
Tetradecylsulfate	5.6	10–11	1×10^6	8.22	4.3	Reynolds et al. (1967)
Dodecylsulfate	5.6	8–9	1.2×10^6	8.22	3.8	Reynolds et al. (1967)
	6.8	8	1.25×10^6	8.34	3.9	Ray et al. (1966)
Decylsulfate	5.6	5–6	1.4×10^6	8.40	2.8	Reynolds et al. (1967)
Octylsulfate	5.6	4–5	6×10^5	7.90	2.3	Reynolds et al. (1967)
Hexylsulfate	5.6	—	$<10^3$	<4.0	—	Steinhardt, unpublished
Dodecylsulfonate	5.6	6	3×10^5	7.50	2.7	Reynolds et al. (1967)
Decylsulfonate	5.6	5	9×10^5	8.18	2.4	Reynolds et al. (1967)
Octylsulfonate	5.6	3	1×10^5	6.85	2.7	Reynolds et al. (1967)
Hexylsulfate	5.6	—	10^3	4.0	—	Steinhardt, unpublished
Linoleate (unsaturated)	7.45	$2^b, 5^b$	1.3×10^7 2.5×10^6	9.26	—	Goodman (1958)

TABLE 7.4 (*Continued*)

	pH		K			Reference
Oleate (unsaturated)	7.45	$2^b, 5^b$	8.0×10^7 / 8.0×10^5	10.9	—	Goodman (1958)
Stearate	7.45	$2^b, 5^b$	1.1×10^8 / 4.0×10^6	11.1	—	Goodman (1958)
Palmitate	7.45	$6–7^b$	6.0×10^7 / 3.0×10^6	10.7	—	Goodman (1958)
Tetradecanoate	7.45	7–8	4.0×10^6 / 1.4×10^6	9.05 / 8.43	—	Goodman (1958)
Dodecanoate	6.8	6–7	2.3×10^5	7.70	—	Reynolds et al. (1968)
		2^b	1.6×10^6	8.50		Goodman (1958)
		5^b	2.4×10^5	7.38		Goodman (1958)
Decanoate	6.8	6–7	6×10^4	6.54	—	Reynolds et al. (1968)
Octanoate	6.8	4–5	5×10^4	6.45	—	Reynolds et al. (1968)
		5	1.2×10^{4c}	5.60		Teresi and Luck (1952)
Dodecanol	5.6	4–5	1.5×10^5	2.10	—	Ray et al. (1966)
Decanol	5.6	4–5	7×10^4	6.62	—	Reynolds et al. (1968)
Octanol	5.6	4–5	3.0×10^3	4.55	—	Ray et al. (1966)
	7.45	5	1.1×10^3	4.90	—	Ray et al. (1966)

[a] The value of K appears to depend on pH. See p. 249 for a demonstration that this appearance is due to the occurrence of unfolding at pH 6.58 at fairly low values of $\bar{v}$, at least in the case of DBS.

[b] Defatted human serum albumin .

ratios of these K's to the K of the 12-carbon alcohol are, for carboxylate 1.5, sulfonate 6, sulfate half-ester over 9; the corresponding ratios for the 8-carbon compounds are for carboxylate 15, sulfonate 30, sulfate about 180. The broader span with the 8-carbon compounds may be merely the result of the low affinity of n-octanol relative to the longer -chain alcohols. Thus if the ratios above were expressed as $K_{ligand}/K_{carboxylate}$ the results would be

          12-carbon: sulfonate, 4   sulfate, 6
          10-carbon: sulfonate, 15   sulfate, 23
           8-carbon: sulfonate, 2   sulfate, 12

a considerably less remarkable spread, and one which reaches a maximum at 10 carbons, where the sulfates and sulfonates appear to reach their maximum affinities to native protein. It will be noted in Table 7-4 that chain length has a rather small effect on affinity, if the polar head remains the same, *as long as at least eight carbon atoms are present*. However, with the sulfates and sulfonates the length of the chain appears to govern the number of available sites. It is possible that multiple contacts contribute to higher free energies of binding. Chains shorter than eight carbons may be incapable of multiple contacts, and thus of high-energy binding. With carboxylates, however, the number of high-energy sites does not depend on chain length. Other evidence will be introduced later which suggests that carboxylates and sulfates may not bind on the same sites.

The differences between chains having different polar heads are harder to account for. It is noteworthy that the polar groups which permit delocalization of their charge over larger areas confer higher affinities than do the heads in which delocalization is not possible (alcohols) or sharply limited (carboxylate). The charge delocalization appears to favor affinity to denatured protein even more than affinity to native protein. Thus dodecylbenzenesulfonate and octylbenzenesulfonate, which combine long aliphatic chains with very highly delocalized charges at one end, unfold at very much lower concentrations of free ligand than do the corresponding sulfates, although their affinity to native protein is only slightly larger than that of dodecyl or decylsulfates.[15]

Reports exist on the complexing of fatty acids with cytochrome c, the effects of such complexing on oxidation of the protein by hydrogen peroxide (Hardesty and Mitchell, 1963), and the effect of fatty acid binding on the electrophoretic patterns of crude preparations of prolactin, growth hormone, hemoglobin, myoglobin, serum albumin, and transferrin.

[15] It has been reported that fatty acids are able to displace the dye bromsulfonphalein from combination with human serum albumin whereas dodecylsulfate is not (Kucerova *et al.*, 1966). This report appears to conflict with the data in Table 7-4. In other respects (higher affinity for longer chain lengths and for increasing unsaturation) it agrees with Goodman's data.

D. Criteria of Unfolding. Viscosity, Deuterium Exchange, ORD, and Difference Spectra

1. *General*

In all the foregoing, references to "unfolded protein" have been largely based on observation of electrophoretic patterns at particular pH values. The validity of the conclusions drawn from such patterns rests on two alternative assumptions: (1) the rate of association and dissociation of ligands must be slower than the separation of the different species by electrophoresis or (2) heterogeneity must exist in an apparently pure protein with respect to its susceptibility to unfolding as a function of H^+ bound or molal ratios of certain "unfolding anions" bound.[16] The phenomenon of unfolding itself is apparent in noticeable changes in viscosity, already mentioned, which are characteristic of any kind of denaturation, and in such short-range physical parameters as optical rotary dispersion, ultraviolet difference spectra, and circular dichroism. Unfortunately, in as complex a phenomenon as unfolding it is not obvious how optical changes are to be related to extents of reaction, since assumptions of linearity and additivity must first be demonstrated experimentally.

Since only one systematic study has been made of the viscosity of a protein as a function of the extent of its interaction with various detergents (Reynolds *et al.*, 1967, 1968), it is easy to summarize the state of our knowledge. The data are given in Figs. 2-2 and 2-3. Carboxylates show no change of viscosity on binding up to $\bar{v} = 14$. Sulfonates produce a *very small* rise in viscosity over the range $\bar{v} = 0$ to 100. It is possible that the maximum effect is reached with *decylsulfonate* at $\bar{v}$ not far above 20. The viscosity is still rising at $\bar{v} = 10$ where the maximum change in $[\alpha]_{233}$ is obtained. The effect with sulfates is more complicated. Octyl- and decylsulfate effect a small rise in viscosity between $\bar{v} = 10$ and $\bar{v} = 30$. The small rise with dodecylsulfate occurs between $\bar{v} = 10$ and 35 and with tetradecylsulfate in the range $\bar{v} = 25$–40. No further change is found at higher $\bar{v}$ except with the two unfolding ligands (12 and 14 carbon atoms), both of which cause the viscosity to rise steeply at $\bar{v}$ values above about 70. Since with dodecylsulfate electrophoretic evidence indicates the existence of the species AD_{38}, it is apparent that this species is only slightly more viscous than A, the native protein. It is

---

[16] The correctness of the assumption of a slowly labile microheterogeneity in susceptibility to *acid* unfolding has been put on a solid footing by the work of Foster and his collaborators (Peterson and Foster, 1965a,b; Peterson *et al.*, 1965; Sogami and Foster, 1968). Recent work on fractionated charcoal-defatted BSA has shown that heterogeneity is not the result of traces of bound fatty acid, as McMenamy has suggested. The heterogeneity applies to susceptibility to unfolding by long-chain aryl detergent anions also (Anderson, 1966; Wong and Foster, 1968).

also paradoxical that the viscosity does not greatly change in the range in which AD_{38} is being transformed to AD_{78} or AD_{80} but that it increases importantly at higher anounts combined. (Fluorescence quenching due to unfolding also occurs at $\bar{v} > 60$, see p. 286). With tetradecylsulfate, solutions of AD_{38}, if it exists, are hardly more viscous than native protein, and the same may be true for solutions of AD_{76} also. The evidence of massive unfolding *in both cases* appears at $\bar{v}$ values which are much too high to agree with inferences drawn from electrophoresis, difference spectra (Polet and Steinhardt, 1968), or the interpretation of the respective isotherms in this chapter.

Two systematic studies of "microscopic" phenomena preceded the work of Ray *et al.* (1966), Reynolds *et al.* (1967), and Polet and Steinhardt (1968), discussed in detail below. Markus and Karush (1957) showed that small changes in levorotation in the visible spectrum were brought about by dodecylsulfate. The levorotation reached a minimum value when 10 to 14 detergent ions per mole of protein were bound. At higher concentrations levorotation *increased* to values higher than those for the native protein—an increase in levorotation in the visible region has often been found whenever protein denaturation occurs. The *decrease* in levorotation occurs in the concentration range in which detergent stabilizes (see p. 268). With increasing concentrations a change from decreased to increased levorotation parallels discontinuities in changes in ultraviolet absorption of BSA and other proteins as a function of detergent concentration. Analogous effects were obtained with decylsulfate and octylsulfate, but progressively higher concentrations were required with the shorter chains; in fact with octylsulfate the reversal at higher concentrations cannot be discerned. Unfortunately, the dialysis experiments of Markus and Karush on which $\bar{v}$ was based were carried out for 14 days and must have been accompanied by considerable hydrolysis of the ligand. No other salts were present and $\bar{v}$ was calculated from a theoretical Donnan ratio, using a flame photometer to determine $[Na^+]$.

Parallel changes in ultraviolet absorption were first studied by the methods of difference spectrophotometry by Bigelow and Sonnenberg (1962) with dodecylsulfate at 0.35% protein in 0.02 M phosphate buffer at pH 6.1. Unfortunately their results are stated in terms of the total detergent concentration instead of equilibrium concentrations or amounts bound, but the affinities are so high that at low concentrations

$$\bar{v} \cong C_{\text{total}}/C_{\text{protein}} \qquad (7\text{-}11)$$

Low concentrations, of the order of 2 or 3×10^{-4} or less, depressed progressively the absorption at 294 mμ and enhanced it at 280 μ (Fig. 7-19). Higher concentrations, while continuing to enhance the depression at 294, had two other effects, a second depression at 287 and a slight reduction of the effect at 280 (Fig. 7-21).

The best estimate, on the basis of the binding data of Ray *et al.* (1966) and Reynolds *et al.* (1967), is that the maximum effect obtained by Bigelow and Sonnenberg (1962) at 280 occurred at a level of $\bar{v} \simeq 6$. However, the depression at 294 increased, although slowly, up to $\bar{v} > 20$. The depression at 287, which does not set in until concentrations are reached at which the effect

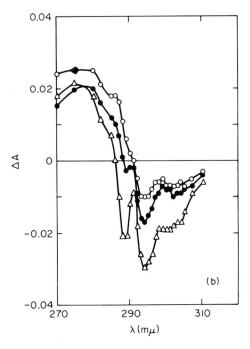

Fig. 7-19. Difference spectra for bovine serum albumin in low concentrations of sodium dodecylsulfate; $\bigcirc$, $0.208 \times 10^{-4}\ M$; $\bullet$, $3.12 \times 10^{-4}\ M$; $\triangle$, $8.68 \times 10^{-4}\ M$. [C. C. Bigelow and M. Sonenberg (1962). *Biochemistry* **1**, 197.]

at 294 is approaching its maximum, increases to the highest concentrations used ($C_{total} = 10^{-2}\ M$). The effect at $\bar{v}$ values above 8–12 was attributed to "an alteration in the environment of the tyrosyl residues." The first and smaller effect was attributed by these investigators to alterations in the environment of tryptophyl residues caused by a small conformation change. A partial effect was visible at concentrations at which $\bar{v}$ is estimated to be no larger than 5 or 6, and was complete at fairly small values of $\bar{v}$. The results of a more thorough investigation with a number of different anions (Polet and Steinhardt, 1968) are discussed in the next section.

Both environmental changes in BSA might be attributed either to charge
effects or to conformation changes, but the tyrosyl blue shift is similar to the
effects observed by Williams and Foster (1959) in the N → F transformation
that occurs in acid solutions. Leonard and Foster (1961) have in fact suggested,
on the basis of a comparison of extinction coefficients, Moffitt constants, and
mean residue rotations as a function of dodecylsulfate concentration, that the
transition caused by dodecylsulfate is identical with that of the N → F transition, and that the same mechanism may underlie both. However, values of $\bar{v}$

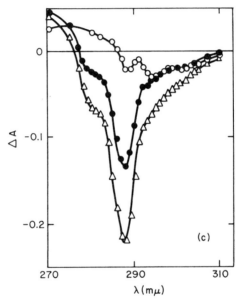

FIG. 7-21. Difference spectra for bovine serum albumin at high concentrations of
sodium dodecylsulfate; ○, 1.04×10^{-3} M; ○, 4.16×10^{-3} M; △, 1.04×10^{-2} M. [C. C.
Bigelow and M. Sonenberg (1962). *Biochemistry* **1**, 197.]

were related to dodecylsulfate concentration on the basis of the data of
Pallansch and Briggs, which are anomalously low. Polet and Steinhardt (1968)
show that absorbance changes due to N → F are smaller than those brought
about by unfolding with dodecylsulfate.

The experiments of Bigelow and Sonnenberg (1962) with BSA have been
repeated by Mullen (1963), who identified each difference spectrum with a
definite but probably erroneous $\bar{v}$ taken from measurements made by Pallansch
and Briggs (1954) over a range of $\bar{v} = 1.8$ to extremely high values. Mullen
also worked with other ligands, to be referred to below, and with modified
protein. His results (Figs. 7-22a, 7-22b, and 7-22c) are interpreted as showing
effects at $\bar{v} < 9$ which differ from those above 9. Even the lowest amount of

binding ($\bar{v} = 1.8$) results in a blue shift for tryptophan, although the effect on tyrosine, also large, is stated to be a red shift which might be interpreted entirely as an increase in the polarizability in the immediate environment, such as might be produced by adsorbed hydrophobic tails, on these chromophores. At $\bar{v}$ above 9 there is a blue shift for tyrosine also, which is interpreted as the exposure of progressively larger numbers of buried tyrosine groups to the aqueous solvent. Substances which are not believed to bind (glycine, urea, sucrose) produce no comparable effects, unless present in very high concentrations. Caprylate, trichloroacetate, *n*-octanol, and *n*-decanol, all of which bind, produce red shifts only, which are not considered to indicate "opening up." It is remarkable that even at $\bar{v} = 40$ only a small part of the maximum blue shift attainable has taken place, although other evidence such as electrophoresis patterns indicates that very little of the native component is present

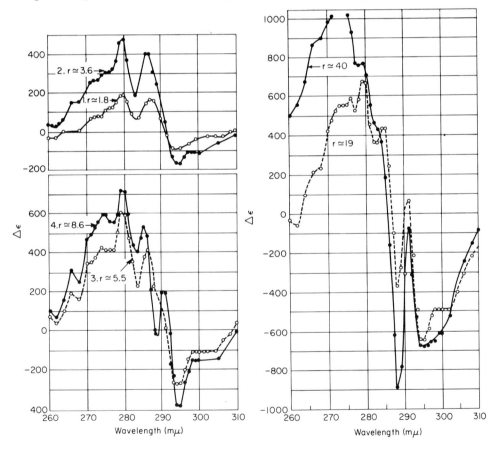

FIG. 7-22a   FIG. 7-22b

when so much detergent is bound. It would appear therefore that progressive changes occur in already unfolded protein which are not manifested in the electrophoretic patterns of Pallansch and Briggs.

Dodecylsulfate was stated to be unique among the large molecules or ions studied in producing a blue shift. Small amounts of this detergent ($\bar{v} < 10$) also inhibit the oxidation of tryptophan in BSA by N-bromosuccimide, although these low concentrations of ligand do not affect the oxidation of free tryptophan. It is concluded, therefore, that tryptophan is directly involved in the 8–10 binding sites of high affinity for dodecylsulfate although there are only two tryptophan residues in a molecule of BSA.

Enhancement of the rate of hydrogen-deuterium exchange has been used as an indication of the unfolding of chicken heart lactic dehydrogenase by dodecylsulfate (Di Sabato and Ottesen, 1965).

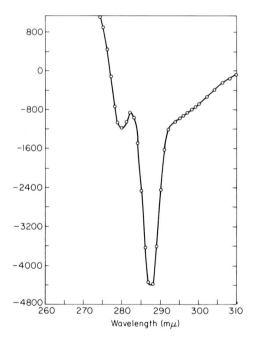

FIG. 7-22c

FIGS. 7-22a,b,c. Difference spectra resulting from addition of dodecylsulfate to serum albumin in phosphate buffer, pH 6.8. Test solutions contained serum albumin and dodecylsulfate at concentrations corresponding to the stated binding levels; reference solutions contained identical concentrations of serum albumin in buffer. [J. D. Mullen (1963). Univ. Microfilms, Ann Arbor, Michigan, Order No. 4356.] The lower figure was obtained with a large excess of detergent.

2. *Recent Data on Binding-Induced Difference Spectra and Changes in Optical Rotation. Further Evidence of the Nature of the Binding Site*

The results of a more exhaustive spectrophotometric investigation of binding-induced difference spectra (Polet and Steinhardt, 1968) are summarized below:

(a) When either aliphatic sulfonates or sulfates having eight or more carbon atoms are bound by BSA, they produce blue shifts with maxima in the difference spectra at 287 and 293 mμ, and much more marked red shifts with a maximum at 232 mμ. These effects increase with $\bar{v}$ but are essentially complete at $\bar{v} = 10$, except for very small effects at 287 Å up to $\bar{v} = 15\text{–}17$. The trough at 293 Å is obviously due to a tryptophan blue shift (Fig. 7-23); the trough at 287 Å contains components due to both tryptophan and tyrosine; and the peak at 232 Å is tentatively assigned to a third chromophore, either phenylalanine or histidine, on the basis of evidence presented below.

(b) Chains shorter than six carbon atoms produce effects that appear to involve only tryptophan and the third chromophore. They are also without effect on the Cotton effect trough at 232 mμ in optical rotatory dispersion alluded to earlier. Octylsulfonate produces a decrease in the 232-mμ ORD trough only at high $\bar{v}$, whereas all the other anions decrease the levorotation at 232 mμ linearly from $\bar{v} = 0$ to 10 up to about 6 percent.

(c) There is no viscosity increase in the range of $0 < \bar{v} \leq 10$, where both $\Delta\varepsilon$ and $\Delta[\alpha]$ approach saturation values.

(d) Only the two "unfolding detergents," dodecyl and tetradecylsulfate, produce additional optical perturbations at $\bar{v} > 10$ (Fig. 7-23). The trough at 287 mμ deepens, a massive maximum appears at 265–280 mμ, and the trough at 293 mμ disappears and is seen as a shoulder. These changes are accompanied by a dramatic reversal of the peak at 232 mμ to a deep trough; all these changes are identifiable as the characteristic blue shifts found in the denaturation of numerous proteins at low pH[17] (Fig. 7-24). These results are summarized in Fig. 7-25.

All of these results are used in concluding that with both sulfonates and sulfates tryptophan residues are at or very close to the set of highest-energy binding sites. With the longer-chain sulfates there are additional sites of slightly lower affinity at, or close to, available tyrosine residues. Octanol, which bears no charge, produces a peak at 230 mμ very similar to the anion peak at 232 mμ, but it has less effect on the tyrosine absorption, and hardly any effect on the tryptophans. It appears that an additional chromophore, either phenylalanine or histidine, is involved in binding at high-energy sites. The small binding-induced changes in optical rotation may be associated with changes at this residue.

---

[17] The effect produced at pH 4 where the N → F transition occurs is very much smaller.

An important addition to these conclusions is provided by the difference spectra of BSA fatty acid anion complexes (Reynolds *et al.*, 1968) and similar HSA complexes (Zakrzanski and Goch, 1968). Figures 7-26a, 7-26b, and 7-26c show that these spectra resemble those of the sulfates and sulfonates just described only in having the same maximum $\Delta\varepsilon$ at 232 mμ which has been attributed to either phenylalanine or histidine. They show no tryptophan effect (trough at 293 mμ) and the large tyrosine effect (two peaks between 270

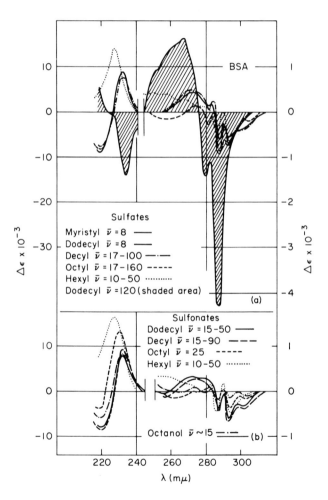

Fig. 7-23. BSA difference spectra due to binding sulfates (A) and sulfonates and octanol (B). The contour of the shaded area represents the difference spectrum due to unfolding by combining with 120 equivalents of dodecylsulfate. Left-hand ordinate refers to $\lambda <$ 2500 Å. [H. Polet and J. Steinhardt (1968). *Biochemistry* 7, 1348.]

and 290 mμ) indicates a tyrosine *red* shift induced by binding, rather than the blue shift produced by long-chain sulfates and sulfonates. In this respect the binding of fatty acid anions is so different from that of sulfates, sulfonates, and such neutral molecules as octanol as to suggest that different binding sites are involved—a fixed number (six to seven) rather than the chain-length-dependent number formed with the other ligands tends to support this interpretation. There is no sign of unfolding, but values of $\bar{v}$ above 10–12 were not investigated in either of these investigations because of solubility limitations.

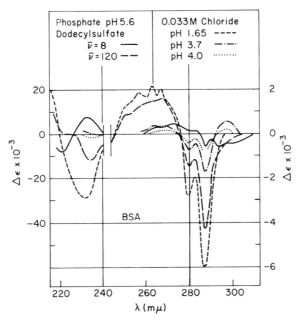

Fig. 7-24. Comparison of the difference spectra of BSA caused by detergent binding, detergent unfolding, the N → F transition (pH 4.0 and 3.7), and unfolding at lower pH. The ionic strength is 0.033. [H. Polet and J. Steinhardt (1968). *Biochemistry* 7, 1348.]

Zakrzanski and Goch, who used essentially Chen's method of defatting human protein, did not observe the effects of bound fatty acid on the Cotton effect trough at 233 mμ, but they reported that b_0 did not change with up to 10 equivalents of dodecanoate bound. The value of a_0 became gradually less negative over this range. Binding reduced the susceptibility of the surface tyrosines to perturbation by methanol, but perturbation by glycerol was not affected.[18]

---

[18] Binding dodecylsulfate or octanol does not affect perturbation of BSA by sucrose Ray *et al.*, 1966).

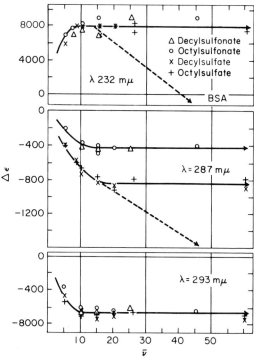

FIG. 7-25. Difference in absorption of BSA at three different wavelengths (λ 232 mμ, top; λ 287 mμ, middle; and λ 293 mμ, bottom) due to binding sulfates and sulfonates, as a function of the molal ratio $\bar{v}$. The dashed lines represent data for the two unfolders dodecyl- and tetradecylsulfate. [H. Polet and J. Steinhardt (1968). *Biochemistry* **7**, 1348.]

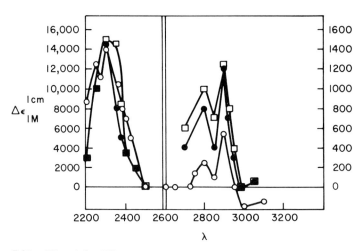

FIG. 7-26a. Ultraviolet difference spectra of BSA as affected by the average number ($\bar{v}$) of octanoate ions bound; λ is given in angstroms; O, $\bar{v} = 5.8$; and □, $\bar{v} = 10.2$. [J. Reynolds, S. Herbert, and J. Steinhardt (1968). *Biochemistry* **7**, 1357.]

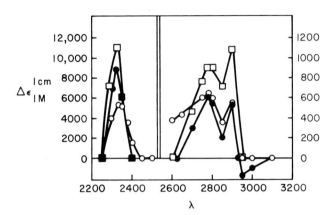

FIG. 7-26b. Ultraviolet difference spectra of BSA as affected by the average number ($\bar{v}$) of decanoate ions bound; λ is given in angstroms; O, $\bar{v} = 2.5$; ●, $\bar{v} = 6$; and □, $\bar{v} = 9.7$. Scale at left applies at $\lambda < 2500$ Å. [J. Reynolds, S. Herbert, and J. Steinhardt (1968). *Biochemistry* **7**, 1357.]

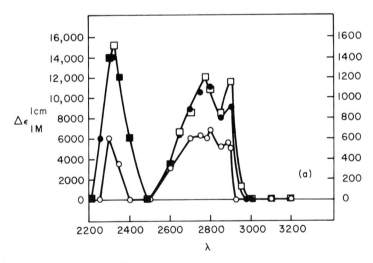

FIG. 7-26c. Ultraviolet difference spectra of BSA as affected by the average number ($\bar{v}$) of dodecanoate ions bound; λ is given in angstroms; O, $\bar{v} = 1.9$; ●, $\bar{v} = 6$, and □, $\bar{v} = 8.9$. Scale at left applies at $\lambda < 2500$ Å. [J. Reynolds, S. Herbert, and J. Steinhardt (1968). *Biochemistry* **7**, 1357.]

Urea denaturation greatly reduced the tyrosine difference spectrum caused by binding carboxylates; if reduction of disulfides also occurred, the difference spectrum practically disappeared, i.e., strong binding may not occur in the completely unfolded form. The involvement of tyrosines in the binding sites is supported by the effect of binding on the apparent pK of the tyrosines, which shifts from about 11.4 to 11.9 as $\bar{v}$ rises to 7. Zakrzanski and Goch propose, on the basis of the disproportionately large effect produced at $\bar{v} = 2$, that two sets of sites, one of two, and one of five, as in Goodman's analysis, are involved.

The effect of tightly bound "residual" fatty acid anions on BSA, and the nature of the binding sites involved, has been explored by comparing the isotherms of various ligands and the resultant difference spectra of solutions of column-deionized crystalline BSA (I), which contains one equivalent of fatty anion, with those of charcoal-defatted BSA (II) which contains none (Gallagher and Steinhardt, 1969). The binding isotherms of up to eight equivalents of dodecylsulfate by either I or II are experimentally indistinguishable. However, the difference spectra due to binding on I and II differ qualitatively when only two equivalents of aliphatic ligands other than carboxylates are bound. Three types of sites which affect tyrosine may be distinguished. One (occupied by residual fatty acid in I) also affects phenylalanine and, when initially empty, produces a red shift on binding fatty acids *or* long-chain sulfates and sulfonates. Another (unoccupied in I and II) is also red-shifted by both short- and long-chain ligands. The next increments of binding to native BSA affect tryptophan if alkyl sulfates, sulfonates, or alcohols are involved, and tyrosine if the ligand is a fatty acid anion, as already shown by Polet and Steinhardt (1968), and by Reynolds *et al.* (1968).

Fluorescence spectroscopy has demonstrated other differences in the binding of long-chain aliphatic anions to column-deionized (I) and charcoal-defatted (II) BSA (Lenz, 1969; Lenz and Steinhardt, 1969). Increasing the binding of such ligands up to 10 equivalents increasingly quenches the intrinsic fluorescence of I and II (tryptophan emitter) but with II no quenching occurs until $\bar{v} > 2$. At pH 5.6 and $\bar{v} = 10$, ligands which do not unfold the tertiary structure produce quenching of just half the emission given by free protein at the emission maximum. Unfolders cause additional quenching at $\bar{v}$ values between 60 and 120. At pH 6.8 the quenching is smaller and the second step sets in at $\bar{v} < 60$. With I there is a fluorescence blue shift in the emission maximum of 11 mμ which is proportional to the quenching and is complete at $\bar{v} = 10$. II undergoes no blue shift when small amounts of ligand are added ($\bar{v} = 2$). Thus the highest available energy sites of II, but not of I (where they are already filled) can bind without changing the immediate emitter environment. This result supports the evidence from difference spectra summarized above (difference spectrum between fully defatted and column-deionized BSA) that tyrosine is present at the one or two sites which bind alkyl ligands most tightly, and that the tryptophan environment is modified when any alkyl ligand fills the remaining high-energy sites of the native protein.

3. *Optical Evidence of Protection by Detergents*

Descriptions of the optical effects of bound large ions would not be complete without inclusion of reported reversals by dodecylsulfate of the effects of optical rotatory dispersion produced by urea or other denaturing agents on some proteins. We have seen (p. 29) that the mathematical model for binding-induced unfolding ($nK \ll mJ$) predicts that the binding of small amounts of high-affinity ions will protect the protein from unfolding by other agents. A few examples which illustrate that this prediction is confirmed are cited: in general, initially nonhelical proteins show a 233-mμ Cotton effect in the presence of long-chain alkyl sulfates even when the viscosity is increased; if however, helices were initially present they are diminished by the same compounds (Jirgensons, 1962a). Jirgensons has shown that dodecyl-sulfate and decylsulfate increase the "helical content" of certain proteins, as interpreted by application of the Moffit-Yang-Doty method (Jirgensons, 1961; 1962b; and 1966).

Simpson and Kauzman (1953) had earlier shown that both dodecylsulfate and 6 M urea increased the levorotation of ovalbumin, although the effect was greater when urea was present. Meyer and Kauzman (1962) more recently have shown that dodecylsulfate or hexadecyltrimethylammonium ions alone (present in same weights as proteins) decrease the Moffit parameter b_0 from -183 to about -270, but the effect of 6 M urea is in the opposite direction, eliminating b_0 completely.

Quantities of dodecylsulfate, equal in weight to the protein, restored b_0 in urea to -182, practically its normal value. The a_0 values were not affected appreciably by detergent but were greatly diminished (from -205 to -955) by 6 M urea (Meyer and Kauzman, 1962). These authors point out that since urea is supposed to denature protein by weakening hydrophobic bonds (Whitney and Tanford, 1962), and since Jirgensons as well as others (Edel-hoch and Lippoldt, 1960) assume that in some proteins hydrophobic bonds interfere with α-helix formation, it is hard to see why the effects of urea and detergent on b_0 should be in the opposite direction "even in each other's presence." Green has commented, however, that the disruption of hydro-phobic bonds by detergent will merely replace them with other hydrophobic bonds, leaving their peptide hydrogen bonds still inaccessible to disruption by water. "In urea, on the other hand, weakening of the hydrophobic inter-actions will facilitate the access of water or urea and cause a complete breakdown of helical structure" (Green, 1963). Thus, "the protection of the hydrogen bonds of an α-helix from the access of water molecules by a matrix of non-polar side chains may be an important factor in determining the most stable configuration of a native protein." It should be noted that in the experiments of Meyer and Kauzman, unlike those of Aoki (1958), both cationic and anionic detergents had the same effect; neither one "stabilized" except when urea had already disordered the protein. Their effect cannot, therefore, be attributed to increasing or decreasing the charge on the protein.

It is appropriate to recall, in this connection, previous allusions to stabilization by dodecylsulfate, starting with the observation of Duggan and Luck (1948) that certain organic anions (not, in general, detergents) protected BSA against the rise in viscosity caused by 6 M urea or heat; stabilization against reversal of the change in levorotation of HSA caused by 6 M urea (Markus and Karush, 1957); stabilization against transformation of BSA by acid to the F form as measured by viscosity (Aoki, 1958); or optical rotation (Klotz and Heiney, 1957). The binding of neutral molecules, butane and pentane, also stabilized the N form (Wishnia, 1963). Two other noteworthy cases of stabilization have been so thoroughly studied that they are added here. Figure 7-28 shows that the large discharge of hydrogen ions by BSA in

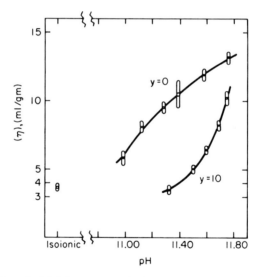

FIG. 7-28. Effect of added detergent on the intrinsic viscosity of BSA at high pH, 25°, ionic strength 0.15 (excluding protein counterions); extrapolated to zero cumulative time after mixing base. [R. Lovrien (1963). *J. Am. Chem. Soc.* **85**, 3679.]

the range 10.5 to 12 in which unmasking of buried tyrosines occurs does not set in until substantially higher pH values are reached when 10 equivalents of dodecylsulfate, assumed to be bound, are present (Lovrien, 1963). The increased viscosity, which occurs in the same pH range in which the abnormal tyrosines are titrated, is also shifted to higher pH (Fig. 7-29). There is a similar shift in fluorescence intensity which has been used as an indication of change in conformation (Steiner and Edelhoch, 1961). If it is assumed that no unmasking of abnormal tyrosines takes place when detergent is absent, then the electrostatic factor w for titration of the phenolic groups falls from 0.025 to 0.014 at 0.15 ionic strength over less than 0.8 pH unit. With detergent present w remains essentially constant. Lovrien concludes that the detergent has no effect other than to prevent the conformation change attested to by the change in viscosity, fluorescence, and electrostatic susceptibility. Stabilization is not to be attributed to changes in the 0.87 wz term in the Linderström-Lang equation (Chapter II), i.e., purely a coulombic effect. Aside from other considerations, the shift in the pH at which particular amounts of H^+ are discharged is in the wrong direction to be explained this way (in alkaline-solution anion binding increases the negative charge on the protein ion

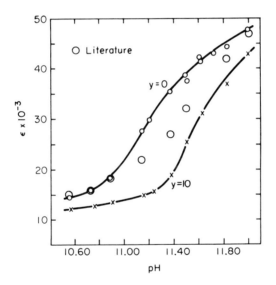

FIG. 7-29. Molar extinction of BSA at 2950 Å, ionic strength 0.15, 25° based on mol. wt. = 69,000. Lower curve represents flattening of a titration curve by binding 10 detergent anions. [R. Lovrien (1963). *J. Am. Chem. Soc.* **85**, 3677.]

rather than diminishing it). At the acid pH values at which the $N \rightleftarrows F$ isomerization occurs, this clear-cut argument cannot be applied. The effect of the detergent is apparently consistent with the concept of Green.

Stabilization of human serum albumin by dodecylsulfate against the changes induced by 6 M urea have been investigated by Markus *et al.* (1964). Fourteen equivalents of dodecylsulfate which are bound very tightly fully

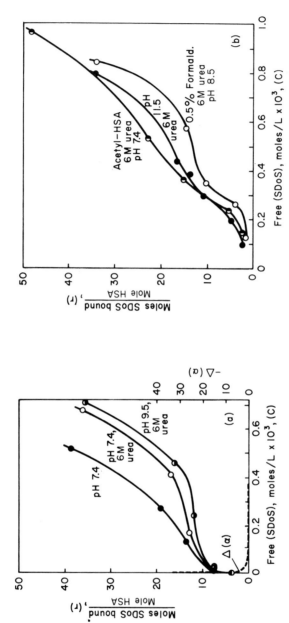

FIG. 7-30. (a) Molar binding ratio of dodecylsulfate (SDoS) as a function of free dodecylsulfate concentration under conditions of protection. Dotted line: Δ[α] at pH 7.4. (b) Same as (a) except it is under conditions of no protection. [G. Markus, R. L. Love, and F. C. Wissler (1964). *J. Biol. Chem.* **239**, 3687.]

reversed the effect of urea as measured by increased levorotation. However, if free ε-amino groups are not also available on the protein, no stabilization occurs, although detergent binding in the presence of 6 *M* urea is only slightly affected (the association constant may be halved), when the amino groups are blocked by acetylation (experiments at pH 7.4) (Fig. 7-30) or by formaldehyde (pH 8.5) or by working at pH 11.5 where there was no reversal (Fig. 7-31). The binding isotherms in 6 *M* urea of acetylated BSA at pH 7.4 are fairly similar to the isotherms of unacetylated protein at pH 11.5 (i.e., the charge due to nonlysine ionization has little effect). The isotherm at pH 8.5 in the presence of 0.5% formaldehyde is also very similar, especially for $\bar{v}$ values up to 14.

The "protective effect" gradually diminishes at pH values between 7.6 and 11.5 (see Fig. 7-31). Formaldehyde, 0.5%, compresses the loss of protection into a much narrower range—practically no protection remains at pH values as low as 7.6. No amount of detergent, including concentrations which give $\bar{v}$ values much greater than 14, will reverse the increased levorotation. It

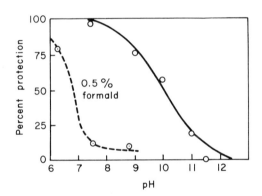

Fig. 7-31. pH dependence of percentage protection with and without 0.5% formaldehyde. The concentration of dodecylsulfate was 1.5 to 1.7×10^{-3} *M*. Conditions: 0.88% human serum albumin in 0.15 *M* NaCl, room temperature. [G. Markus, R. L. Love, and F. C. Wissler (1964). *J. Biol. Chem.* **239**, 3687.]

should be noted (Fig. 7-30) that 4×10^{-3} *M* free detergent produces complete protection at 6 *M* urea at pH 7.4 and almost complete protection at pH 9.5, but none at all if the protein is acetylated, or if HCHO is present, or if the pH is raised to 11.5, although $\bar{v}$ has nearly the same value in all these cases.

It is concluded by Markus *et al.* that "the protection is in part based on the electrostatic interaction between the positively charged ε-ammonium group of some lysine residues and the negatively charged sulfate moiety of the bound detergent ions.[19] Binding of the detergent by both electrostatic and non-polar forces suggests that the protection might be the result of a cross-linking function." At high urea concentrations (7 to 8 M) the protection begins to diminish, and is wholly lost at 10 M (Fig. 7-32). At 8.5 M, where about half

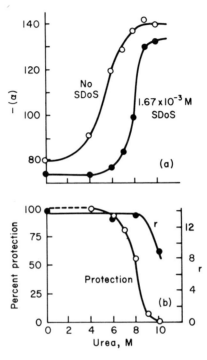

FIG. 7-32. (a) Specific rotation as a function of urea concentration with and without dodecylsulfate (SDoS). (b) Percentage protection and molar binding ratio (r) of dodecyl-sulfate as functions of urea concentration. The average total SDS concentration in the dialysis bags at equilibrium in the binding experiment was 1.9×10^{-3} M. Conditions: 0.88% human serum albumin in 0.15 M NaCl, 0.02 M phosphate buffer, pH 7.4, room temperature. [G. Markus, R. L. Love, and F. C. Wissler (1964). *J. Biol. Chem.* **239**, 3687.]

of the protection is already lost, the number of ions bound remains the same, although it does diminish from 14 to 8 at 10 M urea where there is no protection. These effects are attributed somewhat arbitrarily to diminution of cross-linking by the "swelling" of the molecule brought about by urea. The fact that the curve for stabilized protein in the upper portion of Fig. 7-32 is steeper than that for the original material is considered to be consistent with

[19] A number of papers report the "blocking" of lysines by long-chain fatty acids, e.g., Green (1963) and Glazer and Sanger (1963).

the hypothesis that the cross-linking results in a larger number of cooperatively interacting units in the stabilized protein, although the Moffit constant b_0 is the same whether or not detergent is present. It is, however, reduced by 6 M urea from -313 to -167, and is restored by detergent to -291.

In addition to optical rotation, hydrodynamic parameters (s and D) and viscosity were used as criteria of reversal of the effects of urea on the protein. Very similar conclusions were arrived at in a study of the binding of phytic acid by native, acetylated, and deaminated HSA, but histidines and arginines were implicated as well as lysines (Barre and Nguyen van Huot, 1965).

If the views of Markus *et al.* are accepted, the bifunctionality they attribute to detergent ions has a number of consequences. It helps to explain the solubilization of protein–detergent precipitates by excess detergent, for which an analogy to antibody–antigen interactions has already been drawn, for the same reason that operates in the antibody–antigen reaction. It may explain why, as has been shown by Reynolds *et al.* (1967), the number of high-energy sites depends on the length of the apolar tail attached to the charged group. If other cross-links can also be formed with unfolded protein, the bifunctionality may also serve to explain the existence to *two* kinds of unfolded molecules, which has been reported repeatedly for serum albumin since the work of Putnam and Neurath (1945): one, at lower concentration, binding just half the number of ligand molecules that is found with the other, formed at higher ligand concentrations. Most important, it might explain the existence of variable numbers of binding sites of very high energy, since the free energies of the two bonds involved in cross-linking should be additive. The latter effect, however, could be accounted for by any generalized mechanism of a binding energy depending on a variable number of multiple hydrophobic contacts. This concept of bifunctionality of ligands would, however, predict an effect of protein concentration on the isotherms of native protein; contrary to earlier reports (Ray *et al.*, 1966) such concentration effects are either very small or nonexistent (Cassel *et al.*, 1969).

A number of other stabilizing effects of dodecylsulfate on other proteins may be related to the above. Imanishi *et al.* (1965) have reported that the secondary structures of human Bence-Jones protein ("nonhelical") and *d*-amylase ("helical") from *Bacillus subtilis* are destroyed by both dodecyl-sulfate (anionic) and dodecyl pyridinyl (cationic) ions, but that *new helical regions* were formed at either very low or very high pH. A neutral detergent, glycol nonyl phenyl ether, did not have this effect. The care that must be taken in defining "stabilization" or "protection" is exemplified by the effects of numerous denaturants, including detergents, on carboxypeptidase A, which they completely inactivate. In the presence of 1 M NaCl the enzyme inacti-vated by detergents is said to retain about 40 % of its helical content (originally

80%), but enzyme inactivated by other agents (including trifluoroacetic acid, guanidine, 1,10-phenanthroline, high pH) is completely disordered (Imahori *et al.*, 1962). On the other hand dodecylsulfate *activates* the esterase activity of trypsin, α-chymotrypsin, papain, and mexicain (Castañeda-Agullo and Castillo, 1964). A cationic detergent, hexadecylmethylammonium ion, inhibited enterase action. Nonionic detergents were again without effect.

Not all detergent interactions at low $\bar{v}$ involve stabilizations of structure. With α-globulin and with soybean trypsin-inhibitor, which are nonhelical proteins, 8- to 12-carbon alkyl sulfates as well as dihexyl and dioctyl sulfosuccinates appear to unfold, as indicated by increased viscosity and increased levorotation. With trypsin inhibitor, however, the decrease of b_0 to negative values gives indications of some helix formation (Jirgensons, 1962b).

In earlier pages of this chapter, reference was made to stabilization by nondetergent organic anions, discovered by Boyer *et al.* (1946) and others. Simple polyvalent anions, such as phosphate and sulfate, are effective in protecting pancreatic ribonuclease from denaturation in $9\ M$ urea. Here, unlike stabilization by detergents, the binding of only a *single* anion, possibly to the active site, suffices to give protection. Among the ions giving protection is a competitive inhibitor of the natural substrate, 1,2-cytidylic acid (Nelson *et al.*, 1962). It is suggested that "the active center may lie across a critical seam in the ribonuclease molecule." All active sites, of course, involve juxtapositions, via tertiary structure, of the side chains of amino acids which are, in general, *noncontiguous* in the primary sequence. There are numerous examples of stabilizations (or conformation changes) in enzymes brought about by their substrates or competitive inhibitors. Only a few examples, including some of ordinary inactivation, are cited here: substrate binding or acyl enzyme formation by chymotrypsin changed the Moffit a_0 constant at both extremes of pH (Parker and Lumry, 1963). *Chymotrypsinogen* is stabilized against heat coagulation by binding such polyanions as DNA, or carboxymethylcellulose. The uv spectrum of the soluble complex is similar to that of the soluble urea-denatured protein (Hofstee, 1965). Trypsin, chymotrypsin, amylose, and alkaline phosphomonoesterase are *inactivated* by fatty acid anions of eight or more carbon atoms (pH 7.5), but not by the shorter-chain anions found by Boyer *et al.* (1946) to protect serum albumin. Pepsin is inactivated by all fatty acid *anions*, but this effect may be due to its inability to withstand the pH of their solutions (Bargoni, 1960).

One effect of high-affinity detergents which simulates "protection" arises when the binding of protein to proteolytic enzymes is inhibited *competitively* by detergent. Fatty acids depress the action of numerous proteases, including pepsin, trypsin, and chymotrypsin (Kondo, 1962; Cann, 1962). Cann has shown electrophoretically that a pepsin–BSA complex is broken up by fatty acids or actyl-L-tryptophan; since these substances also inhibit denaturation,

Cann concludes that pepsin only binds and attacks denatured protein. Markus (1965) finds that numerous high-affinity ligands protect HSA from trypsin and chymotrypsin although they are demonstrably without effect on the enzymes. Although his observation is consistent with Cann's, Markus interprets the detergent effect as due to displacement of an equilibrium between conformations, possibly by complexing with lysine side chains, which reduces the fraction present in the susceptible form.

E. EFFECTS OF pH ON ANION BINDING

Changes in the binding isotherm of BSA due to pH are shown in Fig. 7-33 (Reynolds *et al.*, 1970). The effects are very pronounced in the region in which unfolding occurs, as indicated by changes in viscosity (Fig. 7-34), but

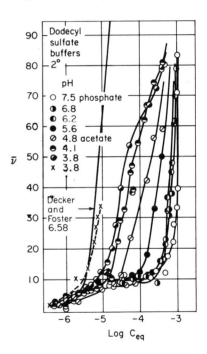

FIG. 7-33. The effect of pH on the binding isotherms of BSA with sodium dodecylsulfate. Ionic strength 0.033 at 2°. The data for pH 3.8 marked × represents a linear ionic strength (about 0.008). The solid line marked Decker and Foster 6.58 was obtained with dodecylbenzenesulfonate at pH 6.58. The obviously greater unfolding power of the latter ion may be due to a larger value of J (Eq. 2-63), greater affinity to sites on unfolded protein.

very small at pH 4.8–5.6 at $\bar{v} \leq 10$ where no viscosity changes occur. It is evident that at high pH unfolding does not occur until much higher equilibrium concentrations of detergent are present, and that in the absence of unfolding, $\bar{v}$ values much above 10 are not obtained. It appears that the effect of pH is on the unfolding constant U in Eq. (2-63) rather than on the association constants K (native protein) or J (unfolded protein). The differences, therefore, are quite distinct from those produced when the choice of unfolding ligand is

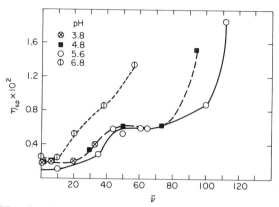

FIG. 7-34. Viscosity of solutions of BSA-dodecylsulfate complexes as a function of pH (Reynolds *et al.*, 1970).

changed (changes in K or J) (as discussed on p. 26, *et seq.*). It is not surprising that the K's do not seem to be sensitive to pH, since the charge on the central ion appears to have no marked influence on the isotherms (p. 237, *et seq.*). The independence of $\Delta F°$ of binding for native protein is also shown by the fact that binding isotherms obtained in buffered solutions, and in NaCl solutions of the same pH and ionic strength, are undistinguishable (Reynolds *et al.*, 1967), although when ligands are bound the protein in buffer is more highly protonated than the protein in salt solutions initially at the same pH. The latter difference is a consequence of the effect of the wZ term on h in the Linderström-Lang equation (Chapter II) when Z changes and pH is held constant.

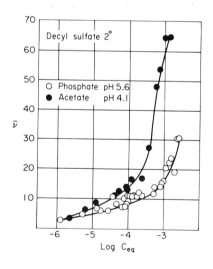

FIG. 7-35. Effect of pH on a non-unfolding ligand–BSA complex (Reynolds *et al.*, 1970).

The reader is referred to Reynolds *et al.* (1970) for an analysis of the isotherms in Figs. 7-33 and 7-35.

The data at pH 3.8 at two ionic strengths in Fig. 7-33 and the viscosity data in Fig. 7-34 show that high ionic strength suppresses or hinders unfolding brought about by detergents just as it does unfolding produced by binding hydrogen ions (Tanford, 1961). Kernahan (1965) has shown that the effect of pH on carbonic anhydrase activity must take into account its effect on the binding of inhibitors which may be present.

F. OTHER EFFECTS OF DETERGENTS ON PROTEINS

One of the destructive effects of detergent anions, probably unrelated to the dissociations and unfoldings treated in these pages, is their powerful catalytic effect on the hydrolysis of amide and peptide bonds of dilute protein, first described by Steinhardt and Fugitt (1942). When the number of equivalents of detergent (or other anion of high affinity) bound is less than or equal to the number of amide groups in the protein, dilute HCl at 60° (0.05 M) hydrolyzes amide bonds quite rapidly, but very few peptide bonds are broken. At higher amounts of detergent bound, both amide and peptide split. A parallel phenomenon has been observed with anionic resins such as Amberlite

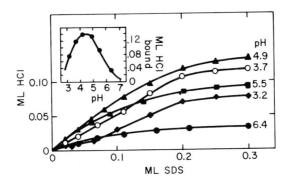

FIG. 7-36. The influence of pH and detergent concentration on the acid binding properties of thyroglobulin in 0.01 M KNO$_3$. Solutions contain 3.0 ml of 0.75% protein. Concentration of HCl was 0.097 M and SDS was 0.10 M. Inset shows effect of pH on the maximum acid binding values; $T = 28.1°$. [H. Edelhoch (1960). *J. Phys. Chem.* **64**, 1771.]

JR 112 (Whitaker and Deatherage, 1955); thus the effect does not depend on the formation of a complex at more than a single site, which must therefore be near the individual bond hydrolyzed. Some investigators attribute the effect to elution of the hydrogen ion on the resin, but the addition of unprotonated resin to an acid solution of hydrolyzing protein increases the rate.

It should be noted that the alkyl sulfate half-esters self-catalyze their own hydrolysis in dilute HCl.

Inhibition of hydrolysis of cationic esters is caused by partially neutralized polymeric acids, as a result of the formation of complexes between the polyanion and the esters (Morawetz and Shafer, 1963).

It is important to note that dodecylsulfate may dissociate molecules, such as the isozymes, with significant changes in sedimentation constant, activity, and certain short-range molecular constants (optical rotation, fluorescence) (di Sabato and Kaplan, 1964). Protection from these effects is afforded by binding to coenzyme. The dissociation into subunits is believed to cause little changes in their structure.

One effect of dilute solutions of dodecylsulfate on some proteins, e.g., thyroglobin, is to dissociate them into subunits as well as to disorganize them completely (Edelhoch and Lippoldt, 1960). (See also p. 266 in this chapter). Another effect (Fig. 7-36), on the titration curve of the same protein (Edelhoch, 1960), seems to be very similar to the effect on the titration curve of wool and of other alkyl sulfates reported by Steinhardt *et al.* (1940a,b; 1941). As may

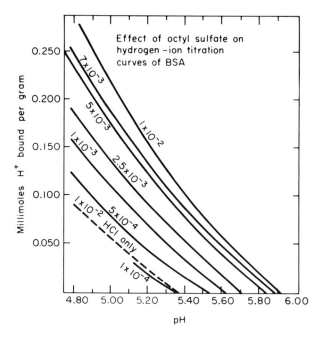

FIG. 7-37. The effect of binding detergent anions on the hydrogen-ion titration curves of 0.32% BSA in 0.01 NaCl. The numbers refer to total detergent concentration except where indicated. With the lowest concentrations practically all the detergent is bound. (J. Cassel and J. Steinhardt, unpublished data.)

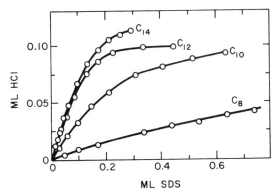

Fig. 7-38. The influence of detergent chain length on the binding of hydrogen ions to thyroglobulin at pH 5.20: $KNO_3 = 0.01$ M; $T = 28.1°$. Detergents were the sodium salts of octylsulfate (C_3); decylsulfate (C_{10}); dodecylsulfate (C_{12}), and tetradecylsulfate (C_{14}); all were in 0.10 M solutions. [H. Edelhoch (1960). *J. Phys. Chem.* **64**, 1771.]

be seen in Fig. 7-37 similar effects have been found by Cassel and Steinhardt (unpublished) with BSA. The effects seem susceptible to interpretation as pH shifts incident to anion binding which have been demonstrated with simpler ions and discussed theoretically by Scatchard and Black (1949). According to their treatment (see p. 74) the difference in pH between the curves with and without detergent at the same amount of acid bound is equal to 0.87 $w\bar{v}$ where $\bar{v}$ refers to the molal ratio of anions bound. Thus a very large number of anions (at least 40) are bound, the maximum occurring when the protein is initially at pH just above 3. Detergents with shorter-chain lengths produce smaller effects (Fig. 7-38). All these effects were obtained with relatively high concentrations of detergent and the native protein conformation had been largely destroyed; w should therefore be quite small, about 0.01, and the number of bound anions given above may be greatly underestimated.

These conclusions are supported by the viscosity data. With octylsulfate, a very small rise in relative viscosity occurs when $\bar{v}$ only slightly exceeds 10–11; with decylsulfate $\bar{v}$ rises to more than 20 before a somewhat larger viscosity effect is seen; with dodecylsulfate, and tetradecylsulfate, successively, larger and larger viscosity effects appear at successively higher values of $\bar{v}$.

Although the $\bar{v}$ values at which the viscosity rise occurs are higher than those at which the isotherms "break," the equilibrium concentrations for both are hardly different; this seeming paradox is due to the steepness of the cooperative region, which is steeper the larger the hydrocarbon chain. Sulfonates show smaller viscosity differences but behave similarly. The relative sizes of the viscosity changes paralleled the increase with chain length of the number of sites made available in the infolded protein.

G. ENTHALPY CHANGE IN BINDING. UNIQUENESS OF TWO HIGHEST ENERGY SITES OF BSA

Nothing has been specified in the foregoing as to the temperature of the experiments cited. It is well established that in multiple equilibria of proteins $\Delta H°$ is often close to zero, as would be expected for entropy-driven associations due to the formation of either hydrophobic or ionic bonds (Kauzmann, 1959). Thus, the multiple binding of five uncharged molecules, n-octanol (Ray et al., 1966), and of eight to nine dodecylsulfate ions (Reynolds et al., 1967) to BSA appears to be only negligibly affected by changes in temperature between 0° and 25°. It is unexpected, therefore, to find that calorimetry may be used to follow the binding of a number of ions if attention is directed to the binding at only the one or two sites which have the highest binding energy (iodide, dodecylsulfate, Lovrien and Sturtevant, 1961; other ions, Lovrien, 1963; Lovrien, unpublished data). The enthalpy changes for dodecyl sulfate binding to serum albumin rise from $-15,000$ for the first to -3500 as an average for the first 14. Substantial negative enthalpies are also found in the binding of uncharged molecules such as tryptophan (Fairclough and Fruton, 1966). (See Chapters III and IV.)[20] The situation with β-lactoglobulin is very similar to the situation with BSA (Lovrien, private communication). The apparent uniqueness of the one or two highest-energy sites of BSA has been investigated by Gallagher and Steinhardt (1969), using uv difference spectroscopy and by Lenz and Steinhardt, (1969) using fluorescence quenching (see p. 286), and it appears that at least the two highest-energy sites of BSA are associated topologically with tyrosine.

H. BINDING OF POLYIONS

1. *Anions*

The formation of complexes between BSA and DNA which prevents thermal coagulation of the protein (Greenstein and Hoyer, 1950) has been demonstrated by light-scattering (Geiduschek and Doty, 1952) and by electrophoresis (Goldwasser and Putnam, 1950). The effect is complex and can be inhibited or enhanced by citrate or Mg^{2+}. RNA in similar complexes can be split by ribonuclease, *in situ*, thereby losing its stabilizing effect. 5′-Ribonucleotides are themselves ineffective in stabilizing against heat-denaturation (Yachmin, 1963).

---

[20] There is a large negative enthalpy for the binding of S-peptide by S-protein to form ribonuclease S′ (Richards et al., 1968). ΔH is -22 kcal mole^{-1} at 5° and -58 kcal mole^{-1} at 40°. The conformational transition near 35°, which is responsible for this difference, has been studied calorimetrically (Danforth, et al., 1967).

However, a number of proteins (e.g., chymotrypsinogen, hemoglobin, and cytochrome c) which complex with such polyelectrolytes as carboxymethyl-cellulose or DNA become less rather than more resistant to heat denaturation (Hofstie, 1967). Chymotrypsins which have undergone structural alterations no longer combine with DNA (Hofstie, 1963).

The interaction of serum albumin with charged polyelectrolytes shows the same difference in affinity between carboxylates and sulfonates in univalent anions that has been described in preceding pages (Noguchi, 1960, 1961).

Some interactions of polyanions with proteins are very clearly not predominantly coulombic in nature. Thus copolymers of glutamic acid with tyrosine, phenylalanine, or leucine are more effective inhibitors of lysozyme than is polyglutamic acid (Sela and Steiner, 1963). The inhibition diminishes at pH above 6 and at high salt concentrations. However, the inhibition of another enzyme, DNAase II, could be reversed by amidating all the acid groups (Tunis and Regelson, 1963). A comparative study has been made of the inhibitory effect of various polyanions (sulfated polysaccharides and polystyrene), including the natural product, heparin, on the inhibition of lipoprotein lipase (Bernfeld and Kelley, 1963).

2. Detergent Cations and Polycations

Observation and measurement of binding of anions by proteins far outstrips observation of cation binding, which appears to be either weaker or rarer. A survey of the binding of cationic dyes and smaller cations is given on p. 337. A systematic study of the binding of cations to purified wool fibers was made by Steinhardt and Zaiser (1950). Small differences in binding effectiveness were found even with univalent inorganic cations; much larger differences were found in a series of alkyl trimethylammonium and tetraalkyl ammonium ions which varied in chain length up to 14 carbon atoms. Tetramethylammonium ion had about the same affinity as potassium ion—all the others had greater affinities, covering approximately the same range as anions of the same size investigated by the same method. For the same molecular weight, the ions having a single long chain were more effective than those containing four identical shorter chains, e.g., a single long chain exercised much of the effect produced by three or four shorter chains. Ions with molecular weights below about 150 differed very little in affinity among one another. The differences in affinity are manifested by much larger pH shifts in the titration curves with base when small amounts of base are bound (shifts up to 3.5 pH units) than when larger amounts are bound (maximum shift 2.3 units).

Early reports of association between BSA and cationic detergents indicated that their affinity was lower than that of comparable anions (Polonovski and Macheboeff, 1948; Glassman, 1950; and Foster and Yang, 1954).

These early results are amplified and confirmed by the binding isotherm of dodecyltrimethylammonium bromide and BSA (Few *et al.*, 1955). Very little is bound at low concentrations ($<4 \times 10^{-3}$ M), but at an equilibrium concentration of about 6.5×10^{-3} M practically all the increment in detergent is bound, until $\bar{v}$ becomes independent of further additions at an equilibrium free ligand concentration of about 9.5×10^{-3} M, where $\bar{v} = 109$. The latter number is close to the BSA content of negatively charged carboxyl groups. Viscosity measurements indicate that the steep rise in amounts bound occurs at $\bar{v} \leq 6$.[21] K for these six sites is obviously much lower than for dodecyl-containing anions, and may indicate that multiple contacts are not made. It is equally obvious that unfolding similar to that found with dodecylsulfate occurs. Unexpectedly, however, the reduced viscosity η_{sp}/c at high detergent protein ratios rises by a factor of about 4 as the protein concentration is raised from 0.2% to 1.0%. Aoki (1958) has described results with other cations.

Fetuin, a protein containing a sialic acid, has a high affinity for, and is unfolded by, hexadecyltrimethylammonium bromide (Verpoorte and Kay, 1966).

Evidence of cation binding by acetylcholinesterase is furnished by the fact that the enzyme is inhibited by numerous quarternary long- and short-chain ammonium derivatives. The results are interpreted as changes in the association constant of the enzyme–inhibitor association constant. The logarithm of this constant is found to vary linearly with the number of methylene groups in the inhibitor (Coleman and Eley, 1962).

Protein interactions with polycations have been investigated with turnip yellow mosaic virus and RNA (Mitra and Kaesberg, 1963). Bis(3-amino-propyl)amine induces a more compact form of the virus as evidenced by sedimentation rates and viscosities. The 2-aminoethyl derivative of synthetic polyglucose reacts with oxidized cytochrome c in such a way as to cause the protein to yield its reduced spectrum (Mora *et al.*, 1965). Polyanions reverse the effect. It is not certain that a polymeric form is necessary for the effect.

Cations affect, by competing, the extent and specificity of binding of poly-L-lysine-ε-DNP-L-lysine to synthetic polynucleotides (Latt and Sober, 1967).

III. Dyes, Dye-like, and Other Cyclic Molecules Binding as Ions

We include in this section not only the interactions of proteins with ions having visible chromophores, but also all other at least partially aromatic or cyclic organic ions, provided they lack pronounced aliphatic hydrocarbon constituents.

---

[21] This is equal to the sum of methionine and tryptophan residues.

A. EARLY WORK

Observations of the binding of dyes by proteins were the earliest indication that proteins combine with ions other than H^+ (see p. 234). Chapman *et al.* (1927), Rawlins and Schmidt (1930), and Fraenkel-Conrat and Cooper (1944) determined the number of basic groups in proteins by determining the amount of dye precipitated by protein in the presence of an excess in acid solutions. The use of dyes as pH indicators in protein solutions has made it important to understand the extent to which they are bound, since errors (" protein errors ") are introduced by such binding. Since injected dyes were often used to determine, by dilution, the total blood volume, and estimates based on dilution alone, ignoring binding, always gave artificially high values for the volume, clinical biochemists have been concerned with determining the necessary corrections, or have attempted to find dyes which bind to negligible extents.

Some of these investigations have been subsequent to and influenced by the quantitative work of Klotz and his collaborators. Klotz used methyl orange, azosulfathiazole, and amaranth in a series of careful equilibrium dialysis experiments which did much to lay the foundations of the subsequent work on the binding of ions by proteins. This work, together with that of Scatchard on smaller ions (described in later pages), established clearly the applicability of stoichiometry and definite association constants, the existence of sites having widely different affinities, and the effect of the binding on the absorption spectra of the bound dyes (Klotz, 1946; Klotz *et al.*, 1946; Klotz and Walker, 1947; Klotz *et al.*, 1950; Klotz, 1954). Klotz also established that dipolar ions were not bound (Klotz and Urquhart, 1949), investigated the effects of the solvent environment on the extent of binding (Klotz and Luborsky, 1959), and advanced theories as to the nature of the binding forces and their relation to the effect of hydration clathrates of the protein (Klotz and Luborsky, 1959) and the balance of side chains of distinct types on the propensity of the protein to bind. Since most of the valid conclusions which were based on this work have already been dealt with in Chapters IV or VII, we merely list here Klotz's value for the $\Delta F°$ of binding to BSA of methyl orange at pH 5.6, which is 5500 cal mole^{-1} for the first ion bound, considerably lower than the values given by the normal aliphatic sulfates or sulfonates described in earlier pages. Klotz also found that dyes having two or more charges (azosulfathiazole which has two and amaranth which has three) bound more tightly than the singly charged methyl orange at pH 5.7.

B. THE AFFINITIES OF SOME DYES TO PROTEINS

In recent years considerable work has been done with a number of dyes, partly because of their use in clinical biochemistry (determination of blood volume or serum pH). Phenol red has been of interest because of its small extent of binding. At low concentrations at physiological pH only one dye molecule is bound to serum albumin ($K = 2.8 \times 10^4$). Up to 10 more equivalents are bound at high concentrations ($K_2 = 3.6 \times 10^2$) but these will not interfere with blood volume tests. Between pH 5 and 10, the univalent ion is bound almost twice as tightly as the divalent dye ion. Caprylate and tryptophan reduce the binding, presumably competitively, and naphthalene sulfonate abolishes it (Rodkey, 1961). Similar studies have been made by Nishida (1961).

It has been remarked already that ligand spectral shifts occur when aryl ligands bind to proteins. These may be complex and vary with stereoconfiguration, especially when two chromophoric ligands are competing with one another (Burkhard et al., 1961). Even without these sources of complexity, spectral shifts may occur which show that the shift depends on the protein site occupied. Thus the dye trypan blue undergoes a spectral shift when it occupies two presumably identical sites in BSA, but the occupation of a third weaker site causes the preexisting two strong sites to disappear, and to be replaced by two weaker sites (Land and Lasser, 1967). If this interpretation is accepted, then this is a case of unfolding BSA at a very low value of $\bar{v}$. It is clear, in any case, that the use of spectral shifts to measure binding equilibria must be accompanied by great caution and preliminary calibrations must be made. Thus, for example, the size of the shifts in the spectra of 4-hydroxyazobenzene-4-sulfonic acid and 4-hydroxyazobenzene-4'-sulfonic acid produced on binding to BSA are not linearly related to the degree of binding (Forbes et al., 1962).

The use of such a shift for measuring the binding of the anionic dye Biebrich scarlet to chymotrypsin (Glazer, 1967) was attended by no such difficulties since complete linearity prevailed. One binding site was found, with $K = 1.1 \times 10^4$, a fairly low value. The hydrolysis of N-acetyl-L-tyrosine ethyl ester by the enzyme is competitively inhibited by the dye, which therefore appears to overlap the active site. Substrates also displace the dye.

Two related proteins, chymotrypsinogen and trypsin, do not bind Biebrich scarlet. This high degree of specificity is not uncommon when only a single binding site exists, and is not to be considered characteristic of "multiple equilibria in proteins."

The cationic dye, thionine, is also subject to uncomplicated behavior in its binding to trypsin. Here again at pH 7 there is a single binding site, and $K = 8 \times 10^4$. The dye competes with substrate and substrate analogues. However, its specificity is lower than that of Biebrich scarlet, and it binds weakly to trypsinogen, and also on a single site on chymotrypsin and chymotrypsinogen ($K = 2 \times 10^3$). This alternative binding, however, shows no inhibition or competition with substrate, and appears to be in a position that is not part of the active site of the latter enzymes.

The acridine dye, proflavine, competes with some of the natural ovomucoid inhibitors of α-chymotrypsin, which it also inhibits (Fernstein and Feeney, 1966). Two out of three ovomucoids investigated could displace proflavine from the enzyme. The reaction was followed by measuring the red shift in the spectrum of the dye caused by binding.

Using the difference spectrum technique described in Chapter III (p. 60), East and Trowbridge (1966) have measured an association constant for trypsin-benzamidine of 4.8×10^4. The same value is obtained by analyzing the inhibiting effect of benzamidine on the tryptic hydrolysis of *p*-toluene-sulfonyl-L-arginine methyl ester and of benzoyl-L-arginine ethyl ester.

Although the binding constants of dyes listed above and in Table 7-6 are considerably smaller than those of the detergents bound by numerous proteins, Glazer (1968) generalizes that strong protein-dye complexes are always found in 1 : 1 ratios, and where enzymes or prosthetic groups are involved, binding is at the "active" site and offers opportunities to investigate the latter.

It was shown many years ago (Klotz, 1946) that the *o*-aminobenzoate is bound more strongly to serum albumin than the para form. *o*-Hydroxy-phenylacetate also has a higher affinity than the *para* form [Luck and Schmidt, 1948), quoted by Klotz]. The methyl reds (dimethylaminoazoben-zenecarboxylic acids) have more complicated distinctions; here the meta form binds more strongly, but the effect is only large at low temperature, since only the meta-form has a high negative enthalpy of binding. The stereoisomers do not compete among one another. Burkhard *et al.* (1961) propose two distinct types of binding sites for ortho and meta forms, as well as hypothesizing that only the para form unfolds the protein. Very clear-cut evidence for the existence of different classes and numbers of sites for *optical isomers* of a dye is shown in Fig. 7-39. The existence of these differences is not entirely unexpected, since the spectral shifts produced in most dyes on binding to proteins indicate that binding to the protein is intimately related to factors affecting the ease of transitions to the π^*-state.

The dyes named above are all bound strongly to serum albumin, but most of them bind only negligibly to the other plasma proteins. The spectral shift which occurs when methyl orange is added to plasma may therefore be used to determine albumin (Girard *et al.*, 1963). Ponceau S appears to bind to β-globulin as well as to albumins and amido black appears to bind to neither (Kupic and Topalovic-Avramov, 1963). Sulfonphthaleins appear to bind to albumins, and to hemoglobins as well (see Chapter IV). Their order of ascending affinity (equilibrium dialysis) is phenol red (least), bromthymol blue,[22]

---

[22] Bromothymol blue has a much higher affinity for the deoxy than for the oxy form of hemoglobin (but not myoglobin), and this has a marked effect on the oxygen equilibrium (see Chapter IV, p. 140). Ten equivalents are bound per heme. Bromophenol blue has been shown to have a higher affinity for denatured hemoglobin than for native hemoglobin (Steinhardt *et al.*, 1966).

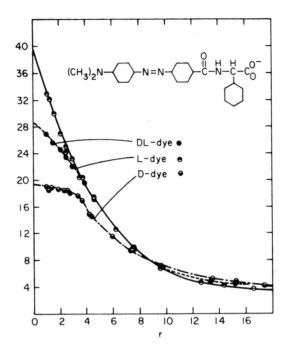

FIG. 7-39. Binding of optically isomeric dyes by bovine serum albumin. [F. Karush (1952). *J. Phys. Chem.* **56**, 70.]

bromphenol blue, bromcresol green (Lee and Hong, 1960). Bromosulfonphthalein is bound very tightly (Boyar and Bradley (1966). Trypan blue is bound so weakly that it is cleared too rapidly to be useful in blood-volume measurements; in this respect Evans blue is recommended (Schwartskopff, 1962).

We include data on certain local anesthetics and other therapeutic agents in this section because of their aromatic character, although they are not dyes. Human serum albumin (HSA) appears to have two sites which bind cationic local anesthetics (procaine, monocaine, xylocaine, and carbocaine). The number of sites is independent of pH, although the association constants depend on pH (Sawiaski, 1964). Tolbutamide and 5-ethylsulfathiazine are bound more strongly to HSA than to BSA; the binding is reduced by high concentrations of urea or dodecylsulfate (Buettner and Portwich, 1967).

We have excluded from this book reactions between proteins and aromatic compounds which, although sometimes reversible, are mediated by the formation of definite chemical bonds. There are many such reactions, some of which, such as the use of Sanger's reagent, are very familiar. Other examples are the formation of trinitrophenylated derivatives of such proteins as G-actin (Tokura and Tonomura, 1963) by treatment with trinitrobenzenesulfonate, or myosin A–adenosine triphosphate (Kubo *et al.*, 1963).

Table 7-5 presents a list of values of n and K for column-deionized BSA and a number of aromatic anions, as determined by both equilibrium dialysis and ΔpH measurements by Cassel and Steinhardt (1969).

An earlier list assembled by Fredericq (1954) is given in Table 7-6. The values listed are nK at 25° in 0.1 M phosphate pH 6.6 at a protein concentration of 0.2% except when otherwise indicated. Where comparisons are possible the values of others appear to be slightly lower than in the table above.

TABLE 7-5

PARAMETERS EXPRESSING THE BINDING OF SEVERAL AROMATIC ANIONS TO BSA AT 2°

	n_1	K_1	$-\Delta F$ (kcal/mole)
2,4-Dinitronaphtholate	5–6(5.52)	750,000	7.5
2,4,6-Trinitrophenolate (picrate)	3	592,300	7.3
2,4,6-Trinitro-*m*-cresolate	4	263,200	6.9
2,5-Dichlorobenzenesulfonate	3	108,600	6.5
2,4-Dinitrobenzenesulfonate	3	80,000	6.2
2-Naphthalenesulfonate	4	44.200	5.9
2-Anthraquinonesulfonate	7	15,100	5.3
Benzenesulfonate	4	9,500	5.05

Fredericq made a careful effort to correlate chemical structure and affinity, with the following very meager conclusions: (a) the affinity rises with the number of aromatic rings, whether or not they are fused; (b) hydroxyl, nitro, and halogen substituents increase the affinity, and amines or nitrogen heterocycles depress it (possibly through charge effects); (c) there are no important position effects; (d) the relative order of affinities is the same for two proteins, serum albumin and insulin. There are indications that delocalization of π-electrons increases the affinity. However, long aliphatic chains with no delocalization have higher affinities than aromatic ions having the same number of carbon atoms.

C. FLUORESCENT LIGANDS

The earliest applications of fluorescence in the measurement of binding isotherms made use of measurements of fluorescence polarization and its dependence on rotational diffusion constants. Since there is a great difference between the rotational diffusion constant of a large and more or less rigid molecule, the protein, and that of a much smaller fluorescent ligand in free solution, the ratio of bound ligand to free ligand can be deduced from the measured polarization of fluorescence if the values for totally bound and totally free ligand are known. The theory of this method was first propounded by Weber (1952) and applied by Laurence (1952) in a study of the binding of a number of anionic dyes by BSA (it was observed that cationic dyes did not combine, and that introducing a heavy substituent, bromine, increased binding).

Eosin at pH 6.9 bound at a single site; fluorescein at two sites (pH 6.9 to 9.2). Two sites were also available for acridylbenzoate (pH 4.4–6.9) and *p*-naphthalene-1-sulfonate (pH 5.9 to 8.0). The binding constants were high, $K = 2.9 \times 10^5$ in the case of fluorescein. The method has been used by Steiner (1954) to determine the interaction between soybean trypsin inhibitor to which a fluorescent dye (dimethylaminonaphthalene-5-sulfonate) had been coupled, and the enzyme; and more recently by Velick (1958) in a study of the binding of NADH to alcohol dehydrogenase, as well as in studies of binding to antibodies and coenzymes (Velick, 1960, 1961). In the use of this method it is important to assure that binding (or extremes of pH) does not induce a degree of unfolding such that rotation about an internal bond is possible (Harrington *et al.*, 1956; Weber and Young, 1964).

Fluorescent dyes have recently come into use for the measurement of binding equilibria by more direct means. The most complete study to date, by Daniel and Weber (1965), presents a determination of an isotherm representing the combination of BSA and 1-anilino-8-naphthalenesulfonate (ANS), by measurements of the quenching of fluorescence. The fluorescence spectrum in the presence of various ratios of bound ligand to protein, $\bar{v}$, was determined. The value of $\bar{v}$ was determined as $(F_c/F_b)(X_0/P_0)$ where F_c is the experimentally determined fluorescence of a protein–dye solution, F_b is the limiting value of the fluorescence in the presence of an excess of the dye, and X_0 and P_0 are the initial concentrations of dye and protein, in a solution which is simply diluted. In the Daniel and Weber experiments $X_0 = 5P_0$ since, as was found, five equivalents of dye could bind. Thus, in Fig. 7-40 each curve was obtained at a dilution which gave the value of $\bar{v}$ specified. The paper is note-worthy in giving a novel way of presenting the data in terms of "probability of binding" (see Chapter II, p. 24) and for a critical discussion of precision. The authors conclude that there are exactly five binding sites, but that the data at pH 7 (see Fig. 3-6) do not obey the law of mass action, even with a free choice permitted of five association constants. This is the kind of "co-operative" phenomenon which the models given in the earlier pages of this chapter (see p. 26) would attribute to unfolding, i.e., the unmasking of sites by the first ions bound. Daniel and Weber, however, conclude:

> We believe that our present results indicate the existence in the protein molecule of relaxation effects upon binding and dissociation of the ligand, with times comparable to or longer than the life-time of the protein-ligand complexes. The direct demonstration of relaxation effects in the protein molecules with times longer than the reciprocal of the dissociation rates of the ligand could be decisive in excluding mechanisms that involve simple tautomeric equilibria governed by detailed balance.

The absolute value of the association constant for the first ion bound is greater than 10^7, as high as any recorded in these pages for molecules of known structure. Theoretical treatment of the fluorescence quenching based on the concept that the decrease is due solely to the transfer of electronic energy among the ligand molecules leads to the conclusions that the average distance between pairs of binding sites is 21 Å, and that the average angle between pairs of emission oscillators is 33° (Weber and Daniel, 1965).

Similar methods were used to determine the binding isotherm of the five forms of beef lactate dehydrogenase (LOH) a tetramer to nicotinamide adenine dinucleotide (NADH). Here two binding sites are found on the horse liver enzyme with $K = 3.4 \times 10^2$ at pH 7.4 (Fig. 7-41); with beef heart protein $K = 2.5 \times 10^6$. Beef muscle LDH and LDH hybrids give more complicated behavior for which $n = 4$ (Anderson and Weber, 1965). With these preparations as more details (" bits ") are obtained, more evidence is found of singularities

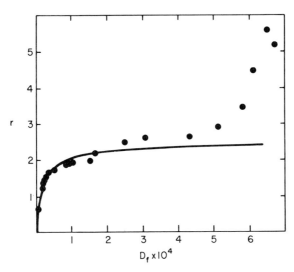

FIG. 7-40. Theoretical isotherm for low detergent level interaction compared with experimentally determined points. [E. Daniel and G. Weber (1965). *Biochemistry* **5**, 1893].

TABLE 7-6

Association Constants (nK) and Free Energies of Association ($-\Delta F^\circ = RT \ln K$)
of Serum Albumin and Various Anions at pH 6.6

	Association constant $nK_1 \times 10^{-3}$	$-\Delta F^\circ$ (cal/mole)	References
A. Aromatic Anions			
o-Chlorobenzenesulfonate	2–3	~4500	*b*
Nitrobenzoate	2–3	~4500	*b*
Phthalate	2–3	~4500	*b*
o-Aminobenzoate	4–5	~5000	*b*
m-Aminobenzoate	4–5	~5000	*b*
o-Aminobenzenesulfonate	4–5	~5000	*b*
m-Aminobenzenesulfonate	4–5	~5000	*b*
o-Hydroxybenzoate (salicylate)	7	5200	*b*
Phenylacetate	1.65	—	*c*($T = 1°$ pH 7.6)
Cinnamate	22.5	—	*c*($T = 1°$ pH 7.6)
Phenoxyacetate	7.8	—	*c*($T = 1°$ pH 7.6)
Phenylbutyrate	13.4	—	*c*($T = 1°$ pH 7.6)
Hippurate	8.5	—	*c*($T = 1°$ pH 7.6)
Dinitrophenolate	190	—	*c*($T = 1°$ pH 7.6)
Trinitrophenolate (picrate)	190	—	*c*($T = 1°$ pH 7.6)
Trinitrophenolate (picrate)	160	7100	*b*
Dichlorophenolate	60[a]	—	*d*($T = 1°$ pH 7.6)
Dodecylbenzenesulfonate	1900	—	*e*($T = 4°$ pH 7.7)
Naphthalene-1-sulfonate	50	6350	*b*
Naphthalene-1-5-disulfonate	15	5650	*b*
2-Naphthol-7-sulfonate	50	6350	*b*
Dinitro-1-naphthol-7-sulfonate	400	7575	*b*
1-amino-2-naphthol-4-sulfonate	40	6225	*b*
Aminonaphthalenedisulfonate	160[a]	—	*f*(pH 7.0)
Aminonaphthalenetrisulfonate	115[a]	—	*f*(pH 7.0)
p-Hydroxyazobenzene-*p*'-sulfonate	40	6200	*b*
2-4-Dihydroxyazobenzene-4'-sulfonate	40	6200	*b*
p-Aminoazobenzene-*p*'-sulfonate	15	5650	*b*
p-Dimethylaminoazobenzene-*p*'-sulfonate (methyl orange)	50	6411	*g*
Hydroxymethylazobenzenecarboxylate	30	—	*h*(pH 7.0)
o-Dimethylaminoazobenzene-*p*-carboxylate	120	6350	*i*(pH 6.8, 0°)
m-Dimethylaminoazobenzene-*p*-carboxylate	390	6980	*i*(pH 6.8, 0°)
p-Dimethylaminoazobenzene-*p*-carboxylate	80	6150	*i*(pH 6.8, 0°)
p-Dimethylaminobenzeneazobenzoy-lacetate	30	—	*j*

[a] Recalculated from experimental data.
[b] Fredericq, E., *Bull. Soc. Chim. Belges* **63**, 158 (1954).
[c] Teresi, J. D., and Luck, J. M., *J. Biol. Chem.* **174**, 653 (1948).
[d] Teresi, J. D., *J. Am. Chem. Soc.* **72**, 3972 (1950).

TABLE 7.6 (*Continued*)

	Association constant $nK_1 \times 10^{-3}$	$-\Delta F°$ (cal/mole)	References
Phenyl-*p*-dimethylaminobenzene-azobenzoylacetate	2.8	—	*j*
p-Phenylaminoazobenzenesulfonate (tropeoline)	120	6900	*b*
β-Naphtholazobenzenesulfonate (Orange II)	225	7325	*b*
Dimethylbenzeneazonaphtholdisulfonate (Ponceau red)	225	7025	*b*
Sulfonaphthaleneazonnaphtholdisulfonate (Amaranth)	250	7125	*b*
Anthraquinone-β-sulfonate	50	6360	*b*
Dihydroxyanthraquinone-β-sulfonate (Alizarin red)	120	6900	*b*
Dihydroxysulfonephthalein (Phenol red)	70	6575	*b*
Dimethyldiisopropylsulfonphthaleine (Thymol blue)	130	6925	*b*
Dimethyldibromosulfonephthalein (Bromcresol purple)	330	7475	*b*
Tetrabromosulfonphthalein (Bromphenol blue)	1200	8225	*b*
Sulfophenylbenesulfonateazopyrazolol-carboxylate (tartrazine)	20	5800	*b*
Indigo disulfonate	10	5420	*b*
Indigo trisulfonate	40	6225	*b*
Indigo tetrasulfonate	40	6225	*b*
Tetraiododichlorofluorescein (Rose bengal)	680	—	*k*(pH 7.0)
Fluorescein	180[a]	—	*f*(pH 6.9)
Eosin (Tetrabromofluorescein)	600[a]	—	*f*(pH 6.9)
B. Aliphatic Anions			
Acetate	0.7[a]	—	*l*(pH 7.6)
Valerate	3[a]	—	
Caproate	4[a]	—	
Heptanoate	9[a]	—	
Caprylate	30[a]	—	
Octylsulfate	3000	—	*m*(pH 5.6)
Decylsulfate	8400	—	*m*(pH 5.6)
Dodecylsulfate	9600	—	*m*(pH 5.6)

[e] Yang, J. T., and Foster, J. F., *J. Am. Chem. Soc.* **75**, 5560 (1953).

[f] Laurence, D. J. R., *Biochem. J.* **51**, 168 (1952).

[g] Klotz, I. M., and Urquhart, J. M., *J. Am. Chem. Soc.* **71**, 847 (1949).

[h] Karush, F., *J. Am. Chem. Soc.* **72**, 2705 (1950).

[i] Klotz, I. M., Burkhard, R. K., and Urquhart, J. M., *J. Phys. Chem.* **56**, 77 (1952)

[j] Karush, F., *J. Phys. Chem.* **56**, 70 (1952).

[k] Oster, G., *J. Chem. Phys.* **48**, 217 (1951).

[l] Teresi, J. D., and Luck, J. M., *J. Biol. Chem.* **194**, 823 (1952).

[m] Reynolds, J. A., *et al.* (1967).

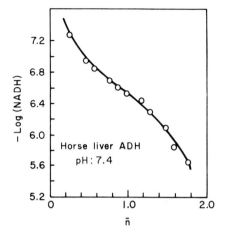

FIG. 7-41. Titration of horse liver ADH with NADH; n is the average number of moles of NADH bound/mole of protein; [NADH] is the concentration of free NADH. Conditions: 15°, 0.042 M potassium phosphate, pH 7.4. [A. Anderson and D. Weber (1965). *Biochemistry* **4**, 1948.]

and cooperativity incompatible with the Adair equation. After discussing and rejecting other alternatives, the authors again advance an explanation in terms of concentration effects.

Brand *et al.* (1967) extended the foregoing studies on liver alcohol dehydrogenase to include various isomeric forms of ANS, its sulfonamide derivatives, and rose bengal, a derivative of fluorescein, all of which compete on a 1:1 basis with NADH for sites on the enzyme. When bound, enhancement of quantum yields occur, and the emission maximum is shifted. K for rose bengal is 3.7×10^5; it is 10^4 for ANS. The two dye binding sites correspond to the two active sites in the enzyme; competitive enzyme inhibitors (e.g., o-phenanthrolene) inhibit dye binding also. Formate ion, which decreases NADH binding, also decreases dye binding; denaturation decreases K for all ligands.

Since the precision of Weber's method is high, and the data more plentiful than is usual in the literature of binding isotherms, the departure from simple binding, even at low $\bar{v}$ values, reported for several systems must be taken seriously and sought in other systems where it may have been overlooked.

Fluorescence enhancement of the sulfonamide (5-dimethylaminonaphthalene-1-sulfonamide) DNSA and quenching (of the protein) have been used by Chen and Kernohan (1967) to study the binding of the sulfonamide by bovine carbonic anhydrase. One equivalent is bound to the same site that binds other sulfonamides (which inhibit the enzyme), with $K = 4 \times 10^6$. Nonsulfonamide "fluorescence probes" did not bind. The binding is remarkable on two counts: (a) it is accompanied by a very large blue shift in the emission maximum found in water (from 580 to 468 mμ) and by an unusual rise in quantum yield, from 0.055 to 0.084; (b) nearly all of the photons absorbed by the seven tryptophans are emitted by the single bound dye molecule; the dimensions of the protein are near the limit which would permit all seven tryptophan residues to be within the critical transfer distance 21.5 Å. The bound ligand quenched 73% of the tryptophan fluorescence, and inhibited the esterase activity of the enzyme. It is argued that the large blue shift is evidence for an extremely hydrophobic environment at the binding site, and for induced hydrogen ion dissociation by the sulfonamide. The hydrophobic region postulated cannot by itself cause significant binding of hydrophobic ligands such as ANS or DNS-amino acids; a second binding group which has affinity for the aromatic nucleus is also required: i.e., the closely bound ligands are "bidentate."

ANS is bound very weakly, if at all, to either myoglobin or hemoglobin, but it is bound in the same proportion as heme to the apoproteins with a binding constant of about 10^5 (Stryer, 1965). Hemin displaces the bound dye. There is a large shift in the emission spectrum (60 mμ from green to blue) when the dye is bound, and the quantum yield increases 200-fold. The fluorescence of the bound dye is excited by light of 280-mμ wavelength; undoubtedly energy transfer occurs from the absorption of the protein to the heme.

An advantage of combining absorption and fluorescence measurements is illustrated by stopped-flow fluorescence studies of the binding of NADPH (reduced nicotinamide adenine dinucleotide phosphate) to NADPH-cytochrome c oxidoreductase (Masters *et al.*, 1967). When the coenzyme is added to the oxidized or half-reduced enzyme, its fluorescence is quenched at a rate which is too rapid to measure by a stop-flow technique. However, changes in absorption continue and their rate can be measured. Binding is apparently extremely fast; the electron-reaction is slower, and can be observed. There are two sites for NADPH, one per FAD (flavin adenine dinucleotide).

D. Dye Interactions with Denatured Protein

Early work indicated that serum albumin heated to 100° lost its power to bind anions, but anion–ovalbumin interaction was increased by protein denaturation (Klotz and Urquhart, 1949; Fish *et al.*, 1949; Lundgren *et al.*, 1943; Oster, 1951). The binding of ions to both ovalbumin and myoglobin increases as soon as denaturation begins (Braun, 1948). Heating serum albumin for long periods at lower temperatures decreased the binding of methyl orange only slightly (Klotz *et al.*, 1950) but increased its binding of Congo red (Haurowitz *et al.*, 1955). The first determinations of the binding to heat-denatured serum albumin (Blei and Carroll, 1960) ascertained that crystal violet had 10 times as great a binding constant for denatured serum albumin as for the native protein, and that the number of binding sites increased 20-fold in denaturation.

When dissolved serum albumin is denatured on air interfaces, the binding of ANS increases; when γ-globulin is similarly denatured, no enhancement of fluorescence occurs (Burgess and Pruitt, 1968). Fluorescence enhancement does not occur when either protein is denatured by heating, or when they are aggregated by exposure to mercaptoethanol.

A much more detailed investigation by Prokopova and Munk (1962), based on measurement of red shifts in the absorption spectrum of methyl orange bound to HSA, indicated 13 sites with an average K of 5×10^3 in native proteins. All of the several sets of binding data given for denatured protein show an increase in the number of sites and decreases in the binding constant, after heating for various periods of time. The results obtained with the milder treatments could be fitted by curves for mixtures of fully denatured and native protein. Sixteen binding sites were reported for methylene blue with $K = 800$. In the denatured protein there were 90 binding sites with $K < 300$. In view of the great discrepancy between the values given for K of the native protein and others in the literature (about 70,000) one cannot accept the values for denatured protein without reservation.

The most general conclusion that can be drawn at this time is that denatured proteins bind dyes at more numerous sites than do native proteins, and that the binding constants are smaller.

The effects of *denaturing agents* on binding may shed light on how they denature proteins. Thus, urea reversibly abolishes the binding of methyl orange by BSA. The synthetic polymer vinylpyrrolidinone also binds the dye, and urea here also suppresses the binding (Klotz and Shickama, 1968). Klotz argues from these observations that the effects of urea are mediated largely through its action on the solvent, rather than on the protein or polymer.

When helical poly-L-glutamic acid (pH 4.7) is exposed to acridine orange, temperature-jump kinetics indicate that a polymer–dye complex is formed very rapidly, followed by a slow intramolecular isomerization. When the non-helical polypeptide (pH 7.5) is used, the isomerization has a much shorter relaxation time, and the dye is more strongly bound. Since the relaxation time depends on polymer concentration, it has been proposed that more than one monomer unit is associated with each dye molecule (Hammer and Hubbard, 1965).

Polylysine takes up 132 equivalents of methyl orange and is precipitated. Wetlaufer and Stohmann have shown that precipitation is complete when less dye is bound, but the precipitate continues to bind as the concentration of dye is increased, the precipitate behaving as an ion-exchange resin (Wetlaufer and Stohmann, 1953).

E. PROTECTION BY DYES AGAINST DENATURATION

Dyes which bind appear to confer protection against denaturation just as detergents do when bound in small quantities. Thus, for example, dipicolinate prevents turbidity from developing and prevents the appearance of un-masked –SH groups, when BSA, HSA, ovalbumin, or human α-globulin are heated to 95° (Mishiro and Ochi, 1966). Bromphenol blue protects BSA from denaturation by all but the highest concentrations of acetamide (Butler *et al.*, 1958). It will be recalled, however, that bromphenol blue makes horse carbonylhemoglobin more susceptible to denaturation at low pH (Steinhardt *et al.*, 1966).

When methyl orange combines with HSA, hydrolysis of the protein by five different proteases proceeds at a reduced rate. Binding to two sites is required for this effect. Other anionic azo dyes also "protect" but do so to varying extents (Markus *et al.*, 1967). The digestion pathway is different from that followed by the protein without dye, and differs with the dye used. Methyl orange reduces the yield of a fragment of molecular weight 51,000 which is characteristic of the usual tryptic digestion of this protein. The distribution of the smaller fragments depends on the ligand. Kinetic analysis indicates that no competition with substrates for enzyme is involved, but that the number of bonds available to attack is affected. Thus each dye produces a different conformation of the protein.

F. PHYTIC ACID

Although phytic acid is not a dye, nor an aromatic compound, its high symmetry and compactness precluded it from inclusion with detergents; and it is not a small ion, such as those treated in the sections that follow. Experiments with phytic acid are therefore placed here, at the conjunction of the larger ions designated in the foregoing as dyes, and the smaller ions which follow.

The detailed investigations of Barre and Nguyen van Huot (1965a) on the combination of phytic acid (inositol hexaphosphoric acid) with HSA are subject to several unfortunate ambiguities: the pH values covered, 2.45 to 4.1, are not those in which HSA is in its most compact state (although it is referred to by those authors as native protein); the protein–ligand complex was precipitated over the whole range at which data were taken; the method of analysis reports the ligand as equivalents of H_3PO_4 esterified with inositol, which suggests that each value of $\bar{v}$ should be divided by 6 unless the unlikely assumption is made that each phosphate is ionized at this low pH value, and that each anionic charge is engaged at a binding site.[23,24] With the latter assumption at pH 4.1, $n = 86$ with an association constant of about 10^6; but

[23] All the numbers given refer to 100,000 gm of protein. The protein–ligand complex precipitates at $\bar{v}$ approximately 60 at pH 4.1. No data were obtained for $\bar{v}$ values at which precipitation did not occur.

[24] In a discussion of their results, the investigators state that they consider that only three of the six phosphates engage binding sites, because the remainder point away from the protein. No numerical adjustments are made for this steric effect.

an additional set of 23 sites is found with $K = 1.4$ to 2.4×10^2, at 37° and 0°, respectively. At pH 2.45, 144 groups appear to have a single K of 2×10^5 at 0° (1.4×10^5 at 37°). The authors associate the quantity 86 with the sum of the terminal amino groups and a lysine content of 84 residues; and the 23 groups with the histidine content. The balance, which do not become available except at the lowest pH, are arginines. After acetylation only 16 groups combine at pH 4.1 ($K = 20$) and 39 at lower pH ($K = 70$). Deamination (nitrous acid) reduces the binding sites at pH 4.1 to 44 but does not greatly affect their high affinity. At pH 2.45, 86 sites are still found with the deaminated protein. One must accept these numbers with caution in view of the possible need to divide all the $\bar{v}$ values by 6 as already referred to. With phosphoric acid itself, however, 86 binding sites are found in the "native protein."

Entirely different results are obtained with hen's ovalbumin. About 80 sites are found for phytic acid, by the same method. The affinity is slightly lower than in HSA, 5×10^4. Here the numbers of sites found add up to the sum of lysines plus arginines (Barre and Nguyen Van Huot, 1965b). The histidines appear to be masked and remain unengaged. Experiments with modified protein lead to the conclusion that the arginines are at the highest-energy sites, rather than the lysines.

Large entropy effects and small enthalpy changes characterize the reaction with both proteins.

IV. Binding of Small Nonaromatic Ions to Proteins

A. EARLY WORK

The binding of *small colorless* ions, other than metallic ions, to proteins was not recognized as early as the binding of dyes or detergents. The delay was due in part to the fact that observation of the binding of such small ions as the halides, for example, requires critical formulation of concepts and application of physicochemical procedures which were not generally available to biochemists until some 30 years ago. Progress could not be made until the formation of definite complexes could be distinguished from unequal distributions of ions around the central protein ion, such as arise from Donnan inequalities, or the presence of gegenions. In order to establish that definite (binding site) rather than general (bulk) interactions occur it is necessary to establish stoichiometry, association constants, ranges of specificity, and the energies involved (both $\Delta F°$ and E, the activation energy). Energy considerations help to distinguish binding effects of salts from thermodynamic activity coefficients, or shielding effects of ions on protein–protein interactions which are predominantly electrostatic in nature [see, for example, Varandani and

Schlamowitz (1963), who show that NaCl accelerates the conversion of porcine pepsinogen to pepsin at pH values near 4].

It has been common practice in work with detergents that unfold proteins to use electrophoretic mobilities as a measure of the ions bound. However, with some proteins the changes in charge (calculated from the titration curve) which accompany changes in pH do not produce changes in mobility as large as would be predicted. Chondromucoprotein behaves in this manner between pH 2 and 5. The disparity has been attributed to the association of counter ions, which is proportionately greater as fewer charged carboxylate groups remain (Warner and Schubert, 1958). The theory of counterion association with macromolecules is reviewed by Tanford (1961) and by Rice and Nagasawa (1961).

It was easy to demonstrate with insoluble proteins, such as wool keratin, that equal numbers of hydrogen ions and anions were associated with the protein phase immersed in solutions of acid or acid plus neutral salt, but the necessary condition of conservation of charge would have been sufficient to account for this phenomenon even if hydrogen ions alone were bound. Demonstration that the binding of small anions contributed to the free energy of the reaction was first accomplished when it was shown that the titration curves obtained with each of 38 strong acids differed among themselves widely, and that the effects of temperature on the various titration curves also were widely different (Steinhardt *et al.*, 1942). On the basis of this demonstration the stoichiometric interpretation of salt effects presented earlier (Steinhardt *et al.*, 1940) acquired qualitative plausibility. The discovery that the binding of high-affinity anions catalyzed the hydrolysis of amide bonds and, at higher binding, peptide bonds, tended to confirm the view that binding occurred at definite sites and could modify the stability of the protein (Steinhardt and Fugitt, 1942). The semiquantitative analysis of these effects in terms of the law of mass action which was offered in these papers was outdated by the more rigorous approaches of Klotz and of Scatchard, but the use of an insoluble protein phase in these early experiments precluded the use of those more rigorous treatments of multiple equilibria. A soluble protein, ovalbumin, however, showed unmistakable signs of combining with a number of anions with markedly different energies (Steinhardt *et al.*, 1941).

Briggs (1940) and Perlmann (1941) had observed that metaphosphoric acid, $(HPO_3)_3$, combines with a number of proteins to form stoichiometric insoluble complexes. The amounts combined were equal to the total number of cationic nitrogen groups in the proteins. We have already seen that similar stoichiometric ratios were reported for some detergents a few years later (see p. 240). Removal of the cationic charge by chemical modification of lysine and arginine led to large reductions in the binding of anions (Klotz and Urquhart, 1949; Teresi, 1950).

As an indirect result of the wartime blood fractionation program, observations were made that the addition of short-chain fatty acids to solutions of serum albumin protected them against denaturation by heating (Duggan and Luck, 1948). References to this work, which soon expanded to the determination of association constants, have been made in the Introduction of this chapter. The affinities of a number of short-chain fatty acid anions were shown ot be measurable. The most important result of this work was to initiate the very extensive investigations of Scatchard and his collaborators on the binding of small ions to human mercaptalbumin and serum albumin. One of the earliest of these studies (Scatchard and Black, 1949) resulted in the valuable ΔpH method of measuring ion binding which has been shown to have almost universal applicability, except in the case of long-chain aliphatic ions or other ions of extremely high affinity (Cassel and Steinhardt, 1969).

B. Thermodynamic Studies (Affinities and Numbers of Sites)

The first extended investigation of the binding of chloride and thiocyanate to HSA was carried out with incompletely deionized material. Since this work has been repeated (Scatchard et al., 1950), and extended by Scatchard and Yap (1964), only the latter will be referred to here; the results are not importantly discrepant. Both inorganic and organic ions will be treated.

Carr (1953) determined by means of potentials across permselective membranes the relative order in which a number of proteins stood in their ability to bind chloride. His results are shown in Fig. 7-42 in terms of equivalents bound per 10^5 g of protein. The order is somewhat the same as that assigned by Klotz and Urquhart (1949) for interactions with methyl orange, on the basis of their theory of binding capacity (see p. 303). Sodium and potassium were not bound at neutral pH. It should be noted that lysozyme stands higher than serum albumin, and far higher than β-lactoglobulin, which have already been shown to have high affinities and capacities for larger anions; it will be remembered that lysozyme, according to Wishnia (see p. 90) showed no tendency at all to combine with hydrocarbons. The data shown in the lower part of Fig. 7-42 at low pH encompass such high molal ratios that they give information, therefore, primarily about the many weaker and nonspecific binding sites (see below) rather than about the smaller number of sites of high affinity which Scatchard's group have shown to have a high degree of ability to discriminate among small ions.

Scatchard et al. (1957) used potentials across permselective membranes (see Chapter III, p. 44) to determine the binding of chloride, iodide, thiocyanate, and trichloracetate to human mercaptalbumin (monomer) in solutions containing only the individual sodium salts, and in solutions containing the conjugate strong acids. The ΔpH method was also used. An exact and

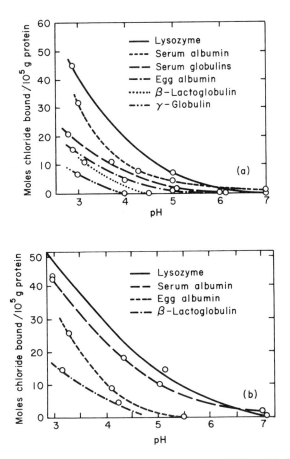

FIG. 7-42. The binding of chloride ion to various proteins. (a) The chloride-ion concentration is 12–19 mmole/liter; (b) the chloride-ion concentration is 100–120 mmole/liter. [C. W. Carr (1953). *Arch. Biochem. Biophys.* **46**, 417.]

explicit treatment of the membrane potentials was used, with only a few plausible assumptions as to the symmetries of the liquid-junction potentials and the effect of the dilute protein on the other components. The values of w used in the ΔpH method were calculated for each ionic strength from the Debye-Hückel theory for a spherical protein molecule with radius 30 Å, corresponding to the volume of the mercaptalbumin molecule, and small ions of radius 2.5 Å in water at 25°. These values have been used by other investigators who have applied electrical interaction theory to multiple equilibria in proteins.

The data for chloride and iodide based on membrane potentials are shown in Fig. 7-43. Here $\alpha = a_A \exp(-2w\bar{Z}_p Z_A)$ where a_A is the activity of the anion A and Z_A is its charge (unity in all the cases in this paper). $\bar{Z}_p$ is the charge on the initially isoionic protein, and is assumed to be equal to the number of anions bound per mole, $\bar{v}_A$. It will be noted that the results for both anions are in close agreement if $\alpha_I = 3.85\alpha_{Cl}$, i.e., the same number of iodide ions are bound at 1/3.85 the equilibrium concentration for chloride.

The results of the analysis can be succinctly stated as follows: There are at least three sets of sites at *pH values near* 5.2. These are described in Table 7-7

TABLE 7-7

Sites for Binding to Human Mercaptalbumin

No. of sites	K_{Cl^-}	K_{J^-}	K_{SCN^-}
1	2400	9240	46,200
8	100	385	1925
18	3.3	13	64

—separate association constants are given for chloride, iodide, and thiocyanate, but they bear a constant ratio to one another of 3.85 and 19.25.

The values of K_i (where i is set one, two, or three in Table 7-7) were determined by application of Eq. (7.12):

$$\bar{v}_A = \sum_i \bar{v}_{i,A} = \frac{n_i K_{i,A} a_A \exp(-2wZ_p Z_A)}{1 + K_{i,A} a_A \exp(-2wZ_p Z_A)} = \sum_i \frac{n_i K_{i,A} \alpha_A}{1 + K_{i,A} \alpha_A} \quad (7\text{-}12)$$

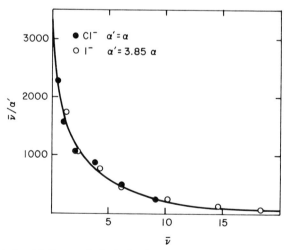

FIG. 7-43. Anion binding to isoionic bovine serum mercaptalbumin. [G. Scatchard *et al.* (1957). *J. Am. Chem. Soc.* **79**, 12.]

in which a_A has already been defined. Since w was different for each point it was calculated from

$$w' = \frac{2w}{2.303} = 0.1034 - \frac{1.017(\Gamma/2)^{1/2}}{1 + 10.663(\Gamma/2)^{1/2}} \qquad (7\text{-}13)$$

where $\Gamma/2$ is the ionic strength.

Note that Eq. (7-12) uses activities rather than concentrations, and that electrostatic corrections are applied to take account of increasing electrostatic repulsion as the anions bound increase. The authors describe a method for extracting the successive K_i from a plot of $\log \bar{v}_A$ vs. $\log \alpha_A$, using the low values of $\bar{v}_A$ to determine n and K, and then repeating the procedure with $\log(\bar{v}_A - \bar{v}_{1A})$ or $\log(\bar{v}_A - \bar{v}_{2A})$ as often as necessary. We have seen that Karush was unable to resolve his detergent data by such a procedure, and have suggested that the failure stemmed in part from unfolding and the creation of new sites.

The analysis cannot distinguish between the numbers of sites given in the table, and an alternative array of 2, 6, and 18. If the latter sets were adopted, K_{Cl^-} would be 1000, 100, and 5. The first thiocyanate ion is practically quantitatively bound at concentrations below $10^{-3} M$ ($\bar{v} = 0.9$ at $C = 5 \times 10^{-4}$).

Analysis of the same data by Saroff (1957) led to 4, 12, and 84 sets of groups, and 2500, 50, and 1 as their K values. Saroff's calculations take into account the effects of pH on the amounts bound on the basis of the assumption that only *protonated* basic side chains participate in the binding, and that hydrogen bonds between carboxylic and basic side chains must be disrupted for binding to occur.

The degree to which the Scatchard-Black (1949) equation (Chapter III, p. 75) is obeyed is shown in Fig. 7-44. The highest $\bar{v}$ value shown (trichloroacetate) is over 30. Since the ionic strength was necessarily variable in these experiments, w was calculated for each point as described above.

When the anions were introduced as strong acids instead of as neutral salts, the results were less satisfactory. Less anion appeared to be bound than when neutral salts were used, and more H^+ was taken up. The results were such as might be expected if one or more prototropic groups in the protein suffered a drop in pK as anions were bound.

It was evident that beyond the third set of sites ($K = 3.3$ to 5), there were numerous still weaker sites. Earlier work with the precipitation of serum albumin by detergents (see p. 240) or by metaphosphoric acid (Perlmann, 1941), had bolstered a natural tendency to identify the anion binding sites with the roughly 100 cationic groups indicated by the amino acid composition of these proteins. It was also natural to seek as a model for the protein–chloride ion combination, similar effects between chloride ion and large

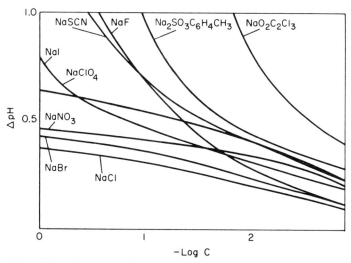

FIG. 7-44. Effect of salts on isoionic point of albumin. [G. Scatchard and E. S. Black (1949). *J. Phys. Colloid Chem.* **53**, 90.]

cations of known composition. Thus Saroff and Healey (1959), using the permselective membrane technique, reported an apparent association constant of 6 for the reaction between chloride and dodecylammonium ions, and 1.5 for the reaction with decylammonium ions. The presence of micelles at higher detergent concentrations raised the association constants by factors of 3–4. Preliminary measurements with hexylammonium ion gave $K = 0.5$. Saroff and Healey suggested that the ratios of affinities of successive sets of sites in serum albumin were analogous to the differences between first and second hydrogen-ion dissociation constants in dicarboxylic acids, in which the acid groups were separated by about six carbon atoms, and that the very high affinities of the strongest set were due to a clustering of charges. A distinctly electrostatic view was taken of the binding phenomenon.[25]

In a later paper (Scatchard *et al.*, 1959) more precise values were given for the binding to mercaptalbumin of the two larger anions, thiocyanate and trichloroacetate; measurements of fluoride binding were added. By using osmotic pressure experiments and treating changes in pressure brought about by the salts added as due entirely to the binding of anions (the standard Donnan equilibrium), higher values of $\bar{v}$ were encompassed. In the lower $\bar{v}$ range, the earlier conclusions as to numbers of sites and their association

[25] Before leaving model compounds, attention is invited to a report that the relatively simple molecule, adrenaline, binds all the amino acids except tyrosine with association constants between 7×10^4 and 2.5×10^1 (Manukhin, 1962).

constants were confirmed for chloride, and extended to the other ions, as
shown in Table 7-8. The values for thiocyanate are only half as great as in the

TABLE 7-8

ANION BINDING TO MERCAPTALBUMIN

No. of sites	1 K_1	8 K_2	18 K_3
Cl^-	2,400	100	3.3
F^-	3,600	150	5.0
SCN^-	24,000	1000	33
CCl_3COO^-	120,000	5000	165

previous paper, but the results with chloride and iodide were in good agreement. A few measurements with chloride and trichloroacetate were made with
HSA, defatted by the method of Goodman, with practically indistinguishable
results. It is not obvious, however, that differences should be expected.
Although it is clear that all the simple ions investigated by Scatchard's group
bind on the same sites, it is not obvious that oleate or palmitate should bind
to these also.

Up to 70 ions were found to bind by the osmotic pressure criterion, but
no large differences appeared between the several ions (Fig. 7-45).

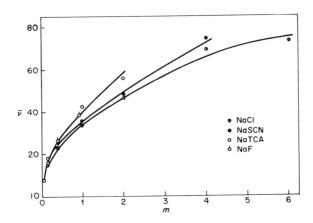

FIG. 7-45. Effect of salts on isoionic point of albumin. [G. Scatchard and E. S. Black
(1949). *J. Phys. Colloid Chem.* **53**, 90.]

The pH data given by trichloroacetate departed noticeably from the simple relationship found with the other ions. The degree of agreement of several of the methods of measuring the binding of trichloroacetate is shown in Fig. 7-46 (Scatchard and Zaromb, 1959). This ligand has a marked poly-

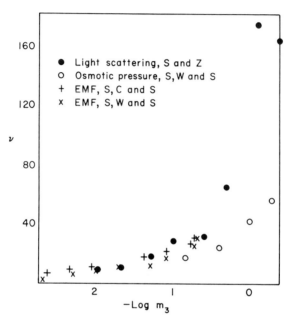

FIG. 7-46. Binding of trichloroacetate ion to bovine serum mercaptalbumin. [G. Scatchard and S. Zaromb (1959). *J. Am. Chem. Soc.* **81**, 6100.]

merizing effect on the protein (it has been used as a protein precipitant for half a century). The values determined by light-scattering experiments are therefore based on the second virial coefficient after correction for large-particle scattering. The difficulties of this method are discussed by Scatchard and Bergman (1959). The unexpected observation with trichloroacetate that the addition of acid or base had very little effect on the apparent total net charge is attributed to the effects of the charge on counteracting aggregation.

Scatchard and Yap (1964) used the potentials developed at collodion-coated silver–silver chloride electrodes (see Chapter III, p. 43) to measure the binding of Cl^-, I^-, and SCN^- to HSA (not mercaptalbumin) at both 0° and 25°. Using a more sensitive graphical procedure and the new more exact data, Scatchard and Yap concluded that the numbers of sites were 1, 4, and 22 rather than 1, 8, and 18 as previously reported. An exceedingly close fit to

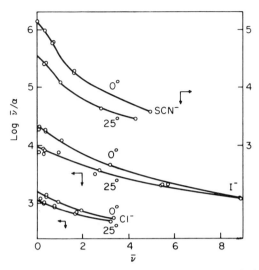

FIG. 7-47. Plots of $\log \bar{v}/\alpha$ vs. $\bar{v}$: at $0°$ and $25°$. Curves are calculated values. [G. Scatchard and W. T. Yap (1964). *J. Am. Chem. Soc.* **86**, 3437.]

the data results (Fig. 7-47). Values of the thermodynamic parameters are given in Table IV of Scatchard and Yap (1964) reproduced here as Table 7-9.

It is noteworthy that, unlike the results with detergents (pp. 27, 244), ΔF and ΔH always have the same sign, and ΔH may even be larger than ΔF (with NaSCN, and in the first site with NaI also). Thus ΔS is usually positive and small, with the exception of the cases just cited.

TABLE 7-9

THERMODYNAMIC PARAMETERS OF BINDING TO HSA

		$\log K$		$-\Delta F°$ (kcal/mole)		$-\Delta H°$ (kcal/mole)	$\Delta S°$ (eu)
		$0°$	$25°$	$0°$	$25°$		
$n = 1$	NaCl	3.054	2.857	3.82	3.91	2.96	3.18
	NaI	4.257	3.789	5.34	5.18	7.03	−6.19
	NaSCN	5.113	4.527	6.40	6.19	8.79	−8.75
$n_2 = 4$	NaCl	1.869	1.785	2.34	2.44	1.26	3.95
	NaI	3.041	2.824	3.82	3.86	3.26	2.03
	NaSCN	3.331	2.894	4.17	3.95	6.56	−8.73
$n_3 = 22$	NaCl	0.996	0.996	1.25	1.36	0.00	4.56
	NaI	1.556	1.556	1.95	2.13	0.00	7.13
	NaSCN	1.589	1.568	1.99	2.14	0.31	6.15

The amounts bound fall as the pH is increased (Fig. 7-48). It is asserted that this effect can be entirely accounted for by the change with pH of the charge on the protein which affects the "electrostatic correction" in the equations used [Eq. (7-12)]. There is also a reduction in the number of cationic sites. It is necessary to assume that 4 of the 16 histidine imidazole groups (pK assumed 6.1) constitute sites for anions, the K_2 group. The K_1 site is assumed to correspond to the α-amino group (pK assumed to be 8.0). A comparison of the new more exact measurements with the older ones on both HSA and bovine mercaptalbumin is given in tabular form, and leads to the conclusion that "with small anion binding there is little or no difference between bovine and human serum albumin, between total albumin and mercaptalbumin, or between reworked and crystalline albumin. The low results of Scatchard, Scheinberg and Armstrong with chloride ion, particularly in dilute solutions, are probably due to the fact that their albumin was not deionized."

C. SUPPORTING DATA AND APPLICATIONS

The meager evidence from crystallography adds to all the other evidence pointing to highly specific spatial relationships in binding. Thus, although *p*-chloromercuribenzene sulfonate (PCMBS) binds to crystals of sperm whale myoglobin (Watson *et al.*, 1964), and analysis of x-ray diffraction data shows the negative sulfonate end of the molecule close to the end of a lysine side chain (Fig. 7-49), in other forms of myoglobin crystals it binds in several

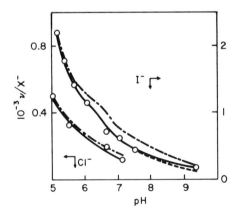

FIG. 7-48. Binding ratio, $\bar{v}/(X^-)$ vs. pH: broken line, calculated for electrostatic effect only; full line, calculated for electrostatic effect and pK_{H_2} 6.1; dotted line calculated for electrostatic effect p$K_{H_2} = 6.1$, p$K_H = 8.0$. [G. Scatchard, W. T. Yap (1964). *J. Am. Chem. Soc.* **86**, 3437.]

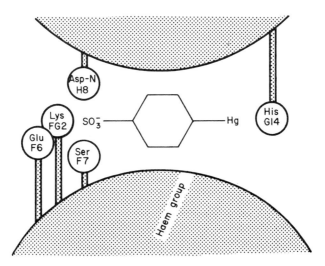

Fig. 7-49. Sketch showing the environment of the PCMBS group in the myoglobin crystal. [H. C. Watson *et al.* (1964). *J. Mol. Biol.* **8**, 168.]

sites, and in still other forms, not at all. As reported, "PCMBS seems to be attached to a specific configuration which might not be repeated, or might be sterically impossible in a different crystal form. Second, a good deal of space is needed to accommodate the PCMBS molecule and some of the sites involved in the non-specific binding in solution may be inaccessible in the crystal. The reason for the failure of PCMB (benzoate) to bind is less obvious." On the other hand, the binding of substrate to cross-linked insoluble *ribonuclease* acid crystals appears to follow a simple mass-law relationship (Bishop *et al.*, 1966) in the crystal as well as in solution.

The data of Scatchard and of others to be listed in the pages that follow have been used to put hydrogen-ion binding data into a form suitable for analysis in terms of the Linderström-Lang equation (p. 20) by converting H^+ bound to net charge by subtraction of anions bound. For example, Carr's data may be used with the ovalbumin titration data of Cannan to bring w_{calc} and w_{exp} into agreement, abolishing the 25% difference between them that exists if chloride binding is neglected (Chapter V). Likewise, Barnett and Bull (1960) determined the binding of chloride, using experiments similar to Carr's, by both ribonuclease and β-lactoglobulin to determine whether such corrections to the titration data for these proteins were required. Above neutral pH no binding of chloride to ribonuclease was found, as the earlier results of Tanford and Hauenstein (1956) had foreshadowed. β-Lactoglobulin, however, bound significant amounts of chloride on both sides of the isoionic point.

One rather special type of anion binding occurs in conjugated proteins, such as hemoglobins and related heme enzymes, in which the anion is bound to one of the coordination places of the iron or other central metal atom of the heme. In these cases, the binding site is completely known, but the complexes formed are characteristic of the prosthetic group rather than of proteins, and are therefore only remotely relevant to the subject of this book. They constitute, however, multiple equilibria, when the heme protein contains subunits, as does hemoglobin, and exhibit both the normal interactions characteristic of multiple equilibria, and anomalous "cooperative" ones such as characterize the formation of oxyhemoglobin (the cyanide complex of ferrihemoglobin is a case of the latter). Values of the equilibrium binding constants for the binding of cyanide, azide, fluoride, and thiocyanate determined prior to 1963 have been tabulated by Steinhardt et al. (1963; see Table 7-10). In recent years, interest has focused on the kinetics of these and related reactions (see, for example, Mohr et al., 1967; Nichols, 1961; and Dunford and Alberty, 1967). In some cases it has been possible to calculate thermodynamic parameters, such as K_1, ΔF°, ΔH°, and ΔS°, from the velocity constants. With horse and human metmyoglobin the following ligands have been studied (Blank, 1966): cyanide, fluoride, azide, imidazole, selenocyanide, nitrite, cyanate, thiocyanate, and formate. The order given above is that of ascending temperature coefficients; the human myoglobin reacted about twice as fast as the horse protein at 20°.

In other cases the binding constant has been assumed to be so great that the kinetic treatment used has been for an irreversible reaction [ferric horseradish peroxidase (Dunford and Alberty, 1967); sperm whale metmyoglobin (Ploeg and Alberty, 1968)].

Difference spectra brought about by temperature differences have been used to study the conversion of ligand–iron bonds from high- to low-spin types in the case of ferrihemoglobin (Scheler et al., 1963).

D. ADDITIONAL DATA

Table 7-11 tabulates some representative values of numbers of sites and association constants for a number of proteins and ligands not already covered. It is not an exhaustive list, even of those cases in which a basis for quantitative analysis has been provided; there are numerous determinations of the same ligands in the case of BSA, and there are numerous cases of enzyme–substrate complexes that have been omitted.

The table does not include studies in which numbers of binding sites and association constants were not determined. Thus, for example, difference spectra have been used as a qualitative indication of the binding of halides and thiocyanate by carbonic anhydrase (Beychok et al., 1966). Changes in the

TABLE 7-10

Hemoglobin–Ligand Binding Constants[a] at Acid pH

	K_{eq}	
	0.2°	24.8°
HCN	0.81 (pH range 4.55–5.55)	5.1 (pH 5.02)
HN_3	0.024 (pH 4.29) 0.048 (pH 5.31)	$(0.23)^b$
HF	—	$(0.09)^b$

	K_{diss}	
	0.2°	24.8°
CN^-	4.8×10^{-11}	2.5×10^{-9}
N_3^-	5.3×10^{-7} (6.3×10^{-7})	— (4×10^{-6})
F^-	(1.2×10^{-2})	$(1.7 \times 10^{-2})^c$
CNS^-	(2.1×10^{-3})	(7.4×10^{-3}) pH 6.7 $(2.24 \times 10^{-3})^d$ pH 4.92

[a] Taken from Steinhardt et al. (1963) K_{eq} refers to the reaction $Hb^+ + HCN \rightleftharpoons HbCN + H^+$, and K_{diss} refers to the dissociation of HbCN, etc.

[b] These values of K_{eq} are derived from the K_{diss} values of Scheler and Jung by dividing the latter by the dissociation constants of HN_3 ($pK = 4.75$ at 25°) and of HF ($pK = 3.3$), respectively. The later value is too high by a factor approaching 2, since another equilibrium (HF + $F^- \rightleftharpoons HF_2^-$; $K = 0.027$) reduces the fluoride ion concentration by such a factor. However, the true value of K_{diss} for fluoride at pH 3–4 is undoubtedly much lower than at the pH of Scheler and Jung's measurements. See footnote c.

[c] There is some doubt concerning the validity of this value in the pH range (3–4). The authors are indebted to C. D. Coryell of Massachusetts Institute of Technology for the opportunity to examine an unpublished thesis (1942) by W. B. Lewis, in which the fluoride-ferrihemoglobin (bovine) equilibrium is investigated and compared with the recalculated results of Lipmann (1929) (pig) which are in close agreement. They find a drop in K_{diss} from 1.55×10^{-2} at pH 4.7 to 5.6×10^{-4} at pH 3.8. Lewis refers to this trend as a "Bohr effect" and attributes it to a dissociable hydrogen ($pK \sim 3$ in the free protein and 4.5 in the bound protein). Such a trend can also be due to an effect of the increase in electrostatic charge on K_{diss} as the protein takes up protons.

[d] This value is given in an unpublished thesis (1942) by T. Vermeulen, made available to us by C. D. Coryell.

TABLE 7-11

ADDITIONAL CASES OF PROTEIN-SMALL ION INTERACTION

Protein	Ligand	Method	pH	n	K	Notes	References
Actin	p-Chloromercuri-benzoate	—	—	—	—	—	Tonomura and Tonomura (1962)
Aldolase (rabbit muscle)	Sulfate	Eq. dialysis	7.8	5.5	~2100	a	Ginsberg and Mehler (1966)
	Phosphate			2.6, 2.9	~1000,28,000	—	
	Hexitol-l-6-di-phosphate or FDP			2.7	830,000	—	
ATP-creatine kinase (rabbit muscle)	Chloride	Permselective membrane electrodes	6–9	9–10	23(pH 5.6–5.8)	b	Floyd and Friedberg (1966)
	Potassium			11–12	16(pH 6.6 –6.7)K^+	—	
	Sodium					—	
	Calcium			Indeterminate	Indeterminate	—	
	Magnesium						
β-Lactoglobulin	Na^+	Eq. dialysis	7.7	—	150	—	Baker and Saroff (1965)
Deaminase-free myosin (rabbit)	ADP	Eq. dialysis	7.7	$1.5/5 \times 10^5$ gm	$1.9 \times 10^5 (Mg^{2+})$	c	Luck and Lowey (1966)
Myosin (rabbit)	ATP	Gel filtration	7.4	$1.7/5 \times 10^5$ gm	$6 \times 10^3 (Ca^{2+})$ $1.4 \times 10^3 (Mg^{2+})$	d	Schliselfeld and Bárány (1968)
Bovine neurophysin	Oxytocin Vasopressin	Eq. dialysis	5.8	2	1.8×10^5	e	Abrash and Breslow (1966)
BSA (deionized)	SCN^-	Eq. dialysis	4.5–10	7 70	400 10	f	McMenamy et al. (1968)
	Iodide	Eq. dialysis (tracer) with Na^+ as Donnan ratio ion	—	1 6 14	4900 440 14	g	Saifer et al. (1964)

Protein	Ligand	Competition with Iodide ion / Method	pH	n	K		Reference
BSA (contd.)	Acetate	Competition with Iodide ion	—	1 6 50	530 50 2	—	Orozlan and Maengwyn-Davies (1962)
	Atropine	Ultrafiltration	5–8	20 (pH 6) 100 (pH 8)	2.3 × 10³ 2.6 × 10³	h	Yoshikawa and Loening (1965)
	Thiopental	Eq. dialysis	7.42	5	1.2 × 10⁴	i	
	Thiocyanate		4.5–10	7 10	700 90	—	McMenamy et al. (1968)
HSA	5-Hydroxytyramine (serotonin)	—	8.8	11	6.5 × 10²	j	Kerp and Kasemir (1962)
	Phosphate	Eq. dialysis	2.6–4.8	85	—	k	Barré and Nguyen van Huot (1964)
	Pyrophosphate,			23	—	—	
Ribonuclease	Chloride	Permselective membrane potentials	9.6 6.6 4.3	0(OH⁺ bound) 0.5(4.3H⁺ bound) 2.0(8.0H⁺ bound)	750	l	Saroff and Carroll (1962)
	Sulfate		6.8 4.5	1.4 2.3	6000	—	
Ribonuclease (bovine)	Chloride	Permselective membrane electrode	2.59–4.43	4 3	200(pH 4.43) 250(pH < 4.05)	m	Loeb and Saroff (1964)
	2′-CMP		5.5	—	—	n	Anderson et al. (1968)
	3′-CMP	—		—	—	—	
	3′-UMP			—	—	—	
	Phosphate			—	—	—	
	Pyrophosphate			—	—	—	
TMV protein	Cl⁻, K⁺, Ca²⁺	Permselective membrane electrodes	3–9	(See Figs. 1 and 2 of ref.)	100	o	Shalaby et al. (1968)
	SCN⁻				200	—	
Trypsin	Phenylguanidinium phenol	Eq. dialysis	7.0	1 1	7 × 10³ 2.3 × 10¹	p	Sanborn and Bregan (1968)

[a] Inactive enzyme with 2.6 equivalents of dihydroxyacetone covalently attached does not show specific binding of either phosphate or hexitol diphosphate. Native fructose diphosphate aldolase thus has three active sites each containing two different phosphate binding sites.

[b] Fig. 1 of ref. shows that in 0.05 M KCl chloride binding falls from $\bar{v} = 10$ at pH 5 to $\bar{v} = 0$ at pH 6.8. Chloride binding rises from 0 at pH 6 to 3 at pH 6.8 and 9 at pH 9.5. Thus both K^+ and Cl^- are bound in the pH interval 6.0–6.8. Although K and n values for the divalent cations could not be calculated, it is clear that Mg^{2+} is bound less effectively than Ca^{2+}.

[c] All binding is eliminated by EDTA. There is no effect of ionic strength. Heavy meromyosin has $n = 1.5$ and $K = 1 \times 10^5$.

[d] Requires Mg^{2+}. Binding inhibited by adenosine diphosphate and pyrophosphate, but not by phosphate.

[e] Deamino oxytocin does not bind; thus, the α-amino group appears to be involved. Various glycine and tyrosine derivatives do not bind. However, 1-hemihomocystine oxytocin, 2-phenylalanine oxytocin and 4-glycine oxytocin have K values close to those of oxytocin itself! It is concluded that hydrophobic interactions between positions 2 and 3 of oxytocin and nonpolar groups on the protein are involved.

[f] The analysis used the electrostatic corrections given by Scatchard, but the numerical results are not in good agreement with Scatchard's data obtained without supporting electrolyte. Normal values of w were found within the pH range indicated. Outside these limits w was much reduced, but n_1 did not change. Larger n_2 values (80) were found at pH 3.5, and smaller ones (45) at pH 10.5. Urea at concentrations above $2M$ affected the n_1 sites but not the n_2 sites; n_1 sites ceased to be found at $8 M$ urea. K_1 was larger at low ionic strengths.

[g] The values given for iodide are about twice as large as those reported by Scatchard et al. (1957) for either human mercaptalbumin or serum albumin.

[h] The binding at low pH is unexpected. Cystine and N-acetylation both inhibit the interaction. The presence of acetylcholine has a slight enhancing effect on the binding of atropine, but is not itself bound.

[i] 7°. There is a small reduction in n and K on adding di-NaEDTA.

[j] Binding is diminished at lower pH. Zn^{2+} and Cn^{2+} reduce it.

[k] $25 \times 10^{-4} M$ phosphate saturates 10^5 gm of protein. Binding decreases as the pH falls. The maximum numbers of sites are said to correspond to the lysine content (phosphate) and the histidine content (pyrophosphate). $\Delta H°$ appears to be negative for all the phosphate esters except phytic acid (see p. 315). No correlations were found between the pK values of the esters, or their rates of hydrolysis by phosphoros-esterase, and their affinities.

[l] The binding and pH data have been interpreted as indicating that each binding site consists of a cluster of charged side chains, containing two imidazole groups and one ammonium or guanidinium group. The calculations, insofar as they take pH effects into account, are based on the assumption that binding of anions occurs only at protonated basic sites.

[m] A maximum of six binding sites is considered to exist; the clustered charge theory is again used, and suggestions are made as to site composition. pH effects are interpreted as signifying that there is competition between the ligand anion and carboxylic side chains.

[n] Association constants as a function of pH were determined. All have the same pH profile except 2'-CMP. The results are explained by assuming that two groups on the enzyme have pK values of about 6.5 and 5, respectively; but that 2'-CMP requires a third group with pK near 5.0. The protonated and nonprotonated species of 2'- and 3'-CMP bind equally well. Association constants in declining order are 2'-CMP, 2'-UMP > 3'-CMP > 3'-UMP > PP > P.

[o] The molal ratios are calculated for a subunit of 17,530 molecular weight. Binding depends strongly on pH and does not occur in the absence of a net charge. Binding by the nucleoprotein is consistently higher than by the apoprotein. Since no binding occurs over a wide region of pH, ion binding is not importantly involved in the endothermic polymerization of nucleoprotein subunits.

[p] The binding of the two ligands listed is not competitive.

activity of the same enzyme in the presence of varying concentrations of anions at pH below 8 have been interpreted in terms of binding (Kernohan, 1965). Precipitation of BSA at pH 3.5–4.5 by thiocyanate has been interpreted as the result of conformation changes induced by SCN⁻ (Aoki and Hori, 1962). A very thorough investigation of chloride binding by BSA, determined electrophoretically, has not been listed because the use of mobilities to determine charge is not fully justified; if the data are accepted at face value they indicate consistently higher binding than in Scatchard's experiments over the pH range 3 to 6 at 0.15 M NaCl. A number of other papers conclude that cationic side chains are involved, e.g., in the binding of ATP by HSA (Drabikowski, 1960).

Although the binding of thyroxine by BSA has been covered in Chapter IV, some of the inhibitors of binding are anions rather than dipolar ions and should be mentioned here. Tabachnik (1964) has ranked the affinities of the following ions on the basis of their inhibition of thyroxine binding: oleate > dodecylsulfate > palmitate > 2,4-dinitrophenolate > octanoate > salicylate. It is noteworthy that carboxylates and sulfate half-esters are found in the same series, although the difference spectra induced when they bind to BSA are entirely different (see p. 284).

The binding constants of a large number of small molecules have been determined in a classical study of competitive inhibition of an enzyme, carboxypeptidase, by Smith and his collaborators (Smith, 1951). The activity of the enzyme against the synthetic carbobenzoxyglycyl-L-tryptophan was measured at a number of concentrations of a number of competitive inhibitors. Figures 7-50 and 7-51 are self-explanatory. It should be noted that Fig. 7-51 is precisely the isotherm of a single association constant, or rather, since competition is involved, a single ratio of binding constants. The results with a wide variety of inhibitors are shown in Figs. 7-51 through 7-54 and in Table 7-12.

Unfortunately, no simple relationship to size or structure reveals itself. In other words, the system behaves like an enzyme in being highly specific, even though only relatively so. In the case of leucine-aminopeptidase, the velocity of hydrolysis gives a very smooth curve when plotted against the molecular weight of the side chain bound to the α-carbon.

With indoleacetic acid, $\Delta F°$ for formation of the complex was determined to be -4300 ± 800 cal/mole. $\Delta H°$ was -3400 ± 100 cal/mole, and ΔS was $+3.0 \pm 5.5$ eu/mole. The negative enthalpy change should be noted.

A nonspecific salting out of myosin A is mitigated or reversed when anions which bind are present (ADP, ATP, pyrophosphate, and others) (Brahms and Bregner, 1961). The 1-to-1 molar ratio of ATP with heavy meromysin is apparently the result of formation of a covalent bond. Both the formation of the complex and its dissolution on dialyzing free of nucleotides are time-dependent reactions (Szent-Gyorgyi, 1968).

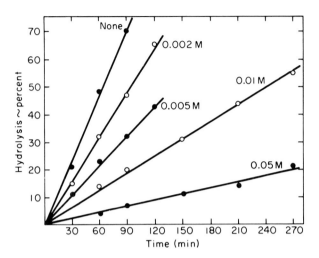

FIG. 7-50. Apparent zero-order hydrolysis of carbobenzoxyglycyl-L-tryptophan (0.05 M) by crystalline carboxypeptidase in the presence of different concentrations of benzylmalonic acid. [E. L. Smith (1951). *In* "Enzymes and Enzyme Systems" (J. T. Edsall, ed). Harvard Univ. Press, Cambridge, Massachusetts.]

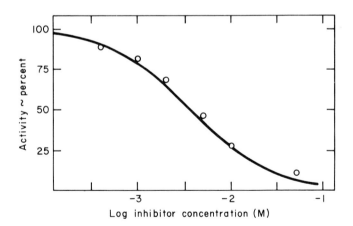

FIG. 7-51. Inhibition of carboxypeptidase by benzylmalonic acid. The solid curve, adjusted to fit the data, is drawn from the mass-law equation for the combination of 1 mole of inhibitor with each active group of enzyme. [E. L. Smith (1951). *In* "Enzymes and Enzyme Systems" (J. T. Edsall, ed.). Harvard Univ. Press, Cambridge, Massachusetts.]

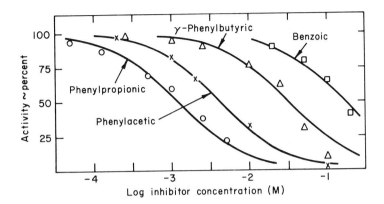

Fig. 7-52. Inhibition of carboxypeptidase by various phenyl acids. The same theoretical curve is drawn as in Fig. 7-51. [E. L. Smith (1951) *in* "Enzymes and Enzyme Systems" (J. T. Edsall, ed.). Harvard Univ. Press, Cambridge, Massachusetts.]

TABLE 7-12

COMPETITIVE INHIBITION OF CARBOXYPEPTIDASE

Competitor	Relative association constant[a]
Indoleacetic	1280
β-Phenylpropionic	830
Valeric, isocaproic	370
Benzylmalonic	250
Phenylacetic	220
Butyric	200
Indolepropionic	180
Caproic	160
Cyclohexylpropionic-8-phenylbutyric	50
Indolebutyric	30
Naphthaleneacetic	22
Propionic	10
Benzoic	7

[a] Reciprocal of concentration producing 50% inhibition of enzyme when substrate concentration is 0.05 M at pH 7.5. Reaction is zero order.

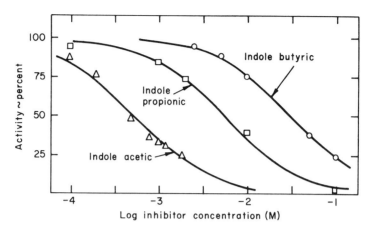

FIG. 7-53. Inhibition of carboxypeptidase by indole acids. The curve drawn is the same theoretical one used in Figs. 7-51 and 7-52. [E. L. Smith (1951). *In* "Enzymes and Enzyme Systems" (J. T. Edsall, ed.). Harvard Univ. Press, Cambridge, Massachusetts.]

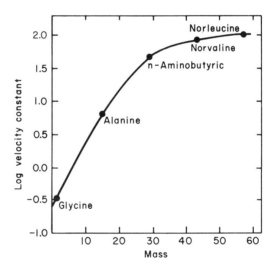

FIG. 7-54. Hydrolysis of aliphatic amino acid amides by leucine-aminopeptidase. The logarithm of the relative first-order velocity constant is plotted as a function of the molecular weight of the side chain bound to the α-carbon. [E. L. Smith (1951) *in* "Enzymes and Enzyme Systems" (J. T. Edsall, ed.). Harvard Univ. Press, Cambridge, Massachusetts.]

E. CATIONS

Data on the binding of a few cations were included in Table 7-11 because they were coupled with data on anions or other ligands. Carr (1956), Carr and Engelstad (1958), and Doremus and Johnson (1958) have all reported binding of alkaline cations to the phosphoproteins, casein and phosvitin. Very little or no binding is observed except at pH values above 5. Nearly 250 moles of sodium are bound to 10^5 gm of phosvitin at pH 9. The affinity is low—about 10% of the sodium present is bound.

Ho and Waugh (1965) have examined the small amount of sodium or potassium binding to deionized α_S-casein (molecular weight 27,300) which occurs at pH 5.16 at 20° by using ion-exchange electrodes similar to those used by Scatchard, and by interpretation of pH changes brought about by KCl and NaCl. The electrode measurements indicate that there are five binding sites for the cations at both isoionic pH (4.8) and pH 7. The ΔpH data suggest that there are two sets, both having low values of K, 323 and 7.

The limited binding of alkaline earths and of other metallic ions to certain special proteins, mostly enzymes, is treated in Chapter VI. An ingenious study of the removal of zinc and exchange with cobalt of cross-linked crystals has been reported by Bishop *et al.* (1966). The essential point here is that while many anions bind to varying extents with many proteins, few cations bind to few proteins. Ion binding, even with very small ions, is not a simple matter of electrostatic interaction.

The binding of mono- and disubstituted tetramethylammonium to antibody binding sites (specific for choline groups) has been studied by an NMR method, by Burgen *et al.* (1967) and Metcalfe *et al.* (1968), in an investigation of the mechanism of such binding. It was determined that acetylcholine and (-)-methacholine are bound as rigid units, unlike, e.g., acetamidophenylcholine, which shows some side-chain interactions with the antibody.

Results obtained by a solubility method (Chapter III) for the binding of a number of amines to BSA (Sahyun, 1964) cannot be accepted without further critical examination. Values of $\bar{v}$ at three different temperatures and two pH values (7.5 and 10.5) were determined. The values of $\bar{v}$, rather than association constants, were then used to calculate ΔH due to binding; large values, 3 to 30 kcal mole^{-1}, were found in the lower temperature interval (9°–17°) and small, or negative values in the higher interval (17°–25°). Failure to use association constants and to distinguish between $\Delta H°$ and ΔH make the results of doubtful value. The tendency of ΔH to fall with increasing T is important, and should be further investigated. Although $\Delta H°$ is almost invariably positive when more than two aliphatic molecules or anions are bound, a negative value appears to be more common for other small ions (Lovrien and Sturtevant, 1961; also Lovrien, 1968; Lovrien, private communication; Fairclough and Fruton, 1966). Whether $\Delta H°$ is initially positive or negative, it appears to tend to rise as the number of ions already bound increases.

It is natural to expect to find ion binding in the case of collagen, since it is a protein that dissolves only when electrolytes are present; it is thus an extreme example of globulin-type behavior. However, the latter has been ascribed to the possession of a high dipole moment (Cohn and Edsall, 1943), rather than to interactions with dissolved ions. There are, however, differences in fibrillar form between collagens dissolved and reprecipitated several times when this is done with different buffers, and the differences have been attributed to binding of the buffer ions (Kahn et al., 1962). Von Hippel and Wong (1962)[26] maintain that the nature of their kinetic data on the formation of the collagen fold and the dependence of the equilibrium constant on salt concentration exclude any possibility that ion binding to the gelatin chain can be responsible for the observed dependences. The reasoning depends, in part, on the assumption that the hypothetical binding sites must be peptide bonds, as has been suggested by Bello, or some other specific groups in the protein. The fraction of sites occupied would then depend on the *concentration* of gelatin, which is contrary to finding a constant increment in melting temperature per mole of salt at all concentrations (Fig. 7-55). The argument

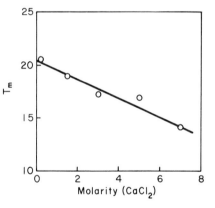

FIG. 7-55. T_m (temperature at the midpoints of the melting profiles shown in Fig 4) for ichthyocol gelatin as a function of $CaCl_2$ concentration. [P. H. Von Hippel and K. Y. Wong (1962). *Biochemistry* **1**, 667.]

appears to be of questionable validity, because while the fraction of ligand bound should depend on the collagen concentration, the fraction of sites occupied ($\bar{v}/n$) at a given free ligand concentration should be independent of the concentration of protein. It is assumed that the melting temperature is

[26] No effort is made here to review the voluminous literature on the striking effects of neutral salts on collagen fibrils and gelatin gels. The reader is referred to von Hippel and Wong (1962) for some of the principal references prior to 1962.

governed by the fraction of sites occupied. The experiments give total salt rather than free salt, so the arguments are at best inconclusive. In experiments with an anion, isotopically labeled thiocyanate, Puett *et al.* (1966) have concluded that binding does occur, but that it occurs to a greater extent on heat-shrunk collagen. It is hypothesized that binding occurs in the more dissolved regions.

F. Evidence from Electrophoresis

In Chapter IV a number of electrophoretic studies were cited which tended to show that undissociated weak acids were bound by serum albumin and some other proteins (p. 112). Some of these papers establish that binding of anions also occurs. Thus Schmidt and Polis (1960) were able to show, by using a particular electrophoretic pattern as a reference standard, that various "stabilizers" such as fatty acids, di- and tribasic organic acids, and aliphatic alcohols, bound to native HSA and in so doing, counteracted the unfolding effect of hydrogen ion in the $N \rightleftharpoons F$ transition. It was necessary to assume that both undissociated and anionic forms of the stabilizing acids were bound, and that they were bound to different sites.

Electrophoresis has been used to detect the existence of complexes between proteins and particular ionic ligands. Unfortunately the method is not sensitive enough to detect the small amounts of free ligand when the ligand is added in small ratios to the protein; and the mobility is an uncertain guide to the amounts bound. Thus isotherms are not commonly obtained. The method has been used with BSA and hyaluronic acid (Gramling *et al.*, 1963) but the interpretation offered is not quantitative; and with various small ions and cytochrome c of ten different species (Barlow and Margoliash, 1966). At pH 6.9 the apparent affinities stood in the ratio $PO_4^{2-} > I^- > Cl^- > SO_4^{2-}$. Cations did not complex. ATP appeared to bind to myosin but not to myosin A (Zaalishvili *et al.*, 1963).

G. Evidence from Conformational Effects

A dependence of protein conformation on the presence of particular ions is not uncommon. Thus ATP radically alters (lengthens) the "ladders" of myosin B which form in solutions of high ionic strengths. The contraction of muscle has been related to this effect (Rice *et al.*, 1963). ATP and other polyvalent anions such as pyrophosphate prevent the precipitation of myosin A at low ionic strengths, and affect its electrophoretic mobility (Brahms and Bregner, 1961). Aspartic transcarbamylase is protected by ATP and its inhibitor, CTP, from digestion by trypsin, while its substrate increases the rate of digestion of the enzyme (McClintock and Markus, 1968). The thermal instability of ribonuclease at pH 2.1, and the conformation (as observed by measurements of optical rotation and rotatory dispersion, uv absorption, and viscosity) varies with the anions present. A more ordered structure seems to exist in the presence of sulfate as compared with chloride; the transition temperature in chloride, 29°, is raised to 43° in sulfate. Both anions give partial protection against unfolding by 5 M guanidine hydrochloride. Phosphate effects are intermediate between those of chloride and sulfate (Ginsberg and Carroll, 1965). The binding of glutamate to glutamic dehydrogenase produces a small conformation effect which perturbs the tryptophan absorption (Cross and Fisher, 1966). Other dehydrogenases show similar effects on tryptophan. K^+, but not Na^+, alters the conformation of pyridine kinase (Mildvan and Cohn, 1966).

H. Protection against Unfolding

Reference has already been made to the early discovery that short-chain fatty acid anions protected HSA from denaturation. Numerous other similar observations have been made with the same and other proteins, sometimes without awareness of the earlier work. A recent example is the prevention of the inactivation of myosin by 2,4-dinitrophenol (Levy *et al.*, 1963) by ATP and pyrophosphates. Inorganic pyrophosphate is 10 times more effective than adenosine diphosphate. Three equivalents of dinitrophenol are bound to the protein in the inactivation process. Since the protecting phosphate does not prevent binding of the dinitrophenol, the protective effect seems to implicate a conformation change. Cyanocobalamin added to the serum globulins of several mammalian species protects the proteins against the effects of 8 M urea when several equivalents are bound. It gives no protection when added subsequent to urea, and no binding then occurs (Rosenthal *et al.*, 1962).

I. Miscellaneous Reports of Small Ion Binding to Proteins

Insulin is reported to bind from one to two fluorescein molecules per mole, probably at the terminal amino group of the β-chain, and possibly at the terminal glycine as well. The complex is hypochromic (Tietze *et al.*, 1962). Vasopressin and oxytocin are bound by proteins in bovine and rabbit neurohypophyses (Ginsberg and Treland, 1964). An effect of EDTA on fibrinogen conformation, *other than by sequestration of metallic ions*, appears to have been demonstrated by Blomback *et al.* (1966). The fluorescence of flavic monophosphates is quenched on binding to cytochrome c reductase (Tsibris and McCormic, 1965). Two nucleotides (ATP or ADP) per subunit of glutamine synthetase—thus 16 moles of nucleotide per mole of enzyme—are bound. Mescaline and other biogenic amines are bound to Cohn Fraction III of human serum but not to other fractions (Oh *et al.*, 1966).

Pande and McMenamy (1968) have shown that the binding of SCN^- by BSA is greatly modified by reduction and blocking of $-SH$.

J. KINETICS OF BINDING PROCESSES

Both binding and dissociation are far too rapid for their rates to be measured in equilibrium dialysis. The rate of increase of fluorescence quenching when thyroxine is bound to albumin indicates that the association is complete in 150 msec (Andreoli *et al.*, 1965). Relaxation techniques have been used by Eigen and his colleagues (Froese *et al.*, 1962) to determine that the binding of certain dyes occurs at a rate almost as fast as a diffusion-limited process (K above 2×10^6 mole^{-1} sec^{-1}). The equilibrium constants ($K = 6.0 \times 10^4$) corresponding to these rates suggest that the dissociation processes should be much slower ($K = 35$ sec^{-1}) but the dissociation rates have not yet been determined experimentally. Measurements by Lenz and Steinhardt (1969) indicate that the *unfolding* of BSA due to binding dodecylsulfate has a half-period of about 80 msec at 25°. The refolding reaction is considerably slower under comparable conditions. There is a small energy of activation for the unfolding reaction, but none for refolding.

The rates of binding of reduced nicotinamide–adenine dinucleotide analogs to liver alcohol dehydrogenase are slow enough to present no problem in measurement by stop-flow methods (Shore, 1969). The " off " reaction is much faster (half-period 1 sec) then the " on " reaction. The results have been analyzed in terms of a possible sequential nature of the binding of the constituent rings of the ligand.

K. EFFECT OF BINDING ON SUBUNIT INTERACTIONS

It should be obvious that the unfolding model described on p. 26 should be applicable to the effects of ligands on dissociation into subunits, a process equivalent to unfolding of a restricted kind. Such a case, for example, is the dissociation of hemerythrin, a non-heme iron-containing protein, which dissociates into eight subunits under the influence of thiocyanate ion (Klapper and Klotz, 1968). Dissociation should occur whenever a ligand is present which binds more strongly to the monomeric than to the oligomeric form. The dissociation into monomers is then accompanied by an increase in bound ligand. The equilibrium constant for the polymerization reaction between subunits can be determined by analysis of this effect (see p. 356).

The very common dissociation into subunits under the influence of H^+ should be susceptible to the same kind of analysis, if no complications, such as changes in conformation prior to dissociation, intervene.

Somewhat more complicated ligand–subunit interactions have been found in the now thoroughly familiar case of aspartic transcarbamylase (Changeux

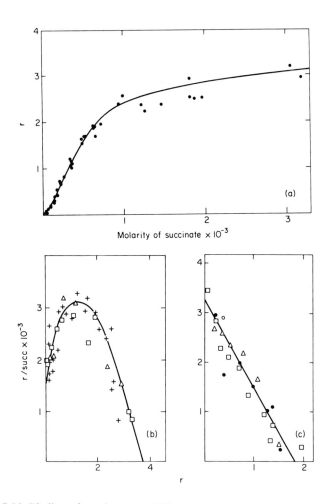

FIG. 7-56. Binding of succinate to ATCase and to the catalytic subunit. Data are expressed as r, the moles of succinate bound per mole of aspartic transcarbamylase (ATCase) or catalytic subunit. Part (a) shows the binding to ATCase plotted as r vs. the concentration of free succinate. The same data appear in (b) as a Scatchard plot, $r/$[free succinate] vs. r. Part (c) is a Scatchard plot for the binding of succinate to the catalytic subunit. Equilibrium dialysis was conducted by the technique of Myer and Schellman (1962) using [^{14}C] succinate. Carbamyl phosphate was present at 4×10^{-3} M. ATCase in (a) and (b) was present in the protein compartment of the dialysis cell at a concentration of 7.5×10^{-5} M (22.5 mg/ml); catalytic subunit in (c) was present at 1.0×10^{-4} M (10.0 mg/ml). Dialysis time at 21° is indicated by the symbols $+$ and $\bigcirc$ for 12 hr, $\triangle$ for 16 hr, and $\square$ for 20 hr. [J. P. Changuex et al. (1968). *Biochemistry* **7**, 534.]

et al., 1968; Gerhart and Schachman, 1968; Changeux and Rubin, 1968). The complications arise because the subunits contain more than one kind of binding site, and respond differently as the two kinds of sites are occupied. The enzyme consists of *two* catalytic and *four* regulatory subunits. There are four specific sites for the *feedback* inhibitor, cytidine triphosphate (CTP) or its analog 5-bromocytidine triphosphate. Dissociation studies indicate that the enzyme is a tetramer, with each monomer containing one regulatory subunit, and *one-half* of a catalytic subunit. The isolated regulatory subunit (molecular weight 50,000) possesses one binding site for CTP, and the isolated catalytic subunit (molecular weight 27,000) contains two sites which bind succinate. Entirely normal binding behavior is found for these isolated subunits. In the native enzyme, however, the binding of succinate is cooperative (Fig. 7-56), and succinate reduces the extent of CTP binding. Both cooperative and antagonistic effects are considered to be the result of conformation changes induced by binding. There is a further complication in that adenosine triphosphate and CTP both compete for the site on the regulatory subunit.

The conclusion that conformation changes are involved was confirmed by determining the effect of the ligands on the reactivity of the sulfhydryl groups of the enzyme. PCMB (*p*-chloromercuribenzene) dissociates the enzyme into subunits. The undissociated subunits reacted with 27 ± 1 equivalents, almost all of them on the regulatory subunits. The rate of reaction of the regulatory units of the intact enzyme with PCMB was increased sixfold by binding succinate and carbamyl phosphate (together, not separately) on the catalytic subunits. The regulatory metabolite CTP or its bromine analogue reversed this effect. Small changes in sedimentation velocity constant accompanied these alterations in reactivity and their reversal by CTP. It was concluded that in the presence of carbamyl phosphate and succinate the intact enzyme exists in either a swollen or more asymmetric state, which facilitates reaction with PCMB or a dissociation into subunits when the latter is present. An analysis of the data in terms of the two-state model of Monod *et al.* (1965) led to the conclusion that succinate is bound to only one of the states postulated, but that CTP, the feedback inhibitor, is bound only slightly more strongly to the other state than to the one already referred to. Details as to all of the equilibria involved are given, including the fact that the transition between states is almost complete when only one-quarter of the substrate binding sites are occupied.

REFERENCES

Abrash, L., and Breslow, E. (1966). ACS Meeting, Sept.
Anderson, D. G. (1966). Univ. Microfilms, Xerox Co., Ann Arbor, Michigan, Order No. 67-3.
Anderson, D. G., Hammes, G. G., and Walz, F. G. Jr., (1968). *Fed. Proc.* **27**, 781, #3180.

Anderson, S., and Weber, D. (1965). *Biochemistry* **4**, 1948.

Andreoli, M., Robbins, J., Rall, J. E., and Bermore, M. (1965). *Proc. Intern. Thyroid Conf., 5th, Rome* 635.

Anson, M. L. (1939). *J. Gen. Physiol.* **23**, 239.

Anson, M. L. (1941). *J. Gen. Physiol.* **24**, 399.

Aoki, K. (1958). *J. Am. Chem. Soc.* **80**, 4904.

Aoki, K., and Hori, J. (1962). *Arch. Biochem. Biophys.* **97**, 175.

Baker, H. P., and Saroff, H. A. (1965). *Biochemistry* **4**, 1670.

Bargoni, N. (1960). *Rev. Espan. Fisiol.* **16**, 173.

Barlow, G. H., and Margoliash, E. (1966). *J. Biol. Chem.* **241**, 1473.

Barnett, L. B., and Bull, H. B. (1960). *Arch. Biochem. Biophys.* **88**, 328.

Barré, R., and Nguyen van Huot, N. (1964). *Bull. Soc. Chem. Biol.* **45**, 661.

Barré, R., and Nguyen van Huot, N. (1965a). *Bull. Soc. Chem. Biol.* **47**, 1399.

Barré, R., and Nguyen van Huot, N. (1965b). *Bull. Soc. Chem. Biol.* **47**, 1419.

Bauer, H., and Burschkies, K. (1933). *Ber.* **66**, 1041.

Bawden, F. C., and Pirie, N. W. (1940). *Biochem. J.* **34**, 1278.

Bernfield, P., and Kelley, T. F. (1963). *J. Biol. Chem.* **38**, 1236.

Beychok, S., Armstrong, J. McD., Lindblow, C., and Edsall, J. J. (1966). *J. Biol. Chem.* **241**, 5150.

Bigelow, C. B., and Sonenberg, M. (1962). *Biochemistry* **1**, 197.

Bishop, W. H., Quiocho, F. A., and Richards, F. M. (1966). *Biochemistry* **5**, 4077.

Blanck, J. (1966). *Abhandl. Deut. Akad. Wiss. Berlin, Kl. Med.* **4**, 411.

Blei, I., and Carroll, B. (1960). *J. Colloid Sci.* **15**, 209.

Blomback, B., Blomback, M., Laurent, T. C., and Pertoff, H. (1966). *Biochem. Biophys. Acta* **127**, 560.

Boyar, K. J. B., and Bradley, S. E. (1966). *J. Clin. Invest.* **43**, 281.

Boyer, P. D., Lum, F. G., Ballou, G. A., Luck, J. M., and Rice, R. G. (1946). *J. Biol. Chem.* **162**, 181.

Brahms, J., and Bregner, J. (1961). *Arch. Biokhimiya. Biophys.* **95**, 219.

Brand, L., Goeke, J. R., and Turner, D. C. (1967). *Intern. Congress of Biochem. 7th (Tokyo)* **IV**, 781.

Braun, A. D. (1948). *Biokhimiya* **13**, 409.

Briggs, D. R. (1940). *J. Biol. Chem.* **134**, 261.

Brunauer, S., Emmett, P. H., and Teller, E. (1938). *J. Am. Chem. Soc.* **60**, 309.

Buettner, H., and Portwich, F. (1967). *Klin. Wochenschr.* **45**, 225.

Burgen, A. S. U., Jardetzky, O., Metcalfe, J. C., and Wade-Jardetzky, N. G. (1967). *Proc. Natl. Acad. Sci. U.S.* **58**, 447.

Burgess, M., and Pruitt, K. M. (1968). Meeting Am. Chem. Soc., Sept.

Burkhard, R. K., Moore, F. A., and Louloudes, S. J. (1961). *Arch. Biochem. Biophys.* **94**, 291.

Butler, J. H. A., Jackson, J. F., Polya, J. B., and Tetlow, J. (1958). *Enzymoligia* **20**, 119.

Cann, J. R. (1962). *J. Biol. Chem.* **237**, 707.

Carr, C. W. (1953). *Arch. Biochem. Biophys.* **46**, 417, 424.

Carr, C. W. (1956). *Arch. Biochem. Biophys.* **62**, 476.

Carr, C. W., and Engelstad, W. P. (1958). *Arch. Biochem. Biophys.* **77**, 158.

Cassel, J. and Steinhardt, J., Unpublished.

Cassel, J., and Steinhardt, J. (1969). *Biochemistry* **8**, 2603.

Cassel, J., Gallagher, J., Reynolds, J., and Steinhardt, J. (1969). *Biochemistry* **8**, 1706.

Castaneda-Agullo, M., and del Castillo, L. M. (1964). *Proc. Intern. Biochem. Cong., 6th.*

Changeux, J. P., and Rubin, M. M. (1968). *Biochemistry* **7**, 553.

Changeux, J. P., Gerhart, J. C., and Schachman, H. K. (1968). *Biochemistry* **7**, 531.

Chapman, L. M., Greenberg, D. M., and Schmidt, C. L. A. (1927). *J. Biol. Chem.* **72**, 707.

Charlwood, P. A., and Ens, M. (1955). *Can. J. Chem.* **35**, 99.

Chen, R. F., and Kernohan, J. C. (1967). *J. Biol. Chem.* **242**, 5813.

Cohn, E. J., and Edsall, J. T. (1943). "Proteins, Amino Acids and Peptides as Ions and Dipolar Ions," Ch. 20. Reinhold, New York.

Coleman, M. H., and Eley, D. D. (1962). *Biochem. Biophys. Acta* **58**, 231.

Cross, D. G. and Fisher, H. F. (1966). *Fed. Proc.* **25**, 346.

Dalton, J., Kirk, P. L., and Schmidt, C. L. A. (1930). *J. Biol. Chem.* **88**, 589.

Danforth, R., Krakaver, H., and Sturtevant, J. M. (1967). *Rev. Sci. Instr.* **38**, 484.

Daniel, E., and Weber, G. (1965). *Biochemistry* **5**, 1893.

Decker, R. V., and Foster, J. F. (1966). *Biochemistry* **5**, 1242.

Decker, R. V., and Foster, J. F. (1967). *J. Biol. Chem.* **242**, 1526.

Di Sabato, G., and Kaplan, Ñ. V. (1964). *J. Biol. Chem.* **239**, 438.

Di Sabato, G., and Ottesen, M. (1965). *Biochemistry* **4**, 422,

Doremus, R. H., and Johnson, P. (1958). *J. Phys. Chem.* **62**, 203.

Drabikowski, W. (1960). *Acta Biochim. Polon. (English Transl.)* **7**, 127.

Duggan, E. L., and Luck, J. M. (1948). *J. Biol. Chem.* **172**, 205.

Dunford, H. B., and Alberty, R. A. (1967). *Biochemistry* **6**, 447.

East, E., and Trowbridge, C. G. (1966). A. C. S. Meeting, Sept.

Edelhoch, H. (1960). *J. Phys. Chem.* **64**, 1771.

Edelhoch, H., and Lippoldt, R. E. (1960). *J. Biol. Chem.* **235**, 1335.

Fairclough, G. F., and Fruton, J. S. (1966). *Biochemistry* **5**, 673.

Fernstein, G., and Feeney, R. E. (1966). A. C. S. Meeting, Sept.

Few, A. V., Otteiwill, R. H., and Parreira, H. C. (1955). *Biochim. Biophys. Acta* **18**, 136.

Fish, W., Miller, H., and Huggins, C. (1949). *Proc. Soc. Exptl. Biol. Med.* **72**, 558.

Floyd, B. F., and Friedberg, F. (1966). *J. Biol. Chem.* **241**, 5533.

Forbes, W. F., Harrap, B. S., and Milligan, B. (1962). *Australian J. Chem.* **15**, 182.

Foster, J. F. (1960). *In* "The Plasma Proteins" (F. W. Putnam, ed.). Academic Press, New York.

Foster, J. F., and Yang, J. T. (1954). *J. Am. Chem. Soc.* **76**, 1015.

Foster, J. F., and Aoki, K. (1958). *J. Am. Chem. Soc.* **80**, 5215.

Fraenkel-Conrat, H., and Cooper, M. (1944). *J. Biol. Chem.* **154**, 239.

Friend, J. P., Harrap, B. S., and Schulman, J. H. (1951). *Nature* **168**, 910.

Fredericq, E. F. (1954). *Bull. Soc. Chim. Belg.* **63**, 158.

Froese, A., Sehon, A. H., and Eigen, M. (1962). *Can. J. Chem.* **40**, 1786.

Gallagher, J., and Steinhardt, J. (1969). *Fed. Proc.* **27**, 853 (Abstract #3325).

Geiduschek, E. P., and Doty, P. (1952). *Biochim. Biophys. Acta* **9**, 609.

Gerhart, J. C., and Schachman, H. K. (1968). *Biochemistry* **7**, 538.

Ginsberg, A., and Carroll, W. R. (1965). *Fed. Proc. Abs.* **24**, #1565.

Ginsberg, A., and Mehler, A. H. (1966). *Fed. Proc.*, **25**, 407.

Girard, M. L., Dechosal, G., Rousselet, F., and Canal, J. (1963). *Ann. Biol. Clin.* **21**, 273.

Glassman, H. N. (1950). *Ann. N.Y. Acad. Sci.* **53**, 191.

Glazer, A. N. (1967). *J. Biol. Chem.* **242**, 4528.

Glazer, A. N. (1968). *Proc. Natl. Acad. Sci. U.S.* **61**, 1147.

Glazer, A. N., and Sanger, F. (1963). *J. Mol. Biol.* **7**, 452.

Goldwasser, E., and Putnam, F. W. (1950). *J. Phys. Colloid Chem.* **54**, 79.

Goodman, D. S. (1958). *J. Am. Chem. Soc.* **80**, 3892.

Gramling, E., Niedermeier, W., Holley, H. L., and Pigman, W. (1963). *Biochim. Biophys. Acta* **69**, 552.

Green, M. L. (1963). *Arch. Biochem. Biophys.* **101**, 186.

Green, N. M. (1963). *Biochim. Biophys. Acta* **74**, 542.

Greenberg, D. M. (1951). "Chemistry of the Amino Acids and Proteins," pp. 461–471. Thomas, Springfield, Illinois.

Greenstein, J. P., and Hoyer, M. L. (1950). *J. Biol. Chem.* **182**, 457.

Groves, M. L., Hipp, N. J., and McMeekin, T. L. (1951). *J. Am. Chem. Soc.* **73**, 2790.

Gurd, F. R. N., and Wilcox, P. E. (1956). *Advan. Protein Chem.* **11**, 312.

Hammer, G. C., and Hubbard, C. D. (1965). Meeting of Am. Chem. Soc., Sept., Abstr. #226, Div. Biol. Chem.

Hardesty, B. A., and Mitchell, H. K. (1963). *Arch. Biochem. Biophys.* **100**, 1.

Harrington, W. F., Johnson, P., and Ottewill, R. H. (1956). *Biochem. J.* **62**, 569.

Haurowitz, F., di Mola, F., and Tekan, S. (1955). *J. Am. Chem. Soc.* **74**, 2265.

Hill, R. M., and Briggs, D. R. (1956). *J. Am. Chem. Soc.* **78**, 1590.

Ho, C., and Waugh, D. F. (1965). *J. Am. Chem. Soc.* **87**, 110.

Hofstee, B. H. J. (1963). *J. Biol. Chem.* **238**, 3235.

Hofstee, B. H. J. (1965). *Biochim. Biophys. Acta* **91**, 340.

Hofstee, B. H. J. (1967). *Intern. Congress Biochemistry (Tokyo)*, *7th* **IV**, 598.

Hutzinger, J. R., Grieger, P. F., and Wall, F. T. (1950). *J. Am. Chem. Soc.* **72**, 2636.

Imahori, K., Fujioka, H., and Ando, T. (1962). *J. Biochem. (Tokyo)* **52**, 167.

Imanishi, A., Momotani, Y., and Isemura, T. (1965). *J. Biochem. (Tokyo)* **57**, 417.

Jirgensons, B. (1956). *Makromol. Chem.* **18/19**, 48.

Jirgensons, B. (1961). *Arch. Biochem. Biophys.* **94**, 59.

Jirgensons, B. (1962a). *Arch. Biochem. Biophys.* **96**, 321.

Jirgensons, B. (1962b). *Makromol. Chem.* **51**, 137.

Jirgensons, B. (1966). *J. Biol. Chem.* **241**, 4855.

Kahn, L. D., Carroll, R. J., and Witnauer, L. P. (1962). *Biochim. Biophys. Acta* **63** 243.

Karush, F. (1952). *J. Phys. Chem.* **56**, 70.

Karush, F., and Sonenberg, M. (1949). *J. Am. Chem. Soc.* **71**, 1369.

Kauzman, W. (1959). *Advan. Protein Chem.* **14**, 1.

Kerlin, D., and Hartree, E. F. (1940). *Nature* **145**, 934.

Kernohan, J. C. (1965). *Biochim. Biophys. Acta* **96**, 304.

Kerp, L., and Kasemir, H. (1962). *Arch. Explt. Pathol. Pharmakol.* **243**, 147.

Klapper, M. H., and Klotz, I. M. (1968). *Biochemistry* **7**, 223.

Klotz, I. M. (1946a). *Arch. Biochem.* **9**, 109.

Klotz, I. M. (1946b). *J. Am. Chem. Soc.* **68**, 2299.

Klotz, I. M. (1950). *Cold Spring Harbor Symp. Quant. Biol.* **14**, 97.

Klotz, I. M. (1953). *In* "The Proteins" (H. Neurath and K. Bailey, eds.), 1st ed., Vol. I Part B, p. 727. Academic Press, New York.

Klotz, I. M., and Walker, F. M. (1947). *J. Am. Chem. Soc.* **69**, 1609.

Klotz, I. M., and Urquhart, J. M. (1949). *J. Am. Chem. Soc.* **71**, 1597.

Klotz, I. M., and Urquhart, J. M. (1949a). *J. Phys. Chem.* **53**, 100.

Klotz, I. M., and Urquhart, J. M. (1949b). *J. Am. Chem. Soc.* **71**, 597.

Klotz, I. M., and Heiney, R. E. (1957). *Biochim. Biophys. Acta* **25**, 205.

Klotz, I. M., and Luborsky, S. W. (1959). *J. Am. Chem. Soc.* **81**, 5119.

Klotz, I. M., and Shikama, K. (1968). *Arch. Biochem. Biophys.* **123**, 551.

Klotz, I. M., Walker, F. M., and Pivan, R. B. (1946). *J. Am. Chem. Soc.* **68**, 1486.

Klotz, I. M., Walker, F. M., and Pivan, R. B. (1948). *J. Am. Chem. Soc.* **73**, 21.

Klotz, I. M., Triwush, H., and Walker, F. M. (1950). *J. Am. Chem. Soc.* **70**, 209.

Kondo, M. (1962). *J. Biochem. (Tokyo)* **52**, 279.

Kronman, M. J., and Foster, J. F. (1957). *Arch. Biochem. Biophys.* **72**, 205.

Kubo, S., Tokura, S., Yoshimura, J., and Tonumura, Y. (1963). *Koso Kagaku Shimpoziumu* **18**, 70.

Kucerova, L., Hoenig, V., Jirsa, M., and Fabian, E. (1966). *Acta Hepato-Splenol.* **13**, 281.

Kuhn, R., Bielig, H. J., and Dann, O. (1940). *Ber Deut. Chem. Ges.* **73B**, 1080.

Kupic, M., and Topalovic-Avramov, R. (1963). *Arkiv Farm. (Belgrade)* **13**, 29.

Land, J. H., and Lasser, E. C. (1967). *Biochemistry* **6**, 2403.

Latt, H. S., and Sober, H. A. (1967). *Biochemistry* **6**, 3307.

Laurence, D. J. R. (1952). *Biochem. J.* **51**, 168.

Lee, K. S., and Hong, S. K. (1960). *Yonsei Med. J.* **1**, 22.

Lenz, D. (1969). *Fed. Proc.* **28**, 871 (Abstract #3436).

Lenz, D., and Steinhardt, J. (1969). ACS Meeting, Sept.

Leonard, W. J., and Foster, J. F. (1961). *J. Biol. Chem.* **236**, 73.

Levy, H. M., Leber, P. D., and Ryan, E. M. (1963). *J. Biol. Chem.* **238**, 3654.

Lipmann, F. (1929). *Biochem. Z.* **206**, 171.

Loeb, G. I., and Saroff, H. A. (1964). *Biochemistry* **3**, 1819.

Lovrien, R. (1963). *J. Am. Chem. Soc.* **85**, 3677.

Lovrien, R. (1968). *Polymer Preprints* #**1**, 218.

Lovrien, R. (1967). Personal communication.

Lovrien, R., and Sturtevant, J. M. (1961). ACS Meeting, Sept.

Luck, J. M., and Schmidt, A. S. (1948). *Std. Med. Bull.* **6**, 133, quoted by Klotz.

Luck, S. M., and Lowey, S. (1966). *Fed. Proc.* **27**, 519 (Abstract).

Lundgren, H. P., Elam, R. W., and O'Connell, R. A. (1943). *J. Biol. Chem.* **149**, 183.

Manukhin, B. N. (1962). *Biokhimiya* **27**, 615.

Markus, G. (1965). Fed. Proc. **24**, 1901 (Abstract).

Markus, G., and Karush, F. (1957). *J. Am. Chem. Soc.* **79**, 3624.

Markus, G., Love, R. L., and Wissler, F. C. (1964). *J. Biol. Chem.* **239**, 3687.

Markus, G., McClintock, D. K., and Castellani, B. A. (1967). *J. Biol. Chem.* **242**, 4402.

Masters, B. S. S., Siegel, L. M., Kamin, H., and Gibson, O. H. (1967). *Intern. Cong. Biochem. (Tokyo), 7th* **IV**, 836.

McClintock, D. K., and Markus, G. (1968). *Fed. Proc.* **27**, 339 (Abstract).

McMeekin, T. L., Polis, B. D., Della Monica, E. S., and Custer, J. H. (1949). *J. Am. Chem. Soc.* **71**, 3606.

McMenamy, R. H., Madeja, M. I., and Watson, F. (1968). *J. Biol. Chem.* **243**, 2328.

Metcalfe, J. C., Burgen, A. S. V., and Jardetzky, O. (1968). *In* "Molecular Association in Biology" (B. Pullman, ed.). Academic Press, New York.

Meyer, M. L., and Kauzman, W. J. (1962). *Arch. Biochem. Biophys.* **99**, 348.

Mirsky, A. S. (1941). *J. Gen. Physiol.* **24**, 709.

Mildvan, A. S., and Cohn, M. (1966). *J. Biol. Chem.* **241**, 1168.

Mishiro, Y., and Ochi, M. (1966). *Nature* **211**, 1190.

Mitra, S., and Kaesberg, P. (1963). *BB Res. Commun.* **11**, 146.

Mohr, P., Scheler, W., Schumann, H., and Mueller, K. (1967). *Eur. J. Biochem.* **3**, 158.

Monod, J., Wyman, J., Jr., and Changeux, J. P. (1965). *J. Mol. Biol.* **12**, 88.

Mora, P. T., Creskoff, E., and Person, P. (1965). *Science* **149**, 642.

Morawetz, H., and Shafer, J. A. (1963). *Biopolymers* **1**, 71.

Mullen, J. D. (1963). Univ. Microfilms, Ann Arbor, Michigan, Order No. 4356.

Nelson, C. A., Hummel, J. P., Swenson, C. A., and Friedman, L. (1962). *J. Biol. Chem.* **237**, 1575.

Neurath, H., and Putnam, F. W. (1945). *J. Biol. Chem.* **160**, 397.

Nichols, P. (1961). *Biochem. J.* **81**, 365.

Nishida, T. (1961). *Igaku to Deibutsugaku* **59**, 33.

Noguchi, H. (1960). *J. Phys. Chem.* **64**, 185.

Noguchi, H. (1961). *Progr. Theoret. Phys.* Supplement No. **17**, 41.

Oh, Y. A., Newrocki, J. W., Leitsch, W. E., and Sanders, B. E. (1966). ACS Meeting, Sept.

Orozhan, S. I., and Maengwyn-Davies, G. D. (1962). *Biochem. Pharmacol.* **11**, 1203.

Oster, G. (1951). *J. Chem. Phys.* **48**, 217.

Pallansch, M. J., and Briggs, D. R. (1954). *J. Am. Chem. Soc.* **76**, 1396.

Pande, C. S., and McMenamy, R. H., (1968). *Biopolymers* **6**, 1487.

Parker, H., and Lumry, R. (1963). *J. Am. Chem. Soc.* **85**, 483.

Perlmann, G. (1941). *J. Biol. Chem.* **137**, 707.

Peterson, A. A., and Foster, J. F. (1965a). *J. Biol. Chem.* **240**, 2503.

Peterson, A. A., and Foster, J. F. (1965b). *J. Biol. Chem.* **240**, 3858.

Peterson, A. A., Foster, J. F., Sogami, M. A., and Leonard, W. J. (1965). *J. Biol. Chem.* **240**, 2495.

Pfankuch, E., and Kansche, G. A. (1940). *Biochem. Z.* **312**, 72.

Ploeg, D. A., and Alberty, R. A. (1968). *J. Biol. Chem.* **243**, 435.

Polet, H., and Steinhardt, J. (1968). *Biochemistry* **7**, 1348.

Polonovski, J., and Macheboeff, M. (1948). *Ann. Inst. Pasteur* **74**, 196, 203.

Prokopova, E., and Munk, P. (1962). *Collection Czech. Chem. Commun.* **28**, 957.

Puett, D., Garmon, R. G., and Ciferri, A. (1966). *Nature* **211**, 1294.

Putnam, F. W. (1948). *Advan. Protein Chem.* **4**, 79.

Putnam, F. W. (ed.) (1953). "The Proteins," 1st Ed., Vol. 1, Part B, p. 828. Academic Press, New York.

Putnam, F. W., and Neurath, H. (1943). *J. Biol. Chem.* **150**, 263.

Putnam, F. W., and Neurath, H. (1944). *J. Am. Chem. Soc.* **66**, 692.

Putnam, F. W., and Neurath, H. (1945). *J. Biol. Chem.* **159**, 195.

Rawlins, L. M. C., and Schmidt, C. L. A. (1930). *J. Biol. Chem.* **88**, 271.

Ray, A. Reynolds, J. A., Polet, H., and Steinhardt, J. (1966). *Biochemistry* **5**, 2606.

Reynolds, J. A., Gallagher, J., and Steinhardt, J. (1970). *Biochemistry* **9** (to be published).

Reynolds, J. A., Herbert, S., Polet, H., and Steinhardt, J. (1967). *Biochemistry* **6**, 937.

Reynolds, J. A., Herbert, S., and Steinhardt, J. (1968). *Biochemistry* **7**, 1357.

Rice, R. V., Asai, H., and Morales, M. (1963). *Proc. Natl. Acad. Sci. U.S.* **50**, 549.

Rice, S. A., and Nagasawa, M. N. (1961). "Polyelectrolyte Solutions," pp. 437–439, Academic Press, New York.

Richards, F. U., Hearn, R. P., Sturtevant, J. M., and Watt, G. (1968). *Fed. Proc.* **27**, 338 (Abstract #694).

Rodkey, F. L. (1961). *Arch. Biochem. Biophys.* **94**, 526.

Rosenberg, R. M., and Klotz, I. M. (1960). *In* "A Laboratory Manual of Analytical Methods of Protein Chemistry," (R. J. Block and P. Alexander, eds.), Vol. 2, p. 131. Pergamon Press, Oxford.

Rosenthal, H., O'Brien, G., and Austin, S. (1962). *Arch. Biochem. Biophys.* **99**, 319.

Sahyun, M. R. V. (1964). *Nature* **203**, 1045.

Saifer, A., Westley, F., and Stergman, J. (1964). *Biochemistry*, **3**, 1624.

Sanborn, B. M., and Bregan, W. P. (1968). *Biochemistry* **7**, 3624.

Saroff, H. A. (1957). *J. Phys. Chem.* **61**, 1364.

Saroff, H. A., and Healey, J. W. (1959). *J. Phys. Chem.* **63**, 1178.

Saroff, H. A., and Carroll, W. R. (1962). *J. Biol. Chem.* **237**, 3384.

Sawiaski, V. J. (1964). Meeting Am. Chem. Soc., Sept., Abstr. #77 Biochem. Division.

Scatchard, G. (1949). *Ann. N.Y. Acad. Sci.* **51**, 660.

Scatchard, G. (1952). *Am. Sci.* **40**, 61.

Scatchard, G., and Black, E. S. (1949). *J. Phys. Colloid Chem.* **53**, 88.

Scatchard, G., and Zaromb, S. (1959). *J. Am. Chem. Soc.* **81**, 610.

Scatchard, G., and Bergman, J. (1959). *J. Am. Chem. Soc.* **81**, 6095.

Scatchard, G., and Yap, W. T. (1964). *J. Am. Chem. Soc.* **86**, 3434.

Scatchard, G., Scheinberg, I. H., and Armstrong, S. H., Jr. (1950). *J. Am. Chem. Soc.* **72**, 540.

Scatchard, G., Hughes, W. L., Gurd, F. R. N., and Wilcox, P. E. (1954). *In* "Chemical Specificity in Biological Interactions," (F. R. N. Gurd, ed.), p. 193. Academic Press, New York.

Scatchard, G., Coleman, J. S., and Shen, A. L. (1957). *J. Am. Chem. Soc.* **79**, 12.

Scatchard, G., Wu, Y. V., and Shen, A. L. (1959). *J. Am. Chem. Soc.* **81**, 6104.

Scheler, W., Blanck, J., and Graf, W. (1963). *Naturwissenschaften* **14**, 500.

Schliselfeld, L., and Bárany, M. (1968). *Fed. Proc.* **27**, 519.

Schmidt, K., and Polis, A. (1960). *J. Biol. Chem.* **235**, 1321.

Shore, J. D. (1969). *Biochemistry* **8**, 1588.

Schwartskopff, W. (1962), *Protides Biol. Fluids, Proc. Colloq.* **10**, 255.

Seibles, T. S. (1969). *Biochemistry* **8**, 2949.

Sela, M., and Steiner, L. A. (1963). *Biochemistry* **2**, 416.

Shalaby, R. A., Bannerjee, K., and Lauffer, M. A. (1968). *Biochemistry* **7**, 955.

Simpson, R. B., and Kauzman, W. K. (1953). *J. Am. Chem. Soc.* **75**, 5139.

Smith, E. L. (1951). *In* "Enzymes and Enzyme Systems" (J. T. Edsall, ed.), p. 49. Harvard Univ. Press, Cambridge, Massachusetts.

Smith, E. L., and Pickels, E. G. P. (1941). *J. Gen. Physiol.* **24**, 753.

Sogami, M., and Foster, J. F. (1968). *Biochemistry* **7**, 2172.

Sorensen, C. P. L. (1909). *Biochem. Z.* **21**, 131.

Sreenivasaya, M., and Pirie, N. W. (1938). *Biochem. J.* **32**, 1707.

Steiner, R. F. (1954). *Arch. Biochem. Biophys.* **49**, 71.

Steiner, R. F., and Edelhoch, H. (1961). *Nature* **192**, 873.

Steinhardt, J. (1941). *Ann. N.Y. Acad. Soc.* **41**, 287.

Steinhardt, J., and Fugitt, C. H. (1942). *J. Res. Natl. Bur. Std.* **29**, 315.

Steinhardt, J., and Zaíser, E. M. (1950). *J. Biol. Chem.* **241**, 3988.

Steinhardt, J., Fugitt, C. H., and Harris, M. (1940). *J. Res. Natl. Bur. Std.* **25**, 519.

Steinhardt, J., Fugitt, C. H., and Harris, M. (1940a). *J. Res. Natl. Bur. Std.* **24**, 335.

Steinhardt, J., Fugitt, C. H., and Harris, M. (1940b). *J. Res. Natl. Bur. Std.* **25**, 519.

Steinhardt, J., Fugitt, C. H., and Harris, M. (1941). *J. Res. Natl. Bur. Std.* **26**, 293.

Steinhardt, J., Fugitt, C. H., and Harris, M. (1942). *J. Res. Natl. Bur. Std.* **28**, 191.

Steinhardt, J., Fugitt, C. H., and Harris, M. (1942). *J. Res. Natl. Bur. Std.* **28**, 201.

Steinhardt, J., Ona, R., Beychok, S., and Ho, C. (1963). *Biochemistry* **2**, 256.

Steinhardt, J., Polet, H., and Moezie, F. (1966). *J. Biol. Chem.* **241**, 3988.

Strauss, G., and Strauss, U. P. (1958). *J. Phys. Chem.* **62**, 1321.

Stryer, L. (1965). *J. Mol. Biol.* **13**, 482.

Szent-Gyorgyi, A. G. (1968). *Fed. Proc.* **27**, 519 (Abstract #1696).

Tabachnik, M. (1964). *Arch. Biochem. Biophys.* **106**, 415.

Tanford, C. (1955). *J. Am. Chem. Soc.* **77**, 6914.

Tanford, C. (1961). "Physical Chemistry of Macromolecules," pp. 499–518. Wiley, New York.

Tanford, C., and Hauenstein, J. D. (1956). *J. Am. Chem. Soc.* **78**, 5287.

Tanford, C., Buzzell, J. G., Rands, D. G., and Swanson, S. A. (1955). *J. Am. Chem. Soc.* **77**, 6421.

Teresi, J. D. (1950). *J. Am. Chem. Soc.* **72**, 3972.

Teresi, J. D., and Luck, J. M. (1952). *J. Biol. Chem.* **194**, 823.

Tietze, F., Mortimore, G. E., and Lomax, N. R. (1962). *Biochim. Biophys. Acta* **59**, 336.

Tokura, S., and Tonomura, Y. (1963). *J. Biochem. (Tokyo)* **53**, 422.

Tonomura, Y., and Tonomura, J. (1962). *J. Biochem. (Tokyo)* **51**, 259.

Tsibris, J. C. U., and McCormick, D. B. (1965). Meeting Am. Chem. Soc. Sept.

Tunis, M., and Regilson, W. (1963). *Arch. Biochem. Biophys.* **101**, 448.

Vallee, B. L. (1955). *Advan. Protein Chem.* **10**, 318.

Varandani, P. T., and Schlamowitz, M. (1963). *Biochim. Biophys. Acta* **77**, 496.

Velick, S. F. (1958). *J. Biol. Chem.* **233**, 1455.

Velick, S. F., Parker, C. A., and Eisen, H. N. (1960). *Proc. Natl. Acad. Sci. U.S.* **46**, 1470.

Velick, S. F. *In* "Light and Life" (W. D. McElroy and B. Glass, eds.), pp. 108–143, Johns Hopkins Press, Baltimore, Maryland.

Verpoorte, J. A., and Kay, C. M. (1966). *Biochim. Biophys. Acta* **126**, 551.

Verpoorte, J. A., and Steinhardt, J. (Unpublished.)

Vijai, K., and Foster, J. F. (1967). *Biochemistry* **6**, 1152.

von Hippel, P. H., and Wong, K. Y. (1962). *Biochemistry* **1**, 664.

Warner, R. C., and Schubert, M. (1958). *J. Am. Chem. Soc.* **80**, 5166.

Watson, H. C., Kendrew, J. C., and Stryer, L. (1964). *J. Mol. Biol.* **8**, 166.

Weber, G. (1952). *Biochem. J.* **51**, 145, 155.

Weber, G., and Young, L. B. (1964). *J. Biol. Chem.* **239**, 1415.

Weber, G., and Daniel, E. (1965). *Biochemistry* **5**, 1900.

Wetlaufer, D. B., and Stohmann, M. A. (1953). *J. Biol. Chem.* **203**, 117.

Wetlaufer, D. B., and Lovrien, R. (1964). *J. Biol. Chem.* **239**, 596.

Whitaker, J. R., and Deatherage, F. E. (1955). *J. Am. Chem. Soc.* **77**, 3360.

Whitney, P. L., and Tanford, C. (1962). *J. Biol. Chem.* **237**, 1735.

Williams, E. J., and Foster, J. F. (1959). *J. Am. Chem. Soc.* **81**, 864.

Wishnia, A. (1963). *J. Phys. Chem.* **67**, 2079.

Wishnia, A., and Pinder, T. W., Jr. (1966). *Biochemistry* **5**, 1534.

Wong, K., and Foster, J. F. (1968). Am. Chem. Soc. Meeting, Sept.

Yachnin, S. (1963). *Biochim. Biophys. Acta* **72**, 572.

Yang, J. T., and Foster, J. F. (1953). *J. Am. Chem. Soc.* **75**, 5560.

Yang, J. T., and Foster, J. F. (1954). *J. Am. Chem. Soc.* **76**, 1588.

Yoshikawa, K., and Loening, L. W. (1965). *Experientia* **21**, 1376.

Zaalishvili, M. M., Surguladae, T. T., Egiazarova, A. R., and Gorgorishvili, D. A. (1963). *Soobskch Akad. Nauk. Gruz.* **30**, 29.

Zakrzanski, K., and Goch, H. (1968). *Biochemistry* **7**, 1835.

VIII

Protein–Protein Interaction

I. Introduction

The study of interactions between protein molecules is such a vast and diversified area that a comprehensive treatment of this subject will appear in another monograph in this series. This chapter will be limited to a brief description of some particularly well-studied systems.

There are two types of equilibria between macromolecules: (1) The interacting species are subunits which associate to form biologically active units. (2) Interaction between distinct macromolecular entities occurs as a step in a biological process (e.g., antigen–antibody reactions, enzyme–coenzyme binding). All of the rigorous, thermodynamic principles in Chapter II apply to macromolecular interaction just as to small molecule–protein binding and, given the appropriate experimental data, association constants, free energies, enthalpies, and entropies of the association process can be determined.

II. Quarternary Structure in Proteins

The term "quarternary structure" was suggested by Bernal (1958) as an extension of the Linderström-Lang terminology for the order and arrangement of amino acid residues in proteins. It refers to that structure which arises through the association of two or more polypeptide chains (which may or may not be identical). There is very little experimental information on the nature of forces which are involved in protein subunit interaction or the mechanism of recognition that leads to specific association. However, the recent X-ray data of Perutz *et al.* (1968) leading to the 2.8 Å resolution model of horse oxyhemoglobin provide some particularly interesting observations. Hemoglobin contains two α-chains and two β-chains in a tetrameric form which is in dynamic equilibrium with a dimer, $\alpha_1\beta_1$, and the monomers. This protein dissociates only into $\alpha_1\beta_1$ dimers, never $\beta_1\beta_2$ or $\alpha_1\alpha_2$. X-ray analysis shows that in the tetramer the interface between α_1 and β_1 contains 34 nonpolar residues in intimate contact, the interface between α_1 and β_2 contains 19 such residues, and the contacts between like chains are apparently entirely ionic in nature. Thus in this protein the strong associative force is apparently largely entropic in origin, coming from " hydrophobic " interactions.

There is also some indirect evidence from solution physical chemistry that some polymeric proteins owe their associative stability to hydrophobic bonding. For example, E. coli alkaline phosphatase subunits which contain a high degree of secondary and tertiary structure associate readily to dimers even at high ionic strength (Reynolds and Schlesigner, 1968). The major problem which arises in an investigation of the formation of quarternary structure in solution, however, is the experimental recognition of alterations in the secondary and tertiary structure of the individual polypeptide chains as separate from the interaction between two such chains.

Most investigations have been concerned with the determination of the number of subunits and their respective molecular weights. In only a very few systems have attempts been made to determine equilibrium constants between subunits and the polymerized form. It is primarily these latter investigations which will be discussed briefly in this chapter.

Table 8-1, from Klotz (1967), is a list of proteins which contain more than one polypeptide chain. Individual references are given in the Klotz paper. Much of this data is still controversial and may be subject to revision.

III. Glutamic Dehydrogenase

Glutamate dehydrogenase (GDH) from bovine liver is an enzyme containing subunits of approximately 30,000–60,000 molecular weight (Frieden, 1962). These polypeptide chains are formed by dissociation of native GDH in the presence of sodium dodecylsulfate, 6 M urea, or at extremes of pH, and could not be reassociated to active enzyme. The " native " form of glutamate dehydrogenase has been isolated as a large aggregate of 1.6–2.0×10^6 molecular weight. This polymer dissociates reversibly upon dilution to a 250,000 and 500,000 molecular weight species (Olson and Anfinsen, 1952; Frieden, 1958). The equilibrium constant between the polymers of GDH is altered by interaction with a large number of small molecules. Thus, dissociation is promoted by the binding of thyroxine (Wolff, 1961), by dioxane (Churchich and Wold, 1963), steroid hormones (Yielding and Thomkins, 1960; Tomkins et al.,

TABLE 8-1

Subunit Constitution of Proteins[a,b]

Protein	Molecular weight	Subunits	
		No.	Molecular weight
Insulin	11,466	2	5733
Thrombin	31,000	(3)	(10,000)
β-Lactoglobulin	35,000	2	17,500
Avidin	53,000	3	18,000
Hemoglobin	64,500	4	16,000
Glycerol-l-phoshpate dehydrogenase	78,000	2	40,000
Alkaline phosphatase	80,000	2	40,000
Enolase	82,000	2	41,000
Liver alcohol dehydrogenase	84,000	2	42,000
Procarboxypeptidase	87,000	1	34,500
		2	25,000
Firefly luciferase	92,000	2	52,000
Hexokinase	96,000	4	24,000
Hemerythrin	107,000	8	13,500
Tryptophan synthetase A	29,000	1	29,000
Tryptophan synthetase B	117,000	2	60,000
Mammary glucose-6-phosphate dehydrogenase	130,000	2	63,000
Glyceraldehyde-3-phosphate dehydrogenase	140,000	4	37,000
Aldolase	160,000	4	40,000
Lactic dehydrogenase	150,000	4	35,000
Yeast alcohol dehydrogenase	150,000	4	37,000
Ceruloplasmin	151,000	8	18,000
Threonine deaminase	160,000	4	40,000
Thetin homocysteine methylpherase	180,000	3–4	50,000
Fumarase	194,000	4	48,000
Serum lipoprotein	200,000	6	36,000
Tryptophanase	220,000	2	(125,000)
Pyruvate kinase	237,000	4	57,200
Catalase	250,000	4	60,000
Phycocyanin	266,000	2	134,000
	134,000	3	46,000
Mitochondrial adenosinetriphosphatase	284,000	10	26,000
Aspartyltranscarbamylase	310,000	2	96,000
		4	30,000
Lipovitellin	400,000	2	200,000
Apoferritin	480,000	20	24,000
Urease	483,000	6	83,000
Phosphorylase	495,000	4	125,000
Fraction I protein, carboyxdismutase	515,000	24	22,000

(*continued*)

TABLE 8.1 (*continued*)

Protein	Molecular weight	Subunits	
		No.	Molecular weight
β-Galactosidase	520,000	4	130,000
	130,000	3–4	(40,000)
Pyruvatecarboxylase	660,000	4	165,000
	165,000	4	45,000
Tyroglobulin	669,000	2	335,000
Propionylcarboxylase	700,000	4	175,000
Lipoic reductase-transacetylase	1,600,000	60	27,000
Glutamic dehydrogenase	2,000,000	8	250,000
	250,000	5	50,000
Hemocyanin	300,000–9,000,000		385,000
			70,000
Chlorocruorin	2,750,000	12	250,000
Bromegrass mosaic virus	4,600,000	180	20,000
Turnip-yellow mosaic virus	5,000,000	150	21,000
Poliomyelitis virus	5,500,000	130	27,000
Cucumber mosaic virus	6,000,000	185	21,500
Alfalfa mosaic virus	7,400,000	160	35,000
Bushy stunt virus	9,000,000	120	60,000
Potato virus X	35,000,000	650	52,000
Tobacco mosaic virus	40,000,000	2130	17,500

[a] Taken from Klotz (1967).
[b] Parentheses indicate doubt.

1961), and DPNH plus GTP (Frieden, 1959a,b). Association to higher polymeric form is promoted by DPNH or TPNH in the absense of other nucleotides (Frieden, 1959). Alternations in the degree of association of this enzyme in the presence of ligands has been interpreted qualitatively by Frieden and Coleman (1967) in terms of the model presented in Chapter II, Section VII. Thus it has been assumed that DPNH binds to the 2×10^6 species with a higher association constant than to the 400,000 species and in the nomenclature of Chapter II, $mJ \gg nK$. In the presence of GTP some alteration of the enzyme occurs which increases the binding constant of DPNH for the 400,000 species, resulting in a transition to the lower molecular weight form.

Churchich and Wold (1963) showed that the dissociation promoted by dioxane produced two species of lower molecular weight, 550,000 and 300,000, which were both enzymatically active. There is some discrepancy between the molecular weights determined by these authors and those of Frieden and

Coleman (1967). However, Churchich and Wold report a molecular number average determined in the ultracentrifuge using the Archibald approach-to-equilibrium method, and Frieden and Coleman have determined a weight average by means of light-scattering measurements. Churchich and Wold visualize the interaction between polymeric species of GDH as involving weakly hydrophobic surface regions which are easily disrupted by dioxane or *sec*-butanol. They observed no change in optical rotatory dispersion on dissociation in these solvents.

IV. Tobacco Mosaic Virus Protein

Tobacco mosaic virus is a rodlike molecule consisting of 2130 protein subunits and a single RNA molecule occupying a hollow core inside the assembly of polypeptide chains (Franklin *et al.*, 1957). The protein component can be separated intact from the RNA and reversibly dissociated by urea, 67% acetic acid, or dilution.

Banerjee and Lauffer (1966) have determined the molecular weight of the smallest subunit by high-speed membrane osmometry in 67% acetic acid and found it to be 18,200. In addition, they have studied the effect of pH and temperature on the molecular weight of a stable aggregate formed during the process of removing the RNA from the intact virus. From pH 6.5 to 8.0 and over the temperature range 4.6° to 15.8° a trimer of molecular weight 53,000 was found. Below 0.1% protein this trimer dissociates. Conventional osmotic pressure plots of π/c vs. c had negative slopes indicating protein–protein interaction at high protein concentrations, which is indicative of the reversible association–dissociation known to occur in this system.

The polymerization process has been shown to be endothermic and involves the release of bound water (Lauffer *et al.*, 1958). The reversible association phenomenon leads to an expression for the concentration dependence of osmotic pressure (Banerjee and Lauffer, 1966)

$$\pi = \frac{(RT)^2}{KM_n}\left(\frac{c}{\pi}\right) - \frac{RT}{K} \tag{8-1}$$

where K is the equilibrium constant, M_n the molecular weight of the associating species, and R, T, π, and c have their usual meanings. Table 8-2 shows the values of K for the polymerization of the trimer of TMV protein at three different temperatures; $\Delta F = -4559$ cal/mole, $\Delta H = 30,000$ cal/mole, and $\Delta S = 124$ eu. If one assumes the entropy change is entirely due to melting of water structure around the interface between two interacting protein species, S corresponds to approximately 23 molecules/mole protein.

TABLE 8-2

POLYMERIZATION OF TMV PROTEIN TRIMERS

T (°C)	K	M_n
4.6°	4.21×10^3	54,000
8.7°	6.99×10^3	53,000
11.0°	12.93×10^3	50,500

V. Hemerythrin

Hemerythrin (molecular weight 107,000) contains eight subunits each of molecular weight 13,500. The protein binds iron which stabilizes the quarternary structure. In the presence of iron-coordinating anions, such as thiocyanate, an equilibrium is observed between the octamer and monomer. No intermediate polymerized species have been detected (Klapper and Klotz, 1968).

It was pointed out in Chapter II that binding to a protein may shift the equilibrium between two or more conformational states. In the hemerythrin–thiocyanate system the anion binds more strongly to the monomer than to the octamer, thus shifting the equilibrium

$$P_8 \overset{K_p}{\rightleftarrows} 8P \tag{8-2}$$

in favor of the monomer. The dissociation constant for this process is

$$K_p = [P]^8/[P_8] \tag{8-3}$$

Since thiocyanate has different affinities for the two species, measurements of binding isotherms at a variety of protein concentrations will give different apparent binding constants; at low protein concentrations more monomer is present and the binding of anion will increase.

Klapper and Klotz (1968) have determined the association constant of thiocyanate for the monomer by extrapolation of the apparent association constant at a number of protein concentrations to zero protein concentration, and the association constant of thiocyanate for the octamer by extrapolation to infinite protein concentration. Using this information, Klapper and Klotz have calculated the equilibrium concentrations of P_8 and P from the apparent binding constants at any protein concentration. The protein–protein interaction constants for the equilibrium of Eq. (8-2) are shown in Table 8-3. Since [P] in Eq. (8-3) is raised to the eighth power, small errors in [P] are reflected as very large errors in K_p. However, the order of magnitude of K_p for the four determinations reported in Table 8-3 is 10^{38}.

TABLE 8-3

EQUILIBRIUM COEFFICIENTS FOR HEMERYTHRIN AS A
FUNCTION OF PROTEIN CONCENTRATION

Protein concn. $(M \times 10^6)$ (in moles of monomer unit)	K_{app} at $\mu = 0.5$ $(M \times 10^{-4})$	$K_p \times 10^{38}$
2.21	4.69	0.03
8.76	3.60	80
18.6	2.90	20
72.9	1.92	0.3

It is very important to note that no other experimental method is available at this time which allows the measurement of such small values of [P], and K's as large as 10^{38}.

REFERENCES

Banerjee, K., and Lauffer, M. A. (1966). *Biochemistry* **5**, 1957.

Bernal, J. D. (1958). *Discussions Faraday Soc.* **25**, 7.

Churchich, J. E., and Wold, F. (1963). *Biochemistry* **2**, 781.

Franklin, R. E. (1957). *Biochim. Biophys. Acta* **18**, 313.

Frieden, C. (1958). *Biochim. Biophys. Acta* **27**, 431.

Frieden, C. (1959a). *J. Biol. Chem.* **234**, 809.

Frieden, C. (1959b). *J. Biol. Chem.* **234**, 809.

Frieden, C. (1962). *J. Biol. Chem.* **237**, 2396.

Frieden, C., and Coleman, R. F. (1967). *J. Biol. Chem.* **242**, 1705.

Klapper, M., and Klotz, J. M. (1968). *Biochemistry* **7**, 223.

Klotz, I. M. (1967). *Science* **155**, 697.

Lauffer, M. A., Ansevin, A. J., Cartwright, J. E., and Brinton, C. C. (1958). *Nature* **181**, 1338.

Olson, J. A., and Anfinsen, C. B. (1952). *J. Biol. Chem.* **197**, 67.

Perutz, M. F., Muirhead, H., Cox, J. M., Goaman, L. C. G. (1968). *Nature* **219**, 131.

Reynolds, J. A., and Schlesinger, M. J. (1968). *Biochemistry* **7**, 2080.

Tomkins, G. M., Yielding, K. L., and Curran, J. (1961). *Proc. Natl. Acad. Sci.* **47**, 270.

Wolff, J. (1961). *J. Biol. Chem.* **237**, 230.

Yielding, K. L., and Tomkins, G. M. (1960). *Federation Proc.* **20**, 238.

IX

Summary and Conclusions

In the foregoing pages an effort has been made to examine from a unified viewpoint (the algebra of which is set forth in Chapter II), the general phenomenon of the complexing of proteins with smaller molecules and ions, including hydrogen ions. In doing so we have avoided extended preoccupation with cases in which some unique feature of the protein, such as possession of a prosthetic group or extremely precise specificity, make the general and unified viewpoint inapplicable or unpromising. An effort has been made to recapitulate the facts as *they are presently known* as to the determinants of binding, both within the protein (binding site structure) and in the environment (effects of concentration, temperature, pH, etc.). The magnitude and the nature of the binding forces involved in complex formation have been reviewed, as have the diversity of bound species; finally and of great importance, the forces responsible for the stability of the native structure have been related, in part, to the effects of the binding of certain ligands on stability and on unfolding, and conditions have been stated which determine whether very low concentrations of a given ligand will act as a stabilizer or as a denaturant.

It has been shown that the most familiar multiple equilibria of proteins, shown by their hydrogen-ion titration curves, have both formal and real parallels with the multiple binding by protein of many other neutral and charged substances. Important, although easily reconciled, differences exist which arise from differences in the nature of the bonds involved in the two classes. The greatest differences (from H^+ binding) arise with the binding of neutral hydrocarbons, where apparently only entropic forces are expressed, and heats of reaction are zero or positive. The difference extends to a possible absence of stoichiometry when some (but not all) proteins bind small hydrocarbons, although here the evidence is inconclusive. Globular proteins differ among themselves more with respect to their tendency to bind hydrocarbons than they do in any other easily measured property; it seems likely that this property gives both qualitative and quantitative information about the nature of their surfaces.

When hydrocarbons are charged by the attachment of sulfate, sulfonate, or carboxylate groups, the affinity for proteins increases and the stoichiometry of binding becomes clear-cut. However, the binding force appears to depend more importantly on the same forces that determined the binding of neutral hydrocarbons than on the coulomb forces exerted by the charged groups. The latter do appear to exert a strong influence on the properties of the resultant complexes, such as spectral dispersion, rotatory dispersion, fluorescence quenching and depolarization, and viscosity.

It will have become obvious to the reader of this book that no simple answers which are entirely adequate can be given to the central questions, which we repeat here:

(A) What are the differences, if any, between the processes that are responsible for multiple equilibria (especially when whole families of substances are involved) and those responsible for the highly specific binding which is characteristic of enzyme–substrate, membrane–protein substrate, and hapten–antibody reactions?

(B) What characteristics must a protein have to be a strong binder of many equivalents of a large variety of ligands or of groups of particular types of ligands (obviously *lysozyme* lacks whatever the characteristics are that are responsible for the binding of hydrocarbons)?

(C) Within homologous groups of chemical substrates, e.g., organic anions, what are the characteristics (parameters) which may make them ligands for proteins in general or for particular proteins?

(D) Why does the binding of a small number of equivalents of certain ligands, such as the longest-chain detergents, result in large conformation changes with most proteins? The total concentration of some such substances which is required to produce extensive unfolding of BSA in 0.1 % protein solutions is considerably less than $10^{-3} M$; thus these substances are far more potent initiators of unfolding than the common denaturation reagents, urea and guanidine hydrochloride.

(E) How are the properties enumerated above utilized physiologically, as for example, in such a versatile transport protein as serum albumin?

The material presented in this monograph permits limited, sometimes tentative, statements to be made about each of these "central questions":

(A) There are some indications that highly specific binding sites are characterized by negative binding enthalpies, while most of the multiple binding sites for broad classes of ligands have negligible enthalpies or even positive values of $\Delta H°$. The negative enthalpies have been attributed to binding-induced conformation changes, but it is hard to see how conformation changes could of themselves account for large negative enthalpies, unless bonds having at least partial low-spin character are involved.[1] With divalent metallic cations there is no question about the formation of low-spin bonds. However, there are sites in some proteins that have large negative enthalpies without accompanying high specificity (Lovrien, 1968). In the last analysis, specificity indicates the need to meet a number of strict steric requirements, and these are compatible with the formation of low-spin bonds, which may, however, also form when other steric requirements are not met. The formation of covalent bonds is usually accompanied by measurable kinetics and large effects of temperature, but hardly a beginning has been made on the study of the kinetics of the binding process. Caution must be exercised with respect to thinking of *any* binding site as a static entity. Among the innumerable configurations in which a protein may exist in aqueous solution, there may be one or more which fulfill the steric requirements for a highly specific substrate. If so, the binding site is "assembled" by the substrate by a simple process of stabilization of one conformation by the spontaneous shift of the conformational equilibrium in that direction (Linderström-Lang and Schellman, 1959). When many equivalents of ligand can bind, many such subconformations would have to be stabilized within the same molecule in concomitant processes. The existence of multiple equilibria may, therefore, give information as to the most probable or *average* conformation of the protein, or of its "surface," whereas such information cannot be expected from a simple protein–substrate interaction.

(B) The answer to the second "central question" is directly related to the lines just above. Proteins that bind metal ions must have functional groups such as amino or imidazole groups in the uncharged (basic) form capable of coordinating with them; and proteins with binding sites for ligands having a pronounced hydrocarbon character must have exposed, or readily accessible, hydrophobic patches, such as would be formed by the side chains of valine, leucine, isoleucine, methionine, phenylalanine, and tryptophan, together with charge constellations that will enhance the interaction (at least locally) rather than detract from it. The peculiar relations between affinities, numbers of binding sites, and size or length of ligand, described in Chapter VII, are

---

[1] A striking and extreme example of a highly specific binding site having a large negative enthalpy (-58 kcal/mole at $40°$) is furnished by the spontaneous reassembly of ribonuclease from the S-protein and S-peptide (Richards *et al.*, 1968).

most readily accounted for by assuming that the highest affinities are attained by this type of compound when the ligand makes multiple contacts with the protein. Thus high affinities for such ligands may well depend on unusually large numbers of hydrophobic patches on the surface, since such a distribution will promote not only a large amount of binding but also tighter binding.

One cannot ignore, however, evidence from difference spectroscopy that perturbations of the aromatic amino acids appear to be closely associated with the binding of many organic substances by many proteins. Such perturbations do not accompany the binding of hydrogen ions, except when tyrosine is involved, unless the pH stability limits are exceeded. Even in the latter case, as, for example, in the $N \rightarrow F$ transition in BSA the aromatic perturbations which appear are very small compared with those that are observed in binding such simple molecules as decylsulfate by the *native* protein. Such perturbations, therefore, may indicate direct involvement of these chromophores in the anion binding process, rather than a more indirect allosteric effect upon the entire molecule. If this tentative conclusion is correct, hydrophobic patches containing the aromatic side chains make binding sites of greater affinity than do those which exclude them, and whose perturbations are invisible in the uv region above $200m\mu$.

(C) The properties of a strongly and multiply bound ligand follow from the preceding section. However, since there are many different classes of ligands, no one group of them need have every kind of binding determinant. Among organic compounds a high affinity to protein will accompany hydrophobic character: thus, in a series of homologous compounds the binding affinity is likely to rise as the solubility in water goes down. Measurement of high affinities associated with low solubility is likely to present special problems. Among organic compounds of the same mass, having different structural features, the situation is not entirely clear. With some proteins, aromaticity seems to reduce the affinity (Steinhardt *et al.*, 1941), but it is not clear whether the cause of the reduction in the affinity of aromatic ligands is lack of conformational adaptability or shorter linear dimensions. Optical isomers of dyes show distinctly different affinities even when multiple rather than single sites are involved (Karush, 1952).

With inorganic metallic ions, potential binding sites would be expected in most proteins at pH values above about 7 or 8. The fact that they appear to be absent in some proteins suggests that special steric requirements must be met. The ubiquity of anion binding is harder to explain. Saroff (1957) has developed a model which depends on the clustering in "cavities" of cationic groups, but in some proteins, such as aldolase (Velick, 1949), electrophoresis shows that the binding of phosphate can reduce the isoelectric point from almost 9 to less than 5 (Fig. 9-1). Thus, at pH 6, for example, the net charge

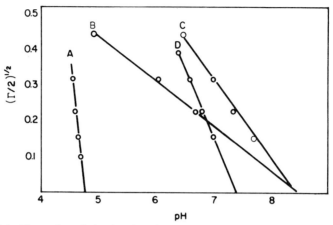

Fɪɢ. 9-1. Electrophoretic isoelectric points as a function of the square root of ionic strength. Curve A, ovalbumin in acetate; curve B, aldolase in phosphate; curve C, aldolase in acetate; curve D, horse carboxyhemoglobin in phosphate. [S. F. Velick (1949). *J. Phys. Colloid Chem.* **53**, 135.]

may vary, as the phosphate present is raised, from $+7$ to -3 or even less (Fig. 9-2), a variation which is difficult to reconcile with a purely coulombic model. The interchangeability of halides in binding to BSA, with a fixed ratio of binding constants, (Scatchard *et al.*, 1957) does, however, support an electrostatic interpretation. Nevertheless, the binding constants are over a hundredfold higher than those which have been demonstrated in any model

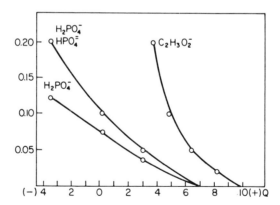

Fɪɢ. 9-2. The net charge of aldolase at pH 6 in phosphate and acetate buffers of different ionic strengths. The curve labeled $H_2PO_4^-$ gives the charge in the same phosphate buffer plotted against the concentration of only the monovalent component of the buffer. For the monovalent species the ionic strength (ordinate) is equal to the concentration. [S. F. Velick (1949). *J. Phys. Colloid Chem.* **53**, 135.]

compounds (Saroff, 1959). It is not easy to think that both iodide and acetate, which compete for the same sites in BSA, are bound entirely electrostatically. Systematic attempts with substituted benzenoid compounds have failed to establish any general rules for the effects of substituents on affinity or numbers of sites (Fredericq and Neurath, 1950). There are suggestions, among aliphatic compounds, that a highly delocalized terminal charge confers a higher affinity than a strictly localized one.

The effect of size is particularly clear in the case of aliphatic compounds, whether neutral or charged. Among the sulfates the free energy of binding is essentially the same for octyl to tetradecyl, but the number of binding sites with this energy increases from 5 up to 10–11. With six-carbon compounds the affinity as well as the number of sites drops severely. A somewhat similar situation obtains with sulfonate, but a large drop in affinity has already occurred at octyl. It is tentatively concluded that two contacts are made wtih chains of eight or more carbon atoms (or eight in addition to an oxygen,) but that shorter chains make only one contact. There are more binding sites for the longer chains because of the way in which contact points are distributed on the surface. Since the energy for two contacts (assumed to be additive) is just under 8 kcal/mole at $2°$, the free energy for a single contact should be just under 4 kcal/mole, and the association contant no higher than about 5000. With $n = 3$ and 1 % protein such a value of K means that only 30% of the ligand is bound when the concentration of free ligand is $10^{-3}M$. At 0.1 % protein (used in the experiments of Reynolds *et al.*, 1967) only 4% would be bound, and there would be a large experimental uncertainty in $\bar{v}$. The actual values of K for chains of less than eight carbon atoms are not known, since sufficiently high concentrations of protein have not been used; thus this simple consequence of the multiple contact hypothesis cannot yet be tested by this means. Since there are some reasons for believing that multiple contacts may also be made in binding to partially unfolded BSA (Ray, 1968; Anderson, 1966), there should be an opportunity to test this criterion in the region of partial unfolding. If " bridging " is found, as suggested by Ray *et al.* (1966) and by Marcus *et al.* (1964), the unfolding model of Reynolds *et al.* (1967) may require simple modifications.

(D) Binding-induced unfolding or denaturation is now well established as confined to certain ligands. Thus, with few exceptions, there are values of $+\bar{h}$ and $-\bar{h}$ at which subunit dissociation, partial unfolding, or massive denaturation occur. The model proposed for unfolding caused by anion binding, with a pH-independent value of U, the unfolding constant (Chapter II), cannot be applied to this case without deep-seated modifications which merit review here. If U is increased as the new charge is increased by either binding

---

² $\bar{h}$ is defined in Chapter V.

very common susceptibility of proteins to partial unfolding by the larger detergents suggests that the generality is there.

It should be clear that there is opportunity and need for much additional work. Some of the need has been specified in the immediately preceding pages. However, the needs are of many kinds: (a) faster and more accurate methods of measuring isotherms, especially with high-affinity ligands (Chapter III); (b) kinetic data on both binding and unfolding or refolding (there are only a few measurements of dissociation obtained with dyes, and a somewhat larger number of unfolding studies, obtained with hydrogen ion); (c) a better understanding of the meaning for multiple equilibria of difference spectra and of fluorescence quenching, wavelength shifts, and depolarization; (d) better specification of the unfolded state or states in terms of experimentally observable quantities; (e) more numerous and more systematic studies of the binding behavior of diverse proteins toward carefully selected ligands, and of the effects on stability which may accompany binding; and finally, more realistic and more sophisticated theoretical models of the binding process and of the unfolding behavior which is sometimes incident to it. Since our present knowledge of hydrogen-ion isotherms and of hydrogen-ion denaturation or subunit dissociation is much more extensive and diverse than that of isotherms of other multiple ligands, the need to study multiple equilibria with neutral molecules or with anions is far greater than for further study of hydrogen-ion equilibria.

More sophisticated elaborations of the model described by Reynolds *et al.* (1967) would include the effects of the existence of more than one set of binding sites in both native and unfolded forms, the effects of possibly bifunctional binding by the longer-chain detergents, and the algebra of the transition between bifunctional binding to monofunctional binding to unfolded protein at high concentrations of free ligand. The latter transition, if it exists, might correspond to the transition between the forms AD_n and AD_{2n} observed by Decker and Foster (1966), among others. There is also need to determine whether the very high molal ratios observed with concentrations of some detergents approaching their CMC are manifestations of mixed-micelle formation, and if so, the architecture of such micelles.

Should binding site compositions and locations become known, there will be an opportunity to attempt to apply such electrostatic models as the Tanford-Kirkwood theory to the binding of anions and cations, and to learn why the electrostatic interactions of the bound ions, or of the sites are so much weaker than with hydrogen ion. The growing number of x-ray analyses of protein structure at moderately high resolution favors such attempts.

Among more detailed questions that require experimental and theoretical study are the numerous unexplained hydrogen-ion titration anomalies which still remain, especially those at high pH, not all of which yield to simple time- and pH-dependent unmasking interpretations; the anomalously low values of w_{exp} which are frequently found in both titration analysis and in the ΔpH method when the latter is applied to long-chain compounds; and the arrangement within native proteins of the *charged* masked groups which they at least occasionally and rather surprisingly appear to contain (see Chapter V); and chemical interpretation of the substantial negative enthalpy of binding the first anion in many multiple equilibria of proteins.

There have been great recent advances in the techniques available for detecting small and local conformation changes in proteins, as distinct from the larger and more general ones we have called unfolding, and which have for many years been followed by viscosity measurements. However, interpretation of the observed effects in terms of specific functional groups and their arrangements in three-dimensional space have lagged behind the means of detecting their existence. There is now considerable evidence that small local conformation changes accompany the binding of many classes of substances which do not unfold. The nature of the binding reaction will be better known when changes in absorption dispersion, ORD, and changes in fluorescence can be better interpreted as well as *exploited*.

It was a great step forward when Kauzman (1959) first made clear how important hydrophobic interactions are to protein structure and to protein interactions. There has been a tendency throughout this book to think of the interactions of multiple equilibria very largely in terms of hydrophobic interaction, modified in some cases by electrostatic effects of smaller magnitudes, and perhaps to a small extent by hydrogen bonding as well. Successful scientific exploration is characterized by a tendency to oversimplify and to overrationalize just before a sharp change of course to a new direction. The binding interactions of proteins may prove no exception to this general rule. Can one really believe that the vast diversity of multiple (and one-step) equilibria, with all their remarkable range of specificities, and the wide range of binding tendencies, can be fully explained eventually by the exploration of so small an arsenal of forces? Can the most remarkable of all specificities, those of antibodies, be explained in this way? The high heats of reaction of many "first" sites with ligands do not fit in, at least at first glance, with so simple (although involved) a picture of nature. What other source of binding interaction energy remains to be discovered, and how shall it be sought?

REFERENCES

Anderson, D. G. (1966). Univ. Microfilms, Xerox Co., Ann Arbor, Michigan.
Decker, R. V., and Foster, J. F. (1966). *Biochem. J.* **5**, 1242.
Fredericq, E. F., and Neurath, H. (1950). *J. Am. Chem. Soc.* **72**, 2684.

Gallagher, J., and Steinhardt, J. (1969). (Unpublished.)

Karush, F. (1952). *J. Phys. Chem.* **56**, 70.

Kauzman, W. (1959). *Advan. Protein Chem.* **14**, 1.

Linderström-Lang, K., and Schellman, J. A. (1959). *In* "The Enzymes" (P. Boyer, H. Lardy, and K. Myrback, eds.), Vol. I, Chapter 10. Academic Press, New York.

Lovrien, R. (1968). *Polymer Preprints* **9**, p. 219.

Markus, G., Love, R. L., and Wissler, F.C. (1964). *J. Biol. Chem.* **239**, 3678.

Ray, A. (1968). *In* "Solution Properties of Natural Polymer." The Chemical Society, Burlington House, London, #23.

Ray, A., Reynolds, J. A., Polet, H., and Steinhardt, J. (1966). *Biochemistry* **5**, 2606.

Reynolds, J. Herbert, S., Polet, H., and Steinhardt, J. (1967). *Biochemistry* **6**, 937.

Richards, F. M., Hearn, R. D., Sturtevant, J. M., and Watt, G. (1968). *Federation Proc.* **27**, 338.

Saroff, H. A. (1957). *J. Phys. Chem.* **61**, 1364.

Saroff, H. A., and Healy, J. W. (1959). *J. Phys. Chem.* **63**, 1178.

Scatchard, G., Coleman, J. S., and Shen, A. L. (1957). *J. Am. Chem. Soc.* **79**, 12.

Steinhardt, J., Fugitt, C. H., and Harris, M. (1941). *J. Res. Natl. Bur. Std.* **26**, 293.

Velick, S. F. (1949). *J. Phys. Colloid Chem.* **53**, 135.

Author Index

Subject Index

A

ATP-creatine kinase, binding of chloride to, 330
Acetate, binding to serum albumin, 310
Acetylcholinesterase, 145
Acridine orange, binding to poly-1-glutamic acid, 314
Acridylbenzoate, binding to serum albumin, 308
Actin
    binding of p-chloromercuribenzoate, 330
    hydrogen ion titration, 186
Activity, biological, 69
Actomyosin, binding of calcum ion, 219
Adair equation, 131
Alcohol dehydrogenase, 149
    binding of DPN, 67
        of ethanol, 67
        of zinc ion, 219
Alcohols
    effect of pH on binding to serum albumin, 98–100
    lipoxygenase binding, 148
    papain binding, 148
    ribonuclease binding, 147
    serum albumin binding, 96–98
Aldolase
    binding of hexitol-1-b-diphosphate, 330
        of phosphate, 330
        of sulfate, 330
Alkaline phosphatase
    binding of metal ions, 220
        of zinc ions, 219
    hydrogen ion titration, 186

Alkanes
    binding of chymotrypsin, 143
        of hemoglobin, 129, 130
        of hemoglobin-S, 130
        of β-lactoglobulin, 125–127
        of lysozyme, 141
        of ribonuclease, 147
        of serum albumin, 88–100, 115
    solubility in micelles, 89
Alkylbenzene sulfonates, binding to serum albumin, 245–261
Alkyl half-esters, binding to serum albumin, 242–245
Alkyl isocyanide, binding to hemoglobin, 140
Alkyl sulfates, 261–270
Alkyl sulfonates, 261–270
p-Aminoazobenzene-p'-sulfonate, binding to serum albumin, 310
Aminobenzene sulfonate, binding to serum albumin, 310
Aminobenzoate, binding to serum, albumin, 310
Aminonaphthalene disulfonate, binding to serum albumin, 310
Aminonaphthalene trisulfonate, binding to serum albumin, 310
1-Amino-2-naphthol-4-sulfonate, binding to serum albumin, 310
β-Amylase, 146
d-Amylase, effect of detergent binding on, 293
Anesthetics, binding to serum albumin, 306
1-Anilino-8-naphthalene sulfonate, binding to serum albumin, 308